ABUNDANCE OF CHEMICAL ELEMENTS

ABUNDANCE OF CHEMICAL ELEMENTS

BY

V. V. CHERDYNTSEV

TRANSLATED BY

WALTER NICHIPORUK

THE UNIVERSITY OF CHICAGO PRESS

Library of Congress Catalog Card Number: 61–11892
First edition published by State Publishing House of
Technical-Theoretical Literature, Moscow, 1956

The University of Chicago Press, Chicago and London
The University of Toronto Press, Toronto 5, Canada

Published 1961.
Composed and printed in the United States of America

Preface to the Russian Edition

The science of the abundance of chemical elements borders upon various scientific disciplines—physics, geochemistry, astronomy, etc. To this question, which is important to contemporary natural sciences, attention is given in many books on nuclear physics and geochemistry. First of all, we should mention the excellent treatise on geochemistry by the academician A. E. Fersman. In this work, however, the physical foundations of the problem are almost untouched. Among foreign publications one can point to summaries by Goldschmidt, Brown, and Rankama and Sahama and to a review by Alpher and Herman in which the theoretical works on the abundance of atomic nuclei are discussed almost completely apart from experimental material. In addition, we should refer to the survey of the data on the isotopic composition of the natural elements—*Isotope Geology*—by Rankama.

A monograph devoted to the survey of the knowledge of the abundance of elements from the viewpoint of the stability of atomic nuclei is lacking in both Soviet and foreign literature.

We consider it timely to offer a book which gives an outline of the current status of the science of the abundance of chemical elements, of the nuclear processes associated with the change in the chemical composition of the cosmos, and of the foundations for a theoretical description of the problem. The book is written for a large circle of readers of diverse specialties (physicists, geochemists, geologists, chemists, astronomers, geophysicists, etc.). We endeavor to present the account so as to make it understandable to the reader who has no specialized knowledge of atomic physics. The fundamental mathematical derivations are not sufficiently rigorous. Probably, a physics expert will consider them too elementary; yet I assume that for many readers these derivations will prove useful. The book takes into account the basic results obtained and published as of the beginning of 1956.

There are, undoubtedly, many deficiencies in this work. This is to some extent inevitable in an attempt to embrace the vast amount of material which is organically connected with the problem at hand. The author will be grateful for suggestions pertaining to the contents of the book.

I take this opportunity to express my gratitude to the corresponding member of the Soviet Academy of Sciences, I. E. Starik, and to Professor A. N. Murin for their review and a valuable criticism of the manuscript.

V. V. CHERDYNTSEV

Preface to the American Edition

This book is neither a textbook nor a work of reference. My aim was to give an account of the vast and varied material on the abundance of the chemical elements. In this objective I was guided by fundamental ideas on the stability of atomic nuclei and on their formation in a neutron environment.

During the preparation of the American edition the book was revised and supplied with many additions from recent literature (including the first half of 1958). The general ideas which underlie the book have in the meantime remained essentially unchanged.

However, the most general idea to which, in my conviction, every scientist should subject his efforts and days, is to aid in the peaceful progress of mankind. If my book finds a response with the reader and will help strengthen friendly connections between the scientists of the Soviet Union and those of the United States, this will be the highest reward for me and the collective faculty of our university, located in the foothills of the Tyan'-Shan'.

V. V. Cherdyntsev

Alma-Ata, U.S.S.R.
S. M. Kirov Kazakh State University

Translator's Note and Acknowledgments

This work is a revised translation of Cherdyntsev's book on the abundances of the elements, first published in 1956. The revisions, supplied by the author, consist of numerous corrections in the original text and of new materials covering the period since 1956 and up to the middle of 1958.

The annotated footnote references, added to the translation in part upon the author's suggestion, supply mainly experimental results not included in the author's revisions and also those published between the middle of 1958 and the end of 1960.

I have also added to the present text a number of footnotes with comments on whatever errors of fact or interpretation in the original pages have been found by those who have carefully read and criticized portions of the translated manuscript. To those critics, for giving me the benefit of their unsurpassed knowledge of the subject, I want to express my deep appreciation.

I also wish to thank Mrs. F. Miko, who typed much of the first draft of the manuscript; Linda Langan and Carolyn Prunty, who shared in the typing of the tables of the Appendix; Mrs. Margareta Roth, who prepared the drawings; and my wife, who typed the greater part of the final manuscript and who in other ways helped in the preparation of this translation.

This work was done in part under Atomic Energy Commission Contract No. AT (11-1)—208.

PASADENA, CALIFORNIA WALTER NICHIPORUK

Contents

Introduction

The solution of many theoretical problems of modern science depends on the study of the abundance of chemical elements, i.e., of their quantitative content in the individual systems of the cosmos. The practical utilization of chemical elements also depends to a large extent on their abundance. Certain groups of elements received their names from their low abundance in the earth's crust; for example, we speak of "rare gases" of the zero group of the periodic table and of the rare-earth elements. The term "rare elements" is widely used in both analytical chemistry and technology.

The primeval cosmic abundance of atoms is determined by the conditions of their formation and by the stability of atomic nuclei. The problem of the origin of atomic nuclei is far from being solved, but it is obvious that the content of atoms in the primordial system depends primarily on their nuclear properties, so that the abundance of isotopes is one of the important parameters among those few which have been used in nuclear physics up to today. S. I. Vavilov [1],[1] in a speech at a triumphant session of the Soviet Academy of Sciences dedicated to the twentieth anniversary of V. I. Lenin's death, said: "There are bases for the belief that such phenomena as the *red shift* in the spectra of the spiral nebulae, the laws of the distribution of chemical elements on the earth and in the universe, and the fundamental biological phenomena will in the future modify modern physics."

The primeval abundance of atoms in the actually accessible cosmic systems is altered by various secondary processes. For example, during the formation of the earth there was a substantial decrease in the earth's content of hydrogen, helium, and many other elements. Therefore, the explanation of the basic regularities of the primeval abundance of atoms is a fairly complex problem. The composition of the matter in the individual cosmic systems is usually not uniform. The quantitative

[1] The brackets contain bibliographical references which are listed at the end of the book. [Author's footnote]

content of chemical elements in the individual zones of the systems we shall call, in accordance with the geochemical literature, the *distribution of atoms.* The distribution of the elements depends in principle on the physicochemical conditions and on the state of the given system. To a certain extent, we contrast the abundance and the distribution of chemical elements, although it is impossible in a number of cases to draw a line between these concepts.

The specific difficulty in the study of the abundance of atoms lies in the fact that, unlike other parameters of atomic physics, the abundance can be determined with sufficient precision only for individual systems: the earth's crust, the sun's atmosphere, the meteorites. In all instances, the original abundance of elements is altered during the migration of matter, i.e., in the process of the distribution of elements. The extent of the effect cannot always be determined quantitatively.

The information on the abundance of elements, isotopes, and atomic nuclei can be found in books on nuclear physics and, of course, in all books on geochemistry. According to Goldschmidt, geochemistry has for its objective the explanation of the quantitative composition of the earth, on the one hand, and the derivation of the laws of the distribution of individual elements, on the other. The first objective depends on the nuclear properties of isotopes, and the second on the structure of the electronic shells. Thus geochemistry is divided into two branches: "nuclear" and "atomic" geochemistry. The basic problem of "nuclear" geochemistry is the abundance of chemical elements in the earth and in the cosmic bodies in general.

By the term "the primeval abundance of atoms in a given system" we mean their quantitative content at the time of the formation of the system. The departures from the primeval abundance are caused not only by the migration of matter but by the nuclear processes as well: spontaneous radioactive decay, thermonuclear reactions in the interior regions of the stars, artificial transmutations of atomic nuclei under the action of cosmic rays, and radioactive decay. Even in the practically isolated systems (for example, in the earth) the abundance of atoms changes continuously. Recent developments in experimental techniques have made possible the discovery of many nuclear processes which modify the composition of the earth. And our knowledge in this field will undoubtedly increase within the next few years. V. I. Vernadskii and A. E. Fersman for the first time gave geochemistry a dynamic direction; they set, as the principal objective of this science, the history of atoms in the earth and the cosmos. This direction should also be preserved in "nuclear" geochemistry—the science of the abundance of cosmic isotopes.

The science of the abundance of atoms is closely connected with a number of scientific disciplines—nuclear physics, geochemistry, astrophysics, etc. Thus the abundance of hydrogen and helium essentially determines the energetics and evolution of the stellar systems. On the abundance of the element in the earth depend its supplies in the mineral deposits of economic interest. One phase of nuclear geochemistry impinges upon cosmogony, but the other is oriented toward practical problems.

The theory of the abundance of atoms should be based on nuclear physics and astrophysics. Until today the theory has not been worked out adequately. The difficulty of the problem could explain the modest success of the attempts, but the fact that the attempts were comparatively few is probably associated with the borderline position of the problem among the various scientific disciplines.

Our first objective (chap. i) is to give a summary of the fundamental material on the abundance of chemical elements in different sectors of the cosmos. Our special attention is directed toward nuclear reactions which alter the composition of matter, such as radioactive decay and the artificial transmutation of atomic nuclei. We emphasize that this chapter does not include a complete review of the material but contains only the fundamental data which help to formulate the regularities in the abundance of isotopes. This is not possible without concepts about the stability of isotopes.

The elementary theory of stability is stated in the second chapter on the basis of some simpler models. At the same time, we try, as far as possible, to trace the connection between the two characteristics of isotopes—the abundance and the stability. The idea is gradually developed that the system of atomic nuclei is far from a state of thermodynamic equilibrium, and therefore the concept of stability has a limited meaning and can be applied only to a specific nuclear process taking place under definite conditions. The theory of stability is indispensable for the study of the existing radioelements and for the explanation of the regularities in the abundance of atomic nuclei.

The third chapter is devoted to the basic regularities in the abundance of isotopes. Here we give a review of the works on the abundance theory. There is presented a theory of the formation of atomic nuclei under conditions of dissociation equilibrium in a neutron environment. This theory most satisfactorily describes the observed regularities.

The abundance theory is closely related to the problem of the origin of atomic nuclei and consequently to the cosmogonic hypotheses. In the study of the problem of the abundance of elements which borders on several basic disciplines, it is easy to encompass the material common to such sciences as geology, geophysics, and cosmogony. However, cosmogony, up to this day, is far from a state of completeness, and some of its fundamental objectives are only formulated in this book. The data of geochemistry and cosmochemistry have only a partial bearing on the development of cosmogony. At a certain stage in the development of sciences it is useful to treat separately some of the problems, and only after these problems have acquired a sufficient degree of completeness and the conclusions from them have a relative probability, does it become necessary to generalize broadly and to combine the results obtained by the various related disciplines. At the present time the main objective of nuclear geochemistry is, in our opinion, the demonstration of the regularities in the abundance of isotopes and the attempt to explain them with a certain working hypothesis as a guide. The next step should be co-ordination of this hypothesis with cosmogonic data, which, as can be judged from the progress of recent years, will soon take on the form of a sufficiently well-organized system.

Modern geochemistry, in studying the abundance of atoms, utilizes extensively the physicochemical methods of investigation—spectral and X-ray analysis, electrochemical methods, mass spectrometry, neutronometry,[2] and other methods of nuclear physics. On the other hand, many investigations in the field of nuclear physics are currently assuming a geochemical direction. In our review we are almost unconcerned with the problems of measurement techniques. Geochemistry has, without question, established its own methods of investigation, but it studies its material by means of experimental techniques developed by the bordering fields of science.

We shall pause for a discussion of terminology. In the old geochemical literature the term *rasprostraneniye* was used instead of *rasprostranennost'*. Despite the fact that *rasprostraneniye* was employed by the classical writers in domestic geochemistry, we shall not retain this term, since in the Russian language it is commonly used in the sense of "expansion" or "development." In astronomical literature, the term *obiliye* is used. It is a literal translation of the French and Anglo-Saxon scientific term "abundance." This word also fails, since it usually means "surplus" or "profusion," both of which make the term unsuitable for the majority of the elements of the cosmos.

[2] This is an exact translation of the term *neitronometriya*. It is difficult to infer from the text what the author means by this term.

I

The Abundance of Chemical Elements in the Earth's Crust and the Cosmic Systems

1. HISTORY OF THE UTILIZATION AND INVESTIGATION OF CHEMICAL ELEMENTS

The majority of the chemical elements are referred to as the "rare elements." This is a conditional idea which is determined by several different factors:

1. The low quantitative content in the earth's crust which can be connected with a low absolute abundance of the given element as well as with its loss during the formation of the earth's crust. In the number of elements lost by the earth to a considerable degree are the rare gases of the zero group of Mendeleyev's table, mercury, and other volatile elements.

2. The peculiarities of the behavior of the element in the earth's crust, namely, its inability to form minerals or mineral deposits. For example, there is more of the "rare" rubidium in the earth's crust than of lead, arsenic, and copper combined, but rubidium, in geochemical processes, follows its homologue element potassium, forms not a single mineral of its own, and only sometimes enriches the minerals of the end phase of the crystallization of magma.

3. The technological difficulties and the small economic importance of the given element. Thus titanium belongs to the group of the most abundant elements of the earth's crust. Its compounds (ilmenite, sphene, titanomagnetite) are common among the accessory minerals or rocks, but negligible utilization has permitted us, up to the present time, to classify this element as belonging to the group of the rare elements.

The evolution of the animal world is often accompanied by the utilization by organisms of the rarer chemical elements. The simplest organisms build their skeletons from silicon (certain sponges, diatoms). The more complex ones use for their skeletons and shells the rarer element calcium, whose salts possess better mechanical properties. Finally, the skeleton of vertebrates consists of calcium phosphate, a compound which is rarer than calcium carbonate. But, at the same time, in evolutionary development those organisms survive which use for their component parts the abundant elements instead of the rarer ones. The blood of lower organisms contains hemocyanin—a copper (in mollusks) or a vanadium (in ascidians) compound. In higher organisms, hemocyanin is replaced by hemoglobin, whose molecule contains the more abundant iron instead of copper. Specialized forms are known which utilize rare elements. Thus the skeletons of the simplest organisms—Acantharia—consist of strontium sulfate; but these organisms, living prior to our time, did not develop broadly.

In the history of mankind the two opposed tendencies—the utilization in man's activities of the valuable properties of new chemical elements and the effort to seek inexpensive substitutes for the rare elements—are displayed consciously. The chemical elements were used at first as oxides. Leaving aside the amorphous varieties of silica (flint, chalcedony, and others)—the basic material for man's implements since the time of primitive man, anthropoid, and up to the beginning of the Iron Age—the first oxides that man familiarized himself with were the iron ochers used mixed with fat for oiling the body. Neanderthal man (the Middle Paleolithic) supplied the burial mounds with a red iron ocher. Approximately at the same time, man employed iron sulfide, the mineral pyrite, for fire-making. The man of the Upper Paleolithic, who lived in Kostenki (the Voronezh District, U.S.S.R.), obtained iron oxides by roasting siderite, this perhaps being one of the first chemo-technological processes. Immediately after iron oxides, oxides and carbonates of copper were utilized. The first native metal—gold—appears in the Neolithic. Man living in Egypt in 5000 B.C. also knew native copper and silver. The cold-forging of metal originated in 4000 B.C. in Elam and Sialk and was soon superseded by the first metallurgical process—smelting. A considerable step forward was the discovery of a eutectic alloy of copper and tin—bronze—with its superior qualities of hardness and ease of fusion. Together with it, there were employed alloys of copper and antimony (in Abkhazia, 3000 B.C.) and also those of copper and arsenic, which were discovered in the ancient culture of the Indus. Evidently, in 2000 B.C. iron was also discovered there. Of interest is the use in Babylon in 3000 B.C. of a ternary alloy—beryllium bronze—whose remarkable anticorrosion properties have been rediscovered in modern times. A rapid growth of metallurgy in 3000 B.C. found its reflection in religion. Thus the King of Ur turned to his deity: "Thou, who mixes copper and tin." Obviously, at that time the practical significance of metallurgy became so indisputable that it was attributed to a supernatural patron of the country as one of his fundamental functions.

Meteoritic iron was diligently gathered by ancient man, but it could in no way supply his need of metal. It rather served as a sign of authority and—what in that epoch meant almost the same—an object of worship. Until the present time in Kaaba, the "faithful" worship what appears to be a meteorite. The difficulties of technology for a long time prevented the introduction of iron. Even in Egypt's New Kingdom—in the period of the "Tel el Amarna" Revolution, which championed the superbly skilled experts, and the leading ideologists, who for the first time proclaimed the principle of equality of nations —iron was as yet extremely rare. In the fantastically rich tomb of Tutenkhamon (1388 B.C.), the mummy lying in a coffin of cast gold was provided only with small articles of iron. The widespread utilization of iron began evidently in the twelfth to thirteenth centuries B.C. in Asia Minor and Armenia, and this marked a genuine industrial revolution in the ancient world.

The utilization of the new elements contributed greatly to the development of human society and its culture. The first periods of the history of primitive man received their names from the materials used in the making of implements: the Stone, the Iron, and the Bronze Ages. At the same time, the production—the techniques of implement-making—shows no direct effect on the evolution of such social forms as, for example, the state. It is possible to give a number of examples in which the cultures of the primitive world gravitated toward the centers of metallurgical raw materials. One of the most important pages of prehistory was written by the Andronian culture of the Bronze Age. This culture extended from the Danube to the Ob' River, and within it were developed the embryos of many historic nationalities. This culture was based on the rich sources of raw materials in the Altai and Kalbinskii Range, where copper and tin deposits are located conveniently close to each other.

The relatively savage race of Dorians gained mastery over the new powerful agent—iron—which gave the long Dorian swords a rapid and decisive victory over the precious bronze daggers of the Greek and non-Greek races of the Creto-Mycenaean world. This was one of the turning points in the early history of contemporary civilization.

At the same time, it should not be forgotten that the development of the major cultures of the ancient world—Egypt, Mesopotamia, the Indus, and China—took place in regions favorable to an intensive growth of agriculture; but in the countries that did not possess ore resources—for example, in the lowlands of Mesopotamia—even stone was deficient. The transition of human society from one socio-economic form to another occurred on different levels of assimilation of materials for making implements. The class society and the state were established in Egypt during the late Neolithic. In Mexico, these entities evolved under conditions of the "Copper" Age, and the state of Kiev Rus' emerged in the epoch of advanced utilization of iron.

The use of the rare elements by man is not always determined by their abundance. The first native metals in man's practice were the rare silver and the very rare gold, the least abundant metals of the earth's crust after rhenium, rhodium, and iridium. Metallurgy begins with the relatively rare copper and tin.

Of the most abundant metals (silicon, aluminum, and iron) of the earth's crust, only iron was used prior to our era.

Metallic aluminum was discovered only in 1829, and during the first decades it was fantastically expensive. Utilization of "metallic" silicon is, even to the present day, comparatively small.

I shall not speak of the exceptional role of the rare elements in the national economies of our times, in which the radioactive isotopes—the raw materials of atomic energy—are becoming increasingly important, especially the artificially prepared plutonium and tritium.

The list of the metals known in antiquity can be supplemented by the addition of mercury and zinc, which were familiar to metallurgists of central Asia during the Hellenic period. Certain elements (sodium, potassium, calcium, aluminum) were known in ancient ages in the form of oxides and salts. Minerals of beryllium and zirconium were used as precious stones.

In the Middle Ages considerable improvement was made in technology and the mining industry, but, at the same time, the list of the useful metals did not expand. Discoveries and studies are being made of the harmful contaminants of the metallurgical processes of that time—tungsten, cobalt, and nickel. But in the metallic form these elements were isolated only as late as the eighteenth century. As in antiquity, primary attention is given to the search for the noble metals. As an admixture for the adulteration of silver, platinum appeared first among the elements used; and, as a substitute for graphite, molybdenum sulfide was utilized. The first element for which the date of the discovery (1669) is known was apparently phosphorus.

The development of technology after the period of the industrial revolution stimulated a widespread and successful search for new elements. From the beginning of the eighteenth and to the middle of the nineteenth century 45 new elements were discovered. During this period many elements were also discovered and isolated in the form of oxides. Such was the case with the element uranium, which was first found by Klaproth in 1789 in pitchblende. Metallic uranium was obtained by Péligot in 1841, and its atomic weight was correctly determined by D. I. Mendeleyev only in 1872.

Improved analytical techniques permitted the prediction of the presence of an unknown element from the deficiency of several per cent in the summation of the results of chemical analysis. In this manner lithium was discovered during the analysis of the mineral petalite, and much later also germanium, during the analysis of the mineral argyrodite. A study of the crystallophysical similarity between beryl and emerald led to the discovery of beryllium.

Toward the middle of the past century, the possibilities of analytical chemistry were to a certain extent exhausted. From 1844, when the Russian chemist C. C. Claus discovered ruthenium, to 1860, the list of the known elements was not supplemented. For further investigations, the application of the new physical methods turned out to be exceptionally important. With the help of spectral analysis, the elements cesium, rubidium, indium, and thallium were discovered in the earth and helium in the spectrum of the solar prominences.

The search for new elements was put on a scientific basis after Mendeleyev, in 1869, came out with his periodic law and predicted a number of elements, of which gallium and scandium were discovered in the following years. The progress of analytical chemistry aided in the in-group separation of the rare-earth elements, and the development of vacuum techniques led to the discovery of the rare gases which fill the zero group of Mendeleyev's system. The discovery of radioactive emission permitted the detection of new radioactive elements—the decay products of uranium and thorium which are present in natural objects in "unweighable" amounts. Finally, by applying X-ray spectral analysis, hafnium (in 1922) and rhenium (in 1925) were discovered, whereupon the table of the stable elements proved to be complete.

A few years earlier, however, Rutherford (in 1919) had split the atomic nucleus, thus opening the possibility of artificial transmutation of the elements. The first isotopes, unknown in nature—the artificially radioactive isotopes—were obtained by Joliot-Curie in 1934. In the following years several hundred new unstable nuclei were discovered. In the 1940's it became possible to obtain artificially not only the new isotopes but the new elements as well, the heavy transuranium elements and the elements of the middle part of Mendeleyev's table, technetium (atomic No. 43) and promethium (atomic No. 61), both of which have no stable isotopes and therefore do not occur in nature. Thus no sooner had completion of the discovery of the chemical elements of the universe been made, than man undertook the creation of the new elements.

The discovery of the new elements was followed by the study of their abundance. This work was so closely connected with the process of the discovery that very often it was continued by the scientists who discovered the element. The first summary of the data on the abundance of the elements in the earth's crust was compiled by Clarke in 1889 [9], who continued to expand these studies for more than thirty years. The investigations of the average composition of the earth's crust were based on the classical methods of analytical chemistry and encompassed only those chemical elements which are contained in rocks in amounts not less than hundredths of 1 per cent. Subsequently, the investigations included the heavy metals and the rare elements. This called for the development and application of the new methods of analysis: spectroscopic, X-ray, polarographic, and others. For example, the Noddacks and Hevesy, the respective discoverers of rhenium [6] and hafnium [8], conducted their classical studies of the geochemistry of these elements by combining the chemical methods of enrichment of the investigated sample with the X-ray method of quantitative determination of the element in the obtained concentrate.

In addition to the formations of the earth's crust, the only objects that can be investigated directly are the meteorites. It should be noted that the fundamental classification of these bodies is based on their composition, that is, on the abundance of the leading elements. The first systematic investigations of the chemical composition of meteorites were conducted by the Noddacks [7] and the school of Goldschmidt [10]. It was assumed that the average composition of meteorites corresponded to the average composition of the earth's crust. Following this assumption, Goldschmidt and later Brown [11], Urey [12],[1] and Suess and Urey [12] relied on meteoritic data in their studies of the abundance of the chemical elements.[2] This tendency appears to us incorrect. Irrespective of the viewpoint which is adopted concerning the origin of meteorites, these objects represent by weight a small part of the planetary system.[3] The conditions of their formation are not explained, and the ratios of the various types of meteorites have not been sufficiently well studied. Undoubtedly, the primeval abundance

[1] In a recent re-examination of Suess's and Urey's abundances, A. G. W. Cameron (*Astrophys. Jour.*, 126: 676–99, 1959) also relied on meteoritic data, i.e., on the chondritic abundances.

[2] The assumption that these authors have actually made is that the average composition of the chondritic variety of meteorites, rather than that of all meteorites, corresponds to the average composition of non-volatile cosmic materials. These authors did not follow the assumption that the average composition of meteorites corresponds to the average composition of the earth's crust.

[3] The author does not consider the fact that meteoritic data yield a smooth abundance curve with many detailed features, all of which can be interpreted theoretically. This claim cannot be made for any other kind of abundance curve.

of the elements in the earth's crust was altered by the secondary processes which also took place in meteorites; only about the latter we know much less than about the migration of the matter of the earth.[4]

There began, together with the investigation of the earth (historically somewhat earlier), a study of the abundance of the elements in the atmospheres of the sun and stars. The study was intensified as soon as the application of spectroscopic data to the determination of the chemical composition of celestial bodies became possible. The hydrogen, metal, and helium contents of the stellar atmospheres were thus established.

On the basis of the spectral types of the stars, the so-called Harvard classification of stars was worked out. Summarizing the data of astrophysics, Lockyer interpreted the spectral sequence as an evolutionary scheme of stars which changed their chemical composition. These studies caused increased interest in the problem of the abundance of the elements and, to a certain extent, prompted Clarke to investigate the chemical composition of the earth's crust. However, Lockyer's viewpoint was subsequently disproved by the studies of the Indian scientist Megh Nad Saha [13], who showed that the different spectral types of the stars do not correspond to the change in chemical composition, but to the differences in the temperature and pressure of the stellar atmospheres and consequently to the differences in the conditions of excitation of atoms of the individual elements; so that the Harvard classification of the spectra represents essentially a temperature scale. However, there are stars with approximately the same temperature in their surface layers but with a different chemical composition.

The most studied astrophysical object is, of course, the atmosphere of the sun. The works of Russell [14] showed a relative similarity between the abundance of the heavy elements in the atmosphere of the sun and in the crust of the earth. Later on, studies were made of the composition of the stellar atmospheres of the principal representatives of the astronomical universe [15, 16], but the completeness and accuracy of these measurements were not too great. The methods of investigation of the abundance of the elements in astrophysical objects possess an advantage over the methods of studying the composition of the earth's crust, in that, if the latter is determined on the basis of many thousands of complex and time-consuming analyses, the former can be ascertained by studying only a few successful spectrograms. However, the completeness of astrophysical investigations is limited by the

[4] Many of the secondary processes which alter the abundance of the elements in the earth's crust did not take place in the meteorites.

excitation conditions of atoms in the stellar envelopes and by the absorption of the short-wave region of the spectrum in the upper layers of the earth's atmosphere.

Unfortunately, the excitation conditions of atoms of the principal components—hydrogen and helium—in the atmospheres of the sun and stars are such that a quantitative determination is associated with great errors. The principal spectral series of hydrogen—the Lyman series—lies in the ultraviolet region of the spectrum, which is absorbed in the upper layers of the atmosphere. In the visible part of the spectrum there is a secondary series, the Balmer series. The determination of the quantitative composition by using the intensity of the lines requires knowledge of the thermodynamic conditions. The assumption of thermodynamic equilibrium for the matter of the sun's envelope is applicable only to a first approximation. In reality, the spectrum of the sun deviates somewhat from the spectrum of an absolute black body. These deviations cause inaccuracies in the determination of the quantitative composition, inaccuracies which are especially large if the determination is conducted by using the lines which correspond to transitions between the higher-energy levels of the atom. This is exactly the case with the hydrogen atom. The content of the rare gases in the sun's atmosphere remains unknown, with the exception of helium, which was discovered under different excitation conditions—in the prominences of the sun.

Interesting are the studies of the composition of the gaseous nebulae. It was shown that the so-called "nebular" lines in their spectra, previously attributed to the elements unknown on the earth, are actually due to atomic transitions from the forbidden metastable states. These transitions are possible only in the extremely rarefied envelopes of the planetary nebulae at low pressures, which are not easily attainable in our laboratories. Most thoroughly investigated is the quantitative distribution of the major elements in the nebula NGC 7027 [17], including the information on the content of the rare gases.

A considerable part (approximately half) of the matter of our Galaxy is in the state of an extremely rarefied interstellar gas. The composition of this gas has been studied, and, like the composition of the stellar atmospheres, it shows a preponderance of hydrogen.

Recently the nature of the primary component of cosmic radiation was explained, that is, the "chemical composition" of matter in this specific state has also been studied.

The problem of the abundance of the elements cannot be separated from the problem of the abundance of isotopes. The isotopes of an element are independent units in the realm of atoms, which unite according to the secondary criterion of a common nuclear charge at a comparatively late stage of their existence (under conditions of relatively low temperatures and pressures), when the atomic nuclei receive their electronic shells. The further history of atoms is determined by their physicochemical properties, the structure of the electronic shells. United by a common charge (atomic number), the isotopes of an element are inseparable, although in other nuclear characteristics they differ no less than the isotopes of different elements.

A systematic study of isotopes was begun by Aston [18] in the early decades of this century, with a mass spectrograph of his own construction. The mass-spectrographic measurements permit the establishment not only of the atomic weights of isotopes but of their mass, their energy states, and their abundance as well. The study of the composition is, generally speaking, within the competence of chemistry. However, the methods used in mass spectrography explain why the study of isotopic composition was for a long time conducted by physicists in nearly complete isolation from the studies of geochemists and astrophysicists, who investigated the abundance of the chemical elements.

A great help in the study of isotopes was provided by the spectral method. In this manner the heavy isotope of hydrogen was discovered, the reason for which was disagreement between the atomic weights of hydrogen as determined by physicists and by chemists. The nuclear methods of the study of isotopes possess definite importance, for example, the "neutronometric" method. During the investigation of the nature of the absorption of neutrons by tantalum, a rare isotope of this element was recently discovered.

At the present time, isotopic analysis permits the solution of many purely geochemical problems. In the field of geochemistry there is a special branch of the geochemistry of isotopes or "isotope geology" to which is devoted the recently published monograph of Rankama. The geochemistry of isotopes overlaps, but is not identical with, the field we have referred to as "nuclear" geochemistry. Many instances of isotope fractionation in nature are caused by physicochemical and not by nuclear processes.

The history of the study of the abundance of chemical elements (or, generally speaking, of atomic nuclei) is distinguished by its uniqueness. The first materials were assembled by chemists and geologists, long before the structure of the atom was established. The studies were aimed at a comparatively limited objective of determining the chemical composition of the earth's crust, and they possessed a practical significance for the foundation of the science of mineral deposits. The first hints of the presence of a certain regularity in the quantitative composition of the chemical elements appeared at the beginning of the last century in the works of Dobereiner, Elie de Beaumont, and

Philipps. Mendeleyev clearly formulated this regularity as the predominance of the light elements over the heavy ones. At the end of the century, geochemistry emerged as a new science. At the present time it leans upon modern physics, chemistry, geology, and astrophysics but has its own problems and methods of investigation.

2. DISTRIBUTION OF CHEMICAL ELEMENTS IN THE EARTH'S CRUST

Naturally, the chemical composition of the earth's crust has been studied more fully than the composition of any other cosmic object. However, in the study of the abundance of the elements we cannot rely on this material as a principal guide. During its formation the earth's crust was relatively impoverished in many elements, and its composition now differs strongly from the primitive composition. Furthermore, the structure of the earth is not uniform, and therefore the data on the minerals and rocks of the earth's surface, assembled and critically averaged, can reflect only the composition of a certain definite shell of the earth. In this section we shall examine the distribution of the chemical elements in the earth's crust, since without such knowledge it is not possible to judge as to what kind of deviations the chemical composition of the earth's crust shows from the composition of the earth as a whole.

Composition of the Interior Parts of the Earth

At the present time, the assumption seems to be generally accepted that the material of the solar system was formed from the matter of the sun. In this process considerable loss of many light and volatile elements took place. The majority of Soviet cosmogonists adhere to the theory of the origin of the solar system developed by O. Yu. Shmidt [19]. According to this theory, the planets originated from a gas-and-dust nebula. The theory is short, by a long distance, of describing the constitution of the earth, but the important fact for us is that the assumption of the unity of origin of the matter of the earth, the planets, and the meteorites is now evidently accepted.

In the study of the composition of the earth it is necessary to utilize supplementary hypotheses regarding its constitution. On the basis of seismic-wave studies, it is possible to obtain some information about the properties of the matter of the geospheres and about the presence of the boundaries which separate them. But the geochemical interpretation of these data has until the present time been uncertain. A rapid change in density at the depth of 400–600 km. is apparently determined by the transition of the principal mineral of this zone—olivine

—into a different state of aggregation which is stable at high pressure.[5] Widely known is the concept of the earth's metallic core, consisting of nickel-iron, in analogy with the principal mineral of the iron meteorites. This concept is used to explain the high specific gravity of the earth as a whole, which is considerably greater than that of the earth's surface rocks. Other bodies of the solar system (Mars, the moon, and, to a lesser degree, Venus) are, with respect to specific gravity, considerably behind the earth; so that the existence of an iron core is, in any event, not necessary for a member of the solar system. The iron meteorites constitute only a small fraction of the total number of meteorites.

Until the present time, the question is under debate whether there is an iron core in the interior of the earth or whether the central zone is made up of the simplest silicates of iron and magnesium possessing a high density at pressures of the earth's deepest layers [20, pp. 65, 81]. If one accepts these limiting cases, the abundance of iron in the earth will change by not more than a factor of 2 or 3. The error within such limits is inadmissible in the study of one system, but in a comparison of different systems it is possible, at the present level of knowledge, to attempt the explanation of only the general features of the deviations in the abundance of the elements, bearing in mind, at the same time, that the incompleteness of our knowledge of the composition of the earth as a whole is not so important.

Geochemical Classification of the Elements

Goldschmidt [21] constructed a geochemical classification of the elements, starting with the hypothesis of the earth divided into an iron core, an intermediate sulfide zone, and an exterior alumosilicate layer. In composition the iron core is similar to iron meteorites, the sulfide zone to the troilite inclusions of meteorites, and the alumosilicate layer to the stony meteorites. According to this classification, the elements are divided into the following groups:

1. Siderophile elements—the elements with high affinity for iron. Their atoms are characterized by electronic shells which are being built up. The elements occupy the minima in the atomic volume curve (iron and platinum groups, molybdenum, and others).

2. Chalcophile elements—the elements with high affinity for sulfur. The ions have eighteen electrons in the outer shell. The elements lie on the rising segment of the atomic volume curve (copper, lead, zinc,

[5] For the laboratory and thermodynamic studies of the transition of olivine into the spinel structure at pressures equivalent to the indicated depth see the papers by A. E. Ringwood (*Geochim. et Cosmochim. Acta,* **13:** 303–21, 1958; **15:** 18–29, 195–212, 1958).

the rare non-ferrous metals, precious metals, arsenic, selenium, tellurium).

3. Lithophile elements—the elements of the lithosphere which lie in the region of the maxima of the atomic volume curve. The ions have eight electrons in the outer shell (the leading elements of the granitic magma: oxygen, sodium, magnesium, aluminum, silicon, and the microcomponents of that magma: lithium, rubidium, tin, niobium, cesium, barium, the rare earths, and the radioactive elements).

4. Atmophile elements—the inert gases of the earth's atmosphere (the noble gases, nitrogen). The atoms with eight electrons in the outer shell.

The scheme of Goldschmidt is based on the atomic volume curve, that is, it has a simple physical interpretation but assumes a definite internal structure of the earth, thus utilizing, in addition, certain hypothetical ideas. These drawbacks do not exist in the classification of Fersman [4, Vol. 3], in which Mendeleyev's table is divided into the following "fields" of the chemical elements:

1. The common field (up to nickel)—the elements of high abundance. For the same period of Mendeleyev's table, the elements with small atomic numbers are specific for the acidic magma,[6] whereas those with large atomic numbers are specific for the ultrabasic magma.

2. The sulfide field—the elements which form sulfides. The ions have eighteen electrons in the outer shell.

3. The acidic field—the elements of the acidic magma: the granites and granitic pegmatites. The heavy elements contain eight electrons in the outer shell of their ions. With increasing atomic number (up to the elements of Group VIII of the periodic table), these elements grade into the elements of the ultrabasic magma.

The closer to the earth's surface the studied layer is, the fuller is our knowledge and the more fortified our theories. Let us consider the conditions of the distribution of the elements following Fersman's principle of geophases which sets forth the development of magma from ultrabasic rocks of the deep-seated zones (protocrystallization) through basic and acidic rocks (mesocrystallization) to postmagmatic derivatives of the end crystallization. An extrapolation into the deep, iron-enriched zone can be made, but it is not necessary for us to invoke this insufficiently reliable material.

Under the term "earth's crust" are conventionally understood the outer layers of the earth down to the depth of approximately 15 km.[7] This depth is somewhat less than the depth of the occurrence of the

[6] This, however, is not true of magnesium.

[7] Actually, this appears to be only a lower limit of crustal thickness. Thicknesses up to 55 km. have recently been reported (F. Press, *Bull. Geol. Soc. America,* **67:** 1647–58, 1956; M. Ewing and F. Press, *Bull. Geol. Soc. America,* **68:** 1725, 1957; **70:** 229–44, 1959).

majority of volcanic chambers and of the earthquake hypocenters. It is considerably less than the depth of the region of the active processes of the earth's crust, which is about 100 km., as can be determined from the depth of the isostatic compensation—the effect which levels off the operation of the active processes.

The earth's crust is inhomogeneous both in depth and across the surface, where the inactive areas (for example, the plateaus) differ in geologic structure and in composition from the active zones—the geosynclines. The movements of geosynclines have an amplitude of the order of 10–20 km., that is, during the time between two orogenic upheavals a substratum is brought up to the surface of the earth from a depth approximately equal to the earth's crustal layer in the indicated sense. According to geochemical indications, the geosynclinal areas are also inhomogeneous, forming "geochemical belts"—for example, the "silver belt" of America or the platinum-palladium zone of the Urals, which gradates into a zone of palladium-platinum enrichment in South Africa. Such belts indicate a non-uniform, unsettled, and unbalanced condition of the earth's envelope. However, the fluctuations in the composition of individual sectors of the earth's crust are much smaller than the change in the composition of the earth with depth.

Distribution of Chemical Elements during the Geochemical Processes

Let us consider the main features of the change of the chemical composition during the geochemical processes. The magma changes under the operation of the following important causes: (*a*) liquefaction (segregation in the liquid magma) and gravitational differentiation of the magma; (*b*) circulation of solutions; and (*c*) liberation of the volatile fraction.

The primary crystallization begins at about 1,500° C. In the course of this crystallization the minerals are formed in approximately the following order: chromite—iron oxides and sphene—orthosilicates (olivines)—metasilicates (pyroxenes)—amphibole—biotite, etc.

The order of the crystallization of minerals is governed by the geoenergetic principle of Fersman. First of all, there are formed minerals of those elements whose crystallization is accompanied by the liberation of a greater amount of energy. The energy of the crystalline lattice is described by the expression

$$E \approx \frac{W_1 W_2}{R_1 + R_2} \times \text{const.,}^{8} \qquad (2.1)$$

[8] The constant in this equation, the so-called Madelung constant, is known to vary slightly for different types of crystal structure (for example, see O. K. Rice, *Electronic Structure and Chemical Binding* [1940], p. 225).

where W_1 and W_2 are the valences and R_1 and R_2 are the ionic radii. It is obvious that minerals which contain ions with small radii and high valence are formed first. Since the ionic radii increase for the heavy elements, the light elements separate earlier than their heavier analogues, in spite of the fact that the gravitational differentiation would have led to an opposite effect.

The separated minerals react with solutions. Because of this, only a limited number of minerals are present in the frozen magma of the primary crystallization; their composition is averaged and approaches the average composition of the starting material. The characteristic elements of the protocrystallization, according to Fersman, are Mg, Si, Fe, Ti, Ni, Cr, and, among the rarer elements, Pt, Zn, and Ge. The light, even-numbered elements predominate (isotopes with atomic weight $A = 4n$, where n is a whole number). This, however, characterizes in general the composition of cosmic matter, that is, the process of liquefaction and of the separation of fluids does not cause a significant change in the macrocomponents of the protocrystallization stage.

Protocrystallization proceeds under conditions of deficiency (from our point of view) of oxygen, sulfur, silicon, and aluminum. The elements usually occur in the lower oxidation states (Fe^{+2}, Ti^{+3}, V^{+3}, Cr^{+3}). There are found such minerals as carbides (for example, cohenite Fe_3C), whose formation in an oxygen environment is not possible. The result of the relative sulfur deficiency is that at this stage, of all sulfides of iron, mainly pyrrhotite (Fe_n S_{n+1}) and not pyrite (FeS_2) is formed.[9] Silicon and aluminum are present in this zone in very small amounts, even when compared with oxygen. For the leading minerals of the deep-seated crystallization—the orthosilicates—the ratio $Si + Al/O = 0.25$. Evidently, the gravitational differentiation of the ultrabasic and basic magma is followed by the segregation of the primary sulfides with limited solubility in the silicate melt. These minerals are enriched in nickel (nickel pyrite) and platinum (sperrylite). If, because of the conditions of the environment, the primary sulfides are not formed, nickel isomorphically substitutes for magnesium in olivines.

The importance of isomorphism in geochemical processes was first shown by V. I. Vernadskii. In 1911 he proposed his isomorphic sequences of the elements upon which modern geochemistry is based.

[9] It is extremely doubtful that this is the case. Pyrite is unstable with respect to pyrrhotite and sulfur under conditions of protocrystallization. Thus, for $T = 1000°$ K, for which data are available, one calculates ΔF for the reaction $2FeS_2$(solid) $= 2FeS$ (solid) $+ S_2$(gas) to be −3,300 cal. (see *Metallurgical Thermochemistry* by O. Kubaschewski and E. LL. Evans [1958], p. 338). Therefore, there is no need to invoke sulfur deficiency for the formation of pyrrhotite at the high temperatures in question.

With large energy reserves in the deep-seated zones, much more extensive isomorphism is possible there than in the surface layers. Thus, under deep-seated conditions, an isomorphic substitution of sodium and potassium takes place in perthites, which later break up into mutually intergrown sodium and potassium feldspars. Usually there is observed an isomorphic entrance of Mg, Fe, and Ni into olivines. Isomorphism is determined, first of all, by the similarity of ionic sizes and by the polarization ability of ions. The ionic radius is approximately described by the expression

$$R = a\frac{n^2}{Z}, \tag{2.2}$$

where a is the Bohr radius of the principal orbit of hydrogen; n is the principal quantum number of the outer shell, which is equal to the period number of Mendeleyev's table; and Z is the charge of the nucleus or the atomic number of the element. With increasing atomic number, the ionic radius decreases, and with increasing period number, it increases. Therefore, the ions of the elements situated along the diagonal which originates at the upper left-hand corner of Mendeleyev's table have similar radii and tend toward isomorphism. Such "diagonal isomorphism," described by Fersman, is often manifested in geochemical processes. Thus Ca^{+2} and Y^{+3}, Mo^{+4} and Re^{+4}, and other ions are isomorphically substituted. From equation (2.1) it is seen that the substitution of ions of low valence by ions of high valence is energetically favorable. This is sometimes manifested, but the development of such a "polar" isomorphism is hindered by the fact that ions of high valence usually belong to the heavy elements (for example, the atomic weight of calcium is 40.08, and that of yttrium is 88.92), and with increasing atomic weight the abundance of the element shows a sharp decrease (the atomic content of calcium in the earth's crust is 1.41 per cent, whereas that of yttrium is 1×10^{-3} per cent).

The transition from the deep-seated to the surface types of magma, according to the petrographic series peridotites—basalts—granites, is connected with a decrease in the content of iron and magnesium. In the atmosphere of the sun there is approximately ten times as much magnesium as calcium, whereas the content of these two leading alkaline-earth metals in the earth's crust is almost the same. Magnesium probably remains in the protocrystallization zone. It should be noted that the volume of the deep-seated zones is considerably larger than the volume of the earth's crust, so that small changes in the composition or the deep-seated matter lead to a large difference in the composition of the residual magma of the final crystallization stage.

On going to the surface rocks, there is an increase in the content of sodium, aluminum, silicon, and potassium and also in that of titanium and calcium, which, however, gravitate preferentially toward the intermediate magma of the gabbroic and basaltic type. That the role of the main alkaline-earth element is conveyed from magnesium to calcium is understandable, because the ionic radius of calcium (1.06 Å) is larger than the ionic radius of magnesium (0.78 Å), that is, the role is explained by a smaller amount of energy contributed by calcium to the crystalline lattice of minerals. The ratio Si + Al/O increases to 0.5 for the acidic magma and its derivatives.

The geochemical paths of nickel and iron—constant companions from iron meteorites to ultrabasic rocks—separate with the formation of the silicate magma. Nickel almost does not participate in the later phases of crystallization. This is explained by the favorable conditions of the isomorphic entrance of nickel into the magnesium minerals of the protocrystallization stage and by the fact that, for nickel, in geochemistry only the valence of +2 is stable, whereas iron in the later geophases is present in the higher oxidation state of +3. In these geophases the usual companions of iron are titanium (in basic rocks), manganese (in pegmatites, pneumatolytes, and partly in the zone of hypergenesis), copper (in sulfide veins), and sometimes aluminum (in laterites).

Distribution of Radioactive Elements in the Earth

Of great importance, not only for geochemistry but also for knowledge of the interior constitution of the earth, is the distribution of radioactive elements in various rocks. There is a regular decrease in the activity of rocks on going from the acidic surface rocks to ultrabasic deep-seated types and to meteorites, whose composition is to some extent similar to the matter of the interior regions of the earth. Radioactive heat, as was shown by Vernadskii [3], constitutes the principal source of the energy of the subcrustal layers of the earth. The active processes are staged in the layers which probably correspond to the depth of the isostatic compensation of the earth's crust (about 100 km.). The data on the radioactivity of rocks [22, 23, 24] are shown in Table 1, which also includes information on meteorites [174, 175, 176, 177].

Let us consider the time, t, needed to melt rocks with their own radioactive heat in the absence of heat emission. Obviously,

$$t \approx \frac{c\Delta T}{q}, \tag{2.3}$$

where $\Delta T \approx 1{,}500°$ is the temperature difference; $c \approx 0.2$–0.3 is the specific heat capacity of rocks; and q is the liberation of radioactive heat in calories per year per gram of rock.

TABLE 1

Radioactivity of Rocks and Meteorites

Name	Radioelement Content in Gm/Ton of Rock			Liberation of Radioactive Heat in 10^{-6} Cal/Gm Year			
	K	Th	U	K	Th	U	Total
Iron meteorites	$\sim 1 \times 10^{-5}$	$6–20 \times 10^{-6}$	$10^{-4}–10^{-6}$	$\sim 5 \times 10^{-7}$	$\leqslant 6 \times 10^{-5}$	$\leqslant 6 \times 10^{-5}$	$\leqslant 1 \times 10^{-4}$
Stony meteorites (chondrites)	0.26*	0.03	0.01	0.01*	0.006	0.006	0.02
Ultrabasic rocks	0.4	0.13	0.04	0.02	0.025	0.025	0.07

* A concentration of 0.105 gm. K^{40} per ton of chondritic material is obtained on the basis of a new average potassium value (880 ppm) reported for chondrites by G. Edwards and H. C. Urey (*Geochim. et Cosmochim. Acta*, **7**: 154–68, 1955). Using this value, Urey (*Proc. Nat. Acad. Sci.*, **41**: 127–44, 1955) calculates the heat liberation from K^{40} in the chondritic meteorites to be 0.98 erg/gm year or 0.024×10^{-6} cal/gm year.

For acidic rocks t is of the order of 10^8 years; for ultrabasic rocks it increases to 10^{10} years, and for iron meteorites it is longer than 10^{12} years. During the time of the existence of the earth's crust (of the order of 10^9 years) it is possible to expect substantial heating of the surface rocks. However, for these rocks the heat emission is high, so that their melting can occur only in isolated parts of the earth where sufficiently deep-seated strata are substantially enriched in radioactive elements. Apparently, such regions form the basis of geosynclines—the regions of geotectonic oscillations. According to V. V. Belousov [25], the period of geotectonic oscillations is 1.5×10^8 years (for the post-Cambrian orogenic upheavals), which coincides, in order of magnitude, with the estimate of the time for the melting of the acidic rocks. In the course of time t the heat flux propagates itself over the distance [26] thus:

$$l = \sqrt{\frac{\lambda t}{\rho c}}, \qquad (2.4)$$

where $\lambda \approx 10^{-2}$ cal per cm per deg per sec is the conductivity and $\rho \approx 3.5$ gm per cm^3 is the density of rocks. If $t = 10^8$ years, $l = 50$–70 km., which is close to the depth at which the active processes of the earth's crust occur.

Radioactive heat is apparently the principal impulse of the active processes, in particular of the geotectonic oscillations of the earth's crust. The consequences of this are the differentiation of rocks, the segregation of the residual magma, and, at the same time, the formation of mineral deposits which are basically associated with the derivatives of the acidic magma. Thus the practical results of a non-uniform distribution of radioactive elements in the subcrustal matter are extremely significant.

The Residual Magma

We shall examine the basic features of the distribution of the elements in the residual magma which produces pegmatite veins. In the geochemical sense, pegmatites differ from the rocks of the late crystallization in the following characteristics [27]:

1. The elements of the acidic field (according to the classification of Fersman) predominate in pegmatites. There begins an extensive replacement of the leading elements of magma by their higher analogues in the periodic table, a replacement which did not take place earlier because it was not favorable energetically. Thus potassium is replaced by rubidium and cesium, silicon by germanium, and so forth. There is observed an enrichment of the elements whose radii are either too large (Ta, Zr, Cs, Rb) or too small (Li, Be, B) for the isomorphic

replacement of other ions during the primary crystallization. The increase in the concentration of these rare elements (essentially the odd-numbered elements) results in some of them being able to form their own minerals.

2. At the beginning of the pegmatitic process, iron separates as magnetic streaks and black tourmaline—the schorl. The process of deferrization leads to important consequences. The iron content decreases so much that, for the pegmatitic minerals, it becomes customary to have their Fe^{+2} ion replaced by the manganous ion Mn^{+2}, a replacement which is not favorable energetically because of the large size of the latter ion.

3. The heavy alkaline-earth elements barium and strontium, which remained in the residual melt because the large radii did not favor energetically their co-crystallization with calcium, are also not retained here but pass into subsequent geophases. By contrast, the pegmatites are enriched in alkali metals which do not form volatile oxides—sodium, lithium, rubidium, and cesium.

The further evolution of the derivatives of magma is connected with the release of the volatile components which produce pneumatolytic and later hydrothermal veins. The dominant mineral of hydrothermal veins is quartz. A considerable fraction of the elements migrate in the form of the light, volatile fluorides. In general, it is probable that many elements, particularly the radioactive elements, are brought up from the deeper parts of the earth as fluorides—for example, SiF_4, SnF_4, ThF_4, UF_4, and others.

High consumption of oxygen in the oxidation processes—for instance, in the conversion of metal fluorides into oxides—leads to oxygen deficiency, and in a number of cases metals precipitate as sulfides.[10] However, in the presence of oxygen, the sulfides are easily oxidized to sulfates, with the liberation of a very large amount of energy. The difference between the hydrothermal and the primary sulfides is that the formation of the former is preceded by a sharp decrease in the content of iron (deferrization during the early pegmatite phase). That is why, instead of the dominant minerals of the primary sulfide bodies—the compounds of iron and nickel—we have a broad representation of a complex of minerals which are composed of the elements of the "sulfide" field, according to the classification of Fersman—Cu, Zn, Pb, As, Sb, Hg, Bi, and others. The ions of these elements contain eighteen electrons in the outer shell. Such ions, because of their large polarization, have only a small ability to substitute isomorphically for the ions of the elements of the "acidic" field, which have eight electrons

[10] The conversion of metal fluorides into oxides is thermodynamically infeasible. For example, for the conversion $SiF_4(gas) + O_2(gas) = SiO_2(solid) + 2F_2(gas)$ $\Delta F_{298} \sim$ 180 K cal., and $UF_4(solid) + O_2(gas) = UO_2(solid) + 2F_2(gas)$ $\Delta F_{298} \sim 190$ K cal.

in the outer shell (with the exception of Sn and Ge). And, because of this, the elements of the sulfide field concentrate to a considerable degree in the derivatives of the magma.

All these elements are sufficiently heavy and consequently not very abundant. In order to be able to form their own minerals, these elements must increase their concentration in comparison with that of the other metals. This is brought about after the precipitation of iron. As for iron itself, it here forms the mineral pyrite under conditions of sulfur excess.

The primeval abundance of some elements of the sulfide field is so low that even under these favorable conditions they are unable to form their own minerals (indium, rhenium) or else form them very seldom (cadmium). In some cases this is explained by the fact that the element yields more stable minerals of a different type (for example, tin occurs usually in the form of oxide—cassiterite—but its pure sulfide—herzenbergite—represents a great rarity). In other cases, this is associated with easy destructibility of the sulfide (for example, greenockite, CdS).

Surface Processes

The penetration of the oxygen atmosphere into the surface layers of the earth causes oxidation reactions. The elements pass into ionic states of higher oxidation (Fe^{+3}, V^{+5}, U^{+6}, and others). In the oxidation zone, sulfides are destroyed and sulfates formed; for example,

$$ZnS + 2O_2 = ZnSO_4.$$

This equation is not applicable to pyrite, where the divalent iron enters into a bisulfide combination of the type FeS_2. The sulfur atoms in pyrite are linked by non-ionic bonds. During the oxidation of pyrite the excess of sulfur leads to the liberation of free sulfuric acid. The balanced reaction has the form

$$12FeS_2 + 45O_2 + 42H_2O = 12Fe(OH)_3 + 24H_2SO_4.$$ [11]

The sulfuric acid–bearing surface solutions favor the migration of a number of elements (vanadium, uranium) and promote the formation of their secondary deposits.

As the temperature and pressure decrease, the thermodynamic boundaries of the deposition of minerals become specific; there are formed clearly separated complexes of the paragenetically associated minerals. At the same time, the amount of foreign impurities in minerals is reduced. The phenomenon of purification of minerals upon

[11] Ferric hydroxide and sulfuric acid should not be given as the final products of a reaction.

their transition into the low-temperature phases is observed over the entire range of the geochemical process. For example, platinum from pyroxenites is considerably purer than platinum from the earlier dunites, particularly from the chromite streaks of the protocrystallization stage. The uraninites from the early pegmatites often contain a large number of foreign admixtures—thorium, the rare earths, and other elements. The thorium content of uranium oxides from the hydrothermal phase falls almost to zero. Especially pure are the minerals of this phase which precipitate during the individual stages of volatilization and circulation of the subsurface solutions.

However, opposite cases are also known. During the late pegmatitic phase, such elements as rubidium and cesium which do not yield volatile oxides are forced, despite the ionic size difference, to enter the minerals of the solidifying vein, inasmuch as their concentration is not sufficient for the formation of their own minerals. The low-temperature beryls of the transparent variety which grow in the empty cavities—*zanoryshy*[12]—of the vein bodies are often enriched in these elements. The uranium minerals of the hydrothermal geophase (pitchblende, uranium black) contain only small or negligible amounts of thorium and the rare earths but are enriched in the non-radiogenic "ore" lead, since lead forms its main accumulations as the sulfide galena precisely during the hydrothermal phase.

Under surface conditions, in the zone of hypergenesis, two opposing processes exist: (1) the deposition of some minerals under strictly defined physicochemical conditions, which leads to the formation of thick beds of such minerals of the biosphere as laterites, phosphorites, bauxites, and others; (2) mechanical and chemical destruction of minerals of the earth's crust, resulting in the deposition of the sedimentary strata whose composition becomes the average composition of the earth's crust.

In the surface layer, many minerals (sulfides, feldspars) which are unstable under new conditions are destroyed, that is, ultimately radioactive energy, which has caused the magmatic processes of mineral formation, is released. Especially important are the biogenic processes, of which the most important unquestionably is the formation of molecular oxygen under the promotion of the energy of solar radiation, that is, in the final analysis, of the energy of thermonuclear reactions in the stellar interiors.

Many investigations have been devoted to the composition of certain individual formations of the earth's crust. Thus Fersman investigated the content of the elements in pegmatites [27] and Vinogradov that of the soils [2] and living matter [28]. These studies, while having

[12] Transliterated term.

contributed a great deal to the development of geochemistry, obviously have no significance in the study of the abundance of the chemical elements in the accepted sense. We shall confine ourselves to the material dealing with the earth's crust as a whole.

3. ABUNDANCE OF CHEMICAL ELEMENTS IN VARIOUS SYSTEMS

We shall describe the abundance in terms of the content of the element in a given system in weight or atom per cent (n), or in terms of the logarithm of the relative concentration of the given element expressed as the number of atoms (Q).

The first investigations of the composition of the earth's crust, carried out by Clarke and Washington [29], consisted of a mechanical averaging of the analytical data on the composition of rocks. In this averaging, the rare rock types and those uncharacteristic of the earth's crust were taken into account with large relative weight. Later on, Goldschmidt, the Noddacks, and other investigators employed the method of studying an average sample made up of different rocks in the ratio proportional to their content. The subjective element in such an approach cannot be fully excluded. However, in the final analysis, the entire material accumulated by geochemistry is used for determining the average composition of the earth's crust, and the reliability of modern data is sufficiently high.

In Table I of the Appendix (p. 265) are given data on the abundance of the chemical elements (in weight per cent) in the earth's crust and meteorites. Separately are presented data on the composition of the lithosphere according to compilations of Goldschmidt [30] (with supplements by Rankama [31]) and Vinogradov [2] and the data on the composition of the earth's crust as a whole, including the atmosphere and hydrosphere, according to Fersman [4]. For the majority of the elements, different authors give similar abundance values. Considerable discrepancies are present in the values for the volatile elements (C, N, F, Cl, Te, Hg) and for some elements of the acidic magma (Nb, Mo, Ta, W). We shall not discuss these discrepancies, which, on the whole, are not so large as to alter the general picture.

In addition to samples of the earth's crust, only the meteorites are accessible to direct analysis in our chemical laboratories. The stony or the silicate meteorites are, according to A. N. Zavaritskii [32], divided basically into chondrites and eucrites.[13] The chondrites contain rapidly cooled droplets—the chondrules, often composed of glass and

[13] In the generally adopted classification of Prior (*Catalogue of Meteorites* by G. T. Prior, revised by M. H. Hey [London, 1953]) the stony meteorites are divided into two broad classes, chondrites and achondrites. Eucrites are a rare subclass of achondrites, not a class as implied by the author.

almost never having undergone full devitrification. The eucrites are similar in composition to ultrabasic rocks of the earth with certain characteristic features (the presence of a high-temperature modification of quartz—tridymite). According to Zavaritskii, the eucrites came from the solid crust of a disrupted planet, whereas the chondrites can be formed from the deeper layers, during a rapid fall of pressure and profuse evolution of gases.[14]

Iron meteorites are fairly rare objects. Their proportion in the total mass of meteorites is not greater than 10 per cent. However, among the meteorites found on the earth's surface, iron meteorites far exceed stony meteorites because of their high degree of preservability under the soil conditions and a conspicuous difference from the matter of the rocks.

For meteorites, solidification in a water- and oxygen-impoverished environment is characteristic. This leads to the formation of a series of specific minerals of the phosphide group (schreibersite, Fe_3P) which are unknown on the earth, and of the minerals of the carbide group (moissanite, SiC, and others), of which only the extremely rare cohenite has been found in the deep-seated rocks of the earth. Of the minerals of the sulfide group, calcium sulfide (oldhamite, CaS) has been discovered in meteorites, while in the accessible regions of the earth calcium is always bound in oxides. The most common sulfide in meteorites is iron sulfide—troilite, FeS. In the surface layers of the earth, iron forms bisulfide, FeS_2 (pyrite or marcasite), but among the sulfides of the primary crystallization the mineral pyrrhotite ($n\mathrm{FeS}\cdot\mathrm{FeS_2}$) is common; its composition is close to that of troilite. It is obvious that, for meteorites, as for the deep zones of the earth, the deficiency of sulfur, which prevents the formation of bisulfides is characteristic. Troilite has not been found in the earth's crust, but in the strongly reducing environment of brine pools, the hydrates of iron sulfate of the type $\mathrm{FeS}\cdot n\mathrm{H_2O}$ (*mel'nikovite* or hydrotroilite) are precipitated.

The meteoritic sulfides are very interesting and have been sufficiently well studied.[15] However, their relative content is small, and for this reason we quote in Table I of the Appendix only the data on the abundance of the chemical elements in the stony and iron meteorites

[14] According to H. C. Urey and H. Craig (*Geochim. et Cosmochim. Acta,* **4:** 36–82, 1953) and especially to R. A. Fish, G. G. Goles, and E. Anders (*Astrophys. Jour.,* **132:** 243–58, 1960), all meteorites came from small planets which were reduced to meteoritic size by mutual collisions. A possibility of lunar origin of chondrites and of asteroidal origin of iron meteorites has recently been suggested by Urey (see the work of P. Eberhardt and D. C. Hess in *Astrophys. Jour.,* **131:** 38–45, 1960).

[15] Actually, only a few studies of meteoritic sulfides (troilites) have been made, nearly all of them in recent years, e.g., A. A. Yavnel' (*Meteoritika,* **14:** 87–91, 1956); J. F. Lovering (*Geochim. et Cosmochim. Acta,* **12:** 253–61, 1957); W. Nichiporuk and A. A. Chodos (*Jour. Geophys. Res.,* **64:** 2451–63, 1959).

(according to Brown [11]), and also in chondrites (according to Urey [12] [16]). The compilation of Brown is based, to a considerable degree, on the data of the Noddacks but is supplemented by those of Goldschmidt, P. N. Chirvinskii, and others. Urey assumes that the composition of chondrites corresponds to the average composition of the meteoritic matter.

Among the celestial bodies, the best known is the composition of the atmosphere of the sun. In addition, fairly complete information is available on the composition of the atmospheres of τ Scorpii and γ Pegasi and also on the composition of the interstellar gas. A summary of the data is given in Table 2.

TABLE 2

ATOMIC CONTENT OF ELEMENTS IN SOME COSMIC OBJECTS
(The Oxygen Content Is Taken as Unity)

ELEMENT	SUN'S ATMOSPHERE		ATMOSPHERE OF τ SCORPII	ATMOSPHERE OF γ PEGASI	INTERSTELLAR MATTER
	[34]	[35]	[35]	[43]	[45]
H	2,700	560	1,000	10,000	2,000
He	595	....	182	2,000	....
C	0.10	0.37	0.17	0.05	....
N	0.32	0.76	0.39	0.23	....
O	1.00	1.00	1.00	1.00	1.0
Mg	0.65	0.062	0.058	0.31	0.001
Na	0.010	0.0035	....	....	0.001
Al	0.0065	0.0040	0.0037	0.011	....
Si	0.20	0.037	0.064	0.09	....
S	0.10	0.016	....	0.04	....
K	0.0032	0.00029	....	....	0.00025
Ca	0.010	0.0031	....	....	0.0001

Of great interest is the study of the planetary nebulae, in the composition of which the rare gases have been discovered.

For a number of F-type stars which predominate among the visible stars of the Galaxy, no outstanding differences were discovered in chemical composition [33]. Similar also is the composition of such diverse formations as the stars, interstellar matter, and the planetary nebulae. However, objects are found among the celestial bodies which have an unusual chemical appearence.

In the atmospheres of cold stars (red giants) one observes the band spectra of various molecular compounds. Thus, in R- and N-type stars the C_2 bands predominate, and oxygen is almost absent. In K- and M-type stars the TiO and in S-type stars the ZrO bands have been

[16] The modified chondritic abundances by Urey as published in the paper by H. Suess and H. C. Urey (*Rev. Mod. Phys.*, 28: 53–74, 1956) have been added to Table I of the Appendix.

found. These oxides, while stable at high excitations of molecules, are transformed on the earth into higher oxidation states. The hot stars of the Wolf-Rayet type are also divided into two groups, according to the presence in their spectra of carbon and nitrogen lines. In general, this group of stars is distinguished by an unusual chemical composition. There is a basis for the belief that there is more helium in these stars than hydrogen, $He/H \approx 2.5$. For the majority of stars, this ratio is reversed, $He/H \approx 0.1$ [36]. It is possible that in the stellar universe there are also bodies relatively enriched in Nb, Sr, Ba, and the rare-earth elements. There is an assumption [178] that the stars of different sectors of the galactic nebulae (the so-called Population I and Population II stars) differ in their chemical composition.

Very interesting are the data on the composition of the primary cosmic rays. Investigations near the upper limit of the atmosphere have detected that the most abundant of these rays are protons. There are also present in them heavier elements from helium to iron in a proportion close to that found in the stellar atmospheres (see Table 3 compiled according to [214]).

TABLE 3

COMPOSITION OF PRIMARY COSMIC RAYS

Atomic Nuclei	Relative Intensity
H^1	10,000
He^4	880
$6 \leqslant Z \leqslant 9$	50
$Z \geqslant 10$	17

The content of nuclei of even elements in cosmic rays is several times higher than the content of odd elements, a relation which is also observed for other systems, so that the "chemical composition" of cosmic rays is close to the composition of the matter of the cosmos [37]. Unfortunately, the information on the heavy nuclei of the primary cosmic rays is contradictory because of extreme experimental difficulties.

The content of the light metals (Li,[17] Be, B) in all studied systems of the cosmos is very small, since their nuclei are easily destroyed in thermonuclear reactions of stellar interiors. A great number of works were devoted to the concentration of these nuclei in the composition of cosmic rays. The latest, most reliable data [179, 180] confirm the presence of isotopes of the light elements in the primary component

[17] An exceptionally high content of Li has been found by W. K. Bonsack and J. L. Greenstein (*Astrophys. Jour.*, **131**: 83–98, 1960) in four T Tauri and a related star. The lithium-to-metals ratio in these stars is 100 times greater than in the sun and approximately equals the terrestrial value.

of cosmic rays. Their amount is approximately one order of magnitude smaller than the amount of the heavier isotopes, whereas at the same time, for example, lithium and beryllium in the sun are seven orders of magnitude less abundant than oxygen. It is possible that the relative enrichment of cosmic rays in the nuclei of the light elements is established as a result of the secondary reactions of the splitting or of the reactions involving the heavy nuclei. It should be noted that the total amount of cosmic matter in the form of cosmic-ray particles is negligible.

A comparison of the abundance of the elements in the sun, $Q_{\odot}$, with that in the planetary nebula NGC 7027 (Q_N), the earth's crust (Q_E), the stony (Q_S) and iron (Q_I) meteorites, and the chondrites (Q_{Ch}), is given in Table II of the Appendix (p. 269). Separately are given the data of Brown on the stony meteorites as a whole and the data of Urey on the chondritic variety of these objects.[18] For convenience of comparison, it is conventionally adopted that $Q_{\text{oxygen}} = 9$. There is no information available on the oxygen content of chondrites[19] and iron meteorites, and the data on the abundance of the elements in these objects are calibrated in terms of iron. It is accepted that $Q_{\text{iron}} = 8.0$, that is, it is the same as for the atmosphere of the sun.[20] The indexes "+" and "−" which appear next to the number in the column Q_N indicate that the abundance is somewhat higher or lower than the given value. In Table II are also given the differences between the Q-values for the earth's crust, the iron and stony meteorites, and the Q-values for the sun's atmosphere, that is, the logarithms of the element abundance ratio for these systems.

The abundance of the elements in the atmosphere of the sun is that by Russell [14] (the data with two significant figures) with some supplements from V. A. Ambartsumian [36] (the data with three figures) and Kuiper [42] (denoted in the table by the letter "K"). In addition, the data of Aller [44], which essentially are close to the compilation accepted by us, have been used.[21] In some cases, the abundance of the ele-

[18] The chondritic abundances by Urey which the author lists in Table II are those published in 1952 (*Phys. Rev.*, **88**: 248–52, 1952) and not the modified abundances which Urey published in 1956 and which have been incorporated in Table I during this translation.

[19] Although no direct determination of oxygen in chondrites has as yet been made, any published analysis contains information on the oxygen content of these meteorites.

[20] H. C. Urey (*Symposium on the Origin of the Earth and Planets,* Tenth General Assembly of the International Astronomical Union, Moscow; abstract in *Geokhimiya,* **7**: 691–92, 1958; also in the paper by A. G. W. Cameron in *Astrophys. Jour.*, **129**: 676–99, 1959) has noted that iron (and other iron-peak elements) is overabundant in meteorites by a factor of about 7.

[21] See more recent element abundances in the sun by L. H. Aller (*Handbuch der Physik* [Berlin: Springer Verlag, 1958], **51**: 324–52.

ments according to Aller is in considerable disagreement with the data of Russell and Ambartsumian. These values are marked in the table by the letter "A." The composition of the planetary nebula NGC 7027 is given according to Bowen and Wyse [17] with some supplements from Ambartsumian [36]. The composition of the earth's crust is quoted from Fersman [4] and that of meteorites from the authors of the compilations given in Table I. The data of Table II are presented graphically in Figure 1.

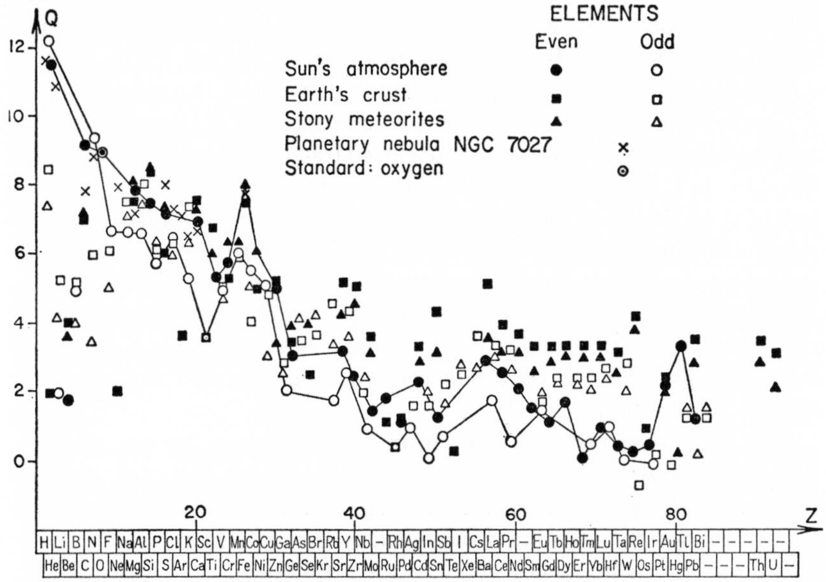

Fig. 1.—Abundance of chemical elements in the sun's atmosphere, earth's crust, stony meteorites, and the planetary nebula NGC 7027. The points, representing the abundance of the even and odd chemical elements in the sun's atmosphere, are connected by a solid line. The accepted standard: $Q_{\text{oxygen}} = 9.0$.

If the ratio of the abundances of two elements varies from one system to another, this can be explained by the addition of one element as well as the escape of another. Sometimes we can label one of these processes as more probable, but, generally speaking, even a comparison of the entire tabulated material is insufficient for the solution of the problem of the migration of the elements and of their proportion in the primeval matter of the solar system. It could be thought that the most reliable in this sense are the data on the sun's atmosphere, but there also the processes of migration are not excluded.

Attempting to approach the problem of the primeval abundance of the elements, Brown [11] utilized the data on meteorites, the sun, the planetary nebulae, and the individual stars (τ Scorpii, γ Pegasi). A.

mechanical combination of this type appears to us to be incorrect in principle.

The abundance distribution of the elements in various systems of the cosmos reveals similar characteristics. The dominant components are hydrogen and helium (both lost by many bodies of the solar system). The light metals—lithium, beryllium, and boron—are contained only in negligible amounts. With increasing atomic weight, the abundance of the elements decreases down to the middle of Mendeleyev's table and then becomes almost constant. There is observed a preponderance of even elements as well as of even isotopes. Such are the basic regularities; they will be examined in detail in Section 15 (p. 188).

Some elements deviate from the general trend of the abundance as a function of atomic weight. This is observed for all considered systems and probably reflects the nuclear characteristics of the individual isotopes. For example, the scandium content is exceptionally low in both the earth's crust and the sun.[22] Contrary to the general regularity, scandium is contained in quantities smaller than those of its heavy analogues—the rare-earth elements. In the earth's crust more than one hundred rare-earth minerals are known (of which, for example, monazite enters into the acidic rocks as one of the common accessory minerals), but there is only one very rare mineral of scandium—the silicate thortveitite.

The individual elements—for example, strontium, barium, cerium, and perhaps zirconium—are present in increased amounts. Let us recall that the presence of a zirconium oxide is characteristic of the spectra of the class S stars. Zirconium is the only heavy element for which local enrichments on such a scale are known.

Differences in the Chemical Composition of the Earth's Crust, the Meteorites, and the Sun's Atmosphere

A comparison of the abundance of the elements in the earth's crust and meteorites with that in the gaseous astronomical objects shows a considerable decrease in the volatile elements in the solid objects, which is obviously explained by the losses during the formation of these bodies. As expected, the inert gases of the zero group were lost to the greatest extent. Their abundances lie on a smooth curve which runs five to six orders of magnitude below the main abundance curve of the elements as a function of atomic weight. The deficiency of the

[22] The meteoritic (chondritic) abundance of scandium ($32Sc/10^6$ Si) reported by G. L. Bate, H. A. Potratz, and J. R. Huizenga (*Geochim. et Cosmochim. Acta,* **18:** 101–7, 1960) is very close to the solar value ($40Sc/10^6$ Si) of L. H. Aller (*Handbuch der Physik,* **51:** 324–52). Compared with these, the terrestrial value of Fersman ($13Sc/10^6$ Si, Table I of the Appendix) is the lowest.

gases of the zero group can be estimated by comparing their Q_Z-values with those of the neighboring even or odd elements:

$$\left.\begin{aligned} \delta Q_1 &= \frac{Q_{Z-1} + Q_{Z+1}}{2} - Q_Z, \\ \delta Q_2 &= \frac{Q_{Z-2} + Q_{Z+2}}{2} - Q_Z. \end{aligned}\right\} \quad (3.1)$$

The numerical values of δQ are given in Table 4, where in parentheses are shown the values for isotopes which under terrestrial conditions are capable of accumulation as a result of the decay of radioactive elements.

TABLE 4

DEFICIENCY OF GASES OF ZERO GROUP IN EARTH'S CRUST

Element	δQ_1	δQ_2
He	(6.6)	...
Ne	5.94	7.33
$Ar^{36} + Ar^{38}$	5.67	5.59
Ar^{40}	(3.24)	(3.16)
Kr	5.15	4.92
Xe	5.00	4.88

A comparison of the abundance of the rare gases in the planetary nebula NGC 7027 and in the earth's crust gives $Q_N - Q_E = 6.1$ for neon and 3.5 for argon. Close agreement of these values and the data of Table 4, obtained by an independent method, confirms the objective character of the calculations.

Hydrogen and nitrogen were lost by the earth's crust to a somewhat lesser extent. The hydrogen content decreased by approximately four orders of magnitude. The loss of hydrogen, the dominant element of the cosmos, leads to important consequences. Instead of a hydrogen-helium gas medium, the earth becomes a solid body, composed mainly of the heavy elements, like a "black concentrate," which separated itself from the primeval matter of the sun. The extent of the loss increases at least by one order of magnitude, if one speaks of the earth as a whole, since the rare gases, hydrogen, and nitrogen are essentially contained in the atmosphere, the hydrosphere, and the surface layers of the lithosphere.

The loss by the earth of carbon (by approximately two orders of magnitude) is unquestionable, and the losses of halogens and of sulfur are probable.

According to the data of astrophysics, the abundance of mercury in the sun is anomalously high, that is, the loss of this element by the earth is evidently also very significant. This is entirely probable.

Metallic mercury is stable under conditions of the earth's crust, and if native mercury is a rare metal, then this is connected with its volatility [46]. For small bodies, such as meteorites, the losses of the volatile elements are naturally still greater than for the earth.[23] The value of $Q_E - Q_{\odot}$ for the elements of the third and fourth periods of Mendeleyev's table is, on the average, close to zero, if oxygen is chosen as a standard of comparison. The greater proportion of the elements of these periods are involatile. Hence it is possible to conclude that oxygen was not lost by the earth in significant amounts (hardly greater than by a factor of 2), so that its selection as a standard turns out to be fortunate. Probably the retention of oxygen was favored by the fact that at comparatively high temperatures it had already formed oxides, which are involatile for a considerable number of metals.

Interesting are the peculiarities of the geochemistry of hydrogen in the bodies of the solar system. The available material is insufficient for a quantitative description, but a general regularity is traced very clearly. The large planets essentially lost molecular hydrogen but retained significant quantities of hydrogen compounds. Methane and ammonia form thick atmospheres of these planets. With decreasing mass of the planet, the relative content of ammonia decreased. On Neptune and Titan (a satellite of Saturn) ammonia has not been found. This fully agrees with a large loss of nitrogen in comparison with carbon under terrestrial conditions. However, the earth also lost hydrocarbons. The basic compound of hydrogen is water. On smaller planets—for example, Mars—only traces of water were retained, which form the polar caps of the planet, probably as a light, frosty deposit.[24] Water in the solid state was found in the particles making up the rings of Saturn [20, p. 63]. On the surface of the moon no traces of water activity have been observed. In meteorites, there is no water, but, as A. N. Zavaritskii [47] has shown, hydrogen is present in the composition of minerals of the chlorite-serpentine type which have been found in the carbonaceous chondrites.[25]

Thus, upon approaching the sun and with decreasing mass of the object of the solar system, the content of hydrogen decreases, and the nature of hydrogen compounds changes.

Among other elements of the earth's crust which are deficient in comparison with the sun's atmosphere are magnesium, the elements of

[23] See also a discussion of the losses of elements from meteorites by H. C. Urey (*Mém. Soc. Roy. Sci. Liège,* **14:** 481–94, 1953).

[24] For an original development of most of these and related ideas see H. C. Urey (*Geochim. et Cosmochim. Acta,* **1:** 209–77, 1951) and H. Brown (*Chem. Eng. News,* **30:** 1622–26, 1952).

[25] A crude chemical analysis of the Cold Bokkeveld carbonaceous chondrite performed by M. Faraday as early as 1839 and communicated to the Royal Society gave 6.6 per cent of water for this meteorite.

the iron-platinum group, and copper, that is, the typical siderophile elements or the elements of the protocrystallization stage. The content of magnesium, iron, and copper is diminished by several times, and that of the platinum metals by one order of magnitude. By contrast, the lithophile elements (aluminum, silicon, potassium, calcium, titanium, and, of the heavier elements, rubidium, tin, the rare earths) are present in the earth's crust in an excess.

In comparison with the sun's atmosphere, the composition of the stony meteorites reveals in principle the same features as the composition of the earth's crust. Meteorites differ from the earth in possessing a considerably higher content of sulfur and a lower content of barium, copper, zinc, and lead. The potassium and barium excess which is characteristic of the earth's crust does not exist in meteorites.

The iron meteorites lost substantially all elements up to iron,[26] and, of the heavier elements, they lost copper and zinc and probably the majority of the heavy lithophile elements for which analytical data are not available. Iron meteorites are enriched in some chalcophile elements (gallium, germanium),[27] in nickel and the platinum-group metals, that is, in the siderophile elements, and in certain lithophile elements (tin, tungsten). This interesting fact shows the relative nature of geochemical ideas. The scheme of Goldschmidt is not justified upon comparing the composition of the sun's atmosphere with that of iron meteorites because it turns out that not the siderophile elements in the conception of Goldschmidt but entirely different elements show affinity for iron.[28]

In Table 5 are given data on the greatest deviations of the earth's crust and of meteorites from the composition of the sun, the volatile elements being excluded.

Certain features of the composition of the earth's crust are explained by the gravitational differentiation of matter during the formation of the earth. The earth's crust is impoverished in the iron-group elements but is enriched in silicon, aluminum, and especially potassium. As to the microcomponents of the crust, their geochemical behavior is practically independent of the weight of the atoms. These elements follow one atom or another by virtue of the geochemical properties or

[26] Phosphorous, however, was not lost from iron meteorites.

[27] From a comparative examination of recent studies on gallium and germanium in the silicate, metal, and sulfide phases of meteorites (H. Onishi and E. B. Sandell, *Geochim. et Cosmochim. Acta,* 9: 78–82, 1956; J. F. Lovering, *ibid.,* 12: 253–61, 1957; J. F. Lovering, W. Nichiporuk, A. Chodos, and H. Brown, *ibid.,* 11: 263–78, 1957; W. Nichiporuk, *ibid.,* 13: 233–47, 1958) it appears that the siderophile tendencies of these elements are greater than their chalcophile tendencies.

[28] This reasoning is an incorrect interpretation of Goldschmidt's classification of elements. Goldschmidt carefully defined geochemical character not as an absolute term but as a relative one. For example, he clearly stated that an element can be chalcophile in the earth's crust and siderophile in the meteorites.

TABLE 5

CHARACTERISTICS OF COMPOSITION OF BODIES OF SOLAR SYSTEM AS COMPARED WITH ATMOSPHERE OF SUN

	Depleted (In Elements)	Enriched (In Elements)
Rocks of the earth's crust...	Mg, Co, Ni, Pt, Hg, Fe, Cu, Cr	Al, Si, K, Ti, Rb, Sn, rare earths, Ba, Ca, W
Stony meteorites..........	Cu, Zn, Pt, Hg, Co, V	Al, Si, Mo, In, Sn, Ti, Zr, rare earths, W
Iron meteorites..........	Light elements up to Fe, Cu, Zn, rare earths (?)	Ni, Pt, Ga, Ge, Sn, W

are carried into the outer region in the form of the volatile compounds. That is why the granitic surface layer is enriched in such heavy elements as rubidium, tantalum, and radioactive elements.

The composition of the earth's crust and the meteorites is similar and in many respects also in contrast to the composition of the sun's atmosphere. However, the earth's crust differs from the sun and the stony meteorites in possessing an increased content of radioactive elements (see Sec. 6) and a decreased content of sulfur. The higher analogues of sulfur, selenium, and tellurium have not been found in the sun, but in the stony meteorites they are more plentiful than in the earth's crust. It is possible that the elements of the sulfur group enrich one of the intermediate layers of the earth.

Together with the difference of the abundance of individual elements there is clearly observed a general increase in the relative abundance of the heavy elements in the earth and meteorites in comparison with the atmosphere of the sun (see Fig. 1). This regularity is illustrated in Table 6.

TABLE 6

AVERAGE DEVIATIONS OF ABUNDANCE OF CHEMICAL ELEMENTS IN EARTH'S CRUST (Q_E) AND METEORITES (STONY AND IRON, Q_S AND Q_I) FROM THEIR ABUNDANCE IN SUN'S ATMOSPHERE*

Period of Mendeleyev's Table	$Q_E - Q_\odot$	$Q_S - Q_\odot$	$Q_I - Q_\odot$
III..........................	0.2	0.3	−2.3
IV..........................	0.1	0.0	−0.3
V..........................	1.4	1.3	1.4
VI..........................	1.6	1.2	1.7

* In this crude table the apparent trends which the author observes are mainly a consequence of the poor quality of solar data.

The average values $\Delta Q = Q - Q_\odot$ increase for the elements of Periods V and VI of Mendeleyev's table in comparison with the elements of Periods III and IV. The data for Period II are not indicative, since some of its elements (N, C, F) have been lost by the solid bodies and others (Li and Be) are present in excess. The effect is not connected with the presence of the volatile elements. Of the volatile and gaseous elements in the sun, only chlorine and mercury have been studied. The abundance of other elements is not known and therefore has not been used in the preparation of Table 6.

The increase in ΔQ is traced regularly for the earth and the stony meteorites. The information on the iron meteorites is incomplete, and the deficiency of the light elements is possibly connected with the differentiation of the matter of that planet from which, according to modern ideas, meteorites were formed. But here relative enrichment in the heavy elements is also observed. The phenomenon cannot be explained by the geochemical conditions of the migration of the elements, inasmuch as in each period of the table there are elements of different geochemical types: the lithophile, chalcophile, and siderophile elements. Only in Period III are the siderophile elements absent and the lithophile elements predominant. Taking into consideration the gravitational differentiation of the earth and the general impoverishment of the siderophile elements in its outer shell, a relative accumulation in the earth's crust of the elements of Period III should be expected. This perhaps takes place, but the predominance of the heavy elements, which is common for the earth's crust as well as the meteorites, is much more strongly manifested. From the data of Table 6, it can be estimated that the earth and meteorites are enriched in the heavy elements by approximately thirty times in comparison with the atmosphere of the sun.

From the standpoint of modern cosmogony, the solar system originated from a primordial gas-and-dust cloud. This cloud either could have been formed from the material ejected by the sun or could have been captured by the sun in the course of its journey. In the latter case the difference between the composition of the solar system and that of the sun is quite possible, since, as is known, objects with diverse composition are found among the astronomical bodies. The majority of astrophysicists consider that the matter of the solar system is of "autochthonous" origin. Perhaps this matter was ejected by the sun during a stage similar to that of the Wolf-Rayet stars.[29] If one agrees with this, then the enrichment of the solar system in the heavy elements may be caused by the operation of two different factors leading to the same result: the gravitational differentiation of the matter of the sun or the loss of the light elements by the bodies of the solar system [48].

[29] Wolf-Rayet stars are class O late-type objects which exhausted much of their hydrogen. The sun still contains most of its hydrogen and could not have gone through a Wolf-Rayet stage earlier in its history.

The gravitational differentiation which leads to the enrichment of the surface layers in the light elements takes place only when the processes of the convectional transport of matter in the interior of the sun are insignificant. It is known that in the surface layers of the sun the gravitational differentiation—the distribution of the elements according to mass—is not observed. The convectional transport of matter equalizes the composition of the sun, and the differentiation, in any event, is smaller than that which would take place if the sun were a system in a static equilibrium. In the deep layers of the sun the transport does not proceed too rapidly, and the difference in the molecular weight of atoms of the sun can lead to a difference between the composition of the surface and the interior layers.

According to a simplified theory of Eddington [49], the convection in the interior of the stars is almost absent. In favor of a slow convectional transport of the matter of the sun is the presence in its atmosphere of traces of the light metals—lithium and beryllium [11, 48],[30] which would have been almost instantaneously destroyed in the center of the sun as a result of nuclear reactions.

The loss of the light elements by the earth and meteorites, which is independent of the chemical properties of the elements,[31] could have occurred only for the gaseous material ejected by the sun, from which subsequently originated the system of the solid bodies—the planets. In this case, it can be assumed that the loss of the light relative to the heavy elements was approximately the same for all bodies that originated from primeval matter. Indeed, this is observed upon comparing the composition of the earth's crust with that of the stony meteorites.

From the viewpoint of the loss of matter and of the change in the chemical composition in the course of the earth's history three stages can be marked down:

1. The stage of the atomic dissipation of matter or the gaseous stage. Even the large planets at the present time are impoverished in molecular hydrogen. If one considers that this hydrogen was lost during the gaseous stage, then the total mass of the matter of the solar system decreased probably by many tens of times. If the dissipation of the matter proceeded slowly, then we should observe a relative enrichment of the heavy elements.

2. The dust stage and the stage of the formation of the planets. The

[30] J. L. Greenstein and E. Tandberg-Hanssen (*Astrophys. Jour.* **119:** 113–19, 1954) found that there is much more beryllium ($10^{2.18}$ Be/10^{12} H) than lithium ($10^{1.26}$ Li/10^{12} H) in the sun, the beryllium abundance being very close to that on the earth and in meteorites ($10^{2.70}$ Be/10^{12} H). From this, the authors conclude that either the solar convection is limited or some unknown processes produce Li and Be in the atmosphere of the sun.

[31] The loss of the light elements by the earth and meteorites definitely depends on the chemical properties of the elements. See, for example, the paper by H. C. Urey in *Mém. Soc. Roy. Sci. Liège,* **14:** 481–94, 1953.

losses of the elements depend on the chemical properties of the elements and on the distance from the sun and are different for the individual sectors of the solar system.

3. The planetary stage. No significant changes in composition take place at the expense of the ejection or capture of the matter.

In Section 15 (p. 188) we shall show that the curve of the abundance of isotopes is in better agreement with the curve of the abundance of the elements on the earth or in meteorites than with a corresponding curve for the sun; that is, the difference between the composition of the elements in the sun and on the earth is apparently connected with the gravitational differentiation of the matter of the sun and not with the loss of the matter of the solar system into a gas phase.[32] This means that the dissipation of the gas proceeded fairly rapidly.

4. GEOCHEMISTRY OF ISOTOPES; FRACTIONATION OF ISOTOPES IN THE EARTH'S CRUST

The isotopes of an element participate together in the chemical and cosmic processes. However, the primeval abundance of isotopes depends on the properties of the nucleus and is not directly connected with the atomic properties. Therefore, in the investigation of the abundance of atoms, the principal object should be the isotopes and not the elements. Unfortunately, the isotopic composition of the elements has been studied only for the earth and not so thoroughly for meteorites. For the other celestial bodies, there are only sporadic data available, which, however, very often turn out to be exceedingly important for astrophysics, geochemistry, and especially the science of the abundance of atoms.

The isotopic composition of the elements of the earth is shown in Table III of the Appendix (p. 272), according to the data of Hollander, Perlman, and Seaborg [50], with additions from White, Collins, and Rourke [51]. The table shows the atomic weight, the per cent content and abundance of each isotope in the earth's crust according to Fersman [4] and also its mass and the binding energy—the characteristics which we shall need later on. Entered in the table are all known stable and also radioactive isotopes which have existed in the earth's crust since the time of its formation. It should be noted that in some instances the isotopic composition of an element is not a primary parameter but changes in the earth's crust under the action of local nuclear processes. Besides, isotope fractionation is possible, so that the assumption of the constancy of the relative abundance of isotopes, which we got used to contrasting with the inconstancy of the distribution of the elements, is useful only as a first approximation.

[32] The poor quality of solar abundance data does not justify such a conclusion.

A great deal of work has been directed toward the comparison of the isotopic composition of the elements of the earth with that of meteorites. By applying the mass-spectrographic and other methods, it was possible to show a practical identity of the isotopic composition for hydrogen, carbon, oxygen, silicon, chlorine, potassium, chromium, iron, cobalt, nickel, copper, gallium, and uranium [11, 52, 54, 55]. For example, according to the data of Valley and Anderson [52], the ratios of the iron isotopes relative to the isotope Fe^{56}, taken as 100, is as follows:

Atomic Weight of Iron Isotopes	Abundance of Given Isotope	
	In Earth's Crust	In Meteoritic Iron
54........	6.32	6.34
57........	2.33	2.34
58........	0.32	0.32

The isotopic composition of carbon in the carbonaceous chondrites was studied by Boato [56]. For the majority of the objects, the composition does not differ from that of terrestrial carbon. In four cases an increased content of deuterium was detected. The enrichment for the meteorite from Tanganyika reaches 35 per cent. This, however, does not exceed the fluctuations in the ratio D/H in terrestrial objects. A. V. Trofimov (quoting from [57]) showed that iron and stony meteorites possess, within the limits of individual fluctuations, the same C^{13}/C^{12} ratio that is close to the average ratio possessed by the magmatic rocks of the earth. The intervals of the fluctuation of this ratio for meteorites are much smaller than for terrestrial objects.

The determination of the relative content of radioactive isotopes of potassium [54] and uranium [55] [33] showed that, within the limits of error, the content is the same for the terrestrial matter as for meteorites. This result is important, inasmuch as it confirms the assumption of a single origin of the matter of the solar system and, above all, the assumption of the simultaneousness of the formation of its atomic nuclei.

The isotopic composition of the elements on the earth can be altered under the action of the following processes:

1. The physicochemical processes connected with the migration of matter. They are especially effective for the light elements taking an active part in the cycle of the matter of the earth's crust. Here the

[33] More recent measurements of radioactive isotopes of uranium in the terrestrial matter and meteorites were made by F. E. Senftle, L. Stieff, F. Cuttita, and P. K. Kuroda (*Geochim. et Cosmochim. Acta,* **11**: 189–93, 1957); K. A. Petrzhak, I. G. Semeniushkin, and M. A. Bak (*Geokhimiya,* **2**: 27, 1956); and H. Hamaguchi, G. W. Reed, and A. Turkevich (*Geochim. et Cosmochim. Acta,* **12**: 337–47, 1957).

total amount of the isotope in the system does not change. As a rule, these processes do not cause a significant fractionation of isotopes, but for the light elements an enrichment of individual isotopes up to 50 per cent is possible.

2. The nuclear processes, which in turn are subdivided into the artificial transmutation of atomic nuclei and the spontaneous decay of the natural radioactive elements. As a result, the isotopic composition of terrestrial elements may change so strongly as to lead to the formation in individual bodies of pure isotopes, for example, He^4, Ar^{40}, Sr^{87}, Os^{187}, Pb^{208}.

We do not as yet know what causes the deviation of the isotopic composition from the normal composition (fluctuations in the Sr^{86}/Sr^{88} ratio in micas and feldspars [58], an anomalous increase in the content of actinium of some hydrothermal minerals [59]).

The study of the isotopic composition of natural objects ordinarily belongs to a new scientific discipline—the geochemistry of isotopes—which, however, mechanically unifies the study of the effects of diverse nature. We shall consider these effects individually. Let us begin with the processes of fractionation of isotopes.

The fractionation of isotopes of the light elements takes place during the evaporation of substances, the deposition of minerals, the exchange reactions between the solid and liquid phases, and, in particular, during the complex reactions of the biosphere. The fractionation is most strongly manifested in the cyclic elements: hydrogen, carbon, and oxygen. Of the possibility of isotopic fractionation in the biogenic processes V. I. Vernadskii [60] spoke as early as 1926. This appears to me to be one of the most remarkable examples of foresight in the history of science. In the first edition of *Outlines of Geochemistry* Vernadskii wrote: "For the present, it is possible to think that life is a force which fractionates isotopes." Now we know that this fractionation is greater than under the action of any other forces.

We shall consider the behavior of hydrogen. Usually, the hydrogen of fresh water is accepted as a standard, and this is justified by the fact that the isotopic composition of this hydrogen is distinguished by a high degree of constancy. The water of the oceans contains an excess of the heavy hydrogen—deuterium—which amounts to 5–15 per cent. Snow and rain water are impoverished in deuterium. As expected, during the distillation of water the isotopic composition of hydrogen changes in the direction of decrease in the content of the heavy isotope. The greatest enrichment (up to 50 per cent) of deuterium in the inorganic realm has been found in the hydrogen from the remnants of the melting glaciers. We note that deuterium was first detected by laboratory methods in the residue of a slowly evaporating mass of solid hydrogen. In biogenic hydrogen, the content of deuterium is strongly increased. Considerable enrichment of deuterium in the hydrogen of petroleums serves as a supplementary proof of the organic origin of petroleum.

The fluctuations of the ratio of the stable isotopes of carbon, C^{12} and C^{13}, in inorganic objects are not large, but in organic samples they are very significant. During the assimilation of carbon by the organic realm, two opposite processes are observed. In photosynthesis, plants extract from the atmospheric carbon dioxide predominantly the light carbon, C^{12}, whereas, during the formation of their skeletons, organisms preferentially absorb the heavy isotope. The ratio C^{12}/C^{13}, according to V. A. Trofimov [61], for various igneous rocks of the earth's crust is concordant within the limits of error and, on the average, equals 92.1. Very close to this value is the ratio of carbon isotopes in meteorites (on the average, 92.0). In the calcitic formations of the earth's crust of animal origin, the ratio C^{12}/C^{13} drops to 90.0–90.1, and in the caustic bioliths of vegetable origin (petroleums, asphalts) it increases to 93.[34]

With these data, it is possible to calculate the proportion in the earth's crust of limestones and caustic bioliths. By studying the isotopic composition, it is possible to succeed in determining the origin of some minerals. Thus it has been proved that among graphites there are two varieties, one of organic and the other of inorganic origin [57].[35] The heavy oxygen isotope, O^{18}, is found in living matter in greater amounts than in river water. Atmospheric oxygen is enriched in this isotope by approximately 3.5 per cent. This contradicts the general fact of the decrease in the heavy isotopes in the gaseous phase but agrees well with the hypothesis of a biogenic origin of the atmospheric oxygen. Yet A. P. Vinogradov [57] assumes that, in photosynthesis, water is dehydrogenated and that its light, not its heavy, organogenic oxygen is released.

It is very interesting that the enrichment of the solid phase in the heavy oxygen during an exchange reaction of the carbonate ion with water depends on temperature. It has been experimentally established that if carbonates are formed at temperature T, then

$$\left(\frac{O^{18}}{O^{16}}\right)_T = \left(\frac{O^{18}}{O^{16}}\right)_0 [1 - 0.0176(T - T_0)].$$

[34] In a concurrent study of the carbon isotopes H. Craig (*Geochim. et Cosmochim. Acta,* 3: 53–92, 1953) has shown, in addition, that organic carbon samples intermediate between calcitic formations and petroleum fall into two well-defined groups —a marine group and a land group, the former being richer in C^{13} than the latter by about 1.2 per cent.

[35] The C^{13}/C^{12} ratio has been rejected by H. Craig (see the preceding reference) as a criterion for the origin of graphites. The reasons are the absence of the exchange equilibrium constants between graphites and other compounds and the lack of chemical evidence on the processes that produce graphites.

This relationship gave Urey and his co-workers [62 and 63, p. 543] a basis for working out an oxygen method of determining the temperature of the deposition of sedimentary formations. By studying successively the isotopic composition of oxygen in the layers of the relics of a Jurassic belemnite, the authors have shown that the animal perished in the spring time, at the age of about four years, after having lived originally in water which was warmer than that in which it spent the last year of its life. Based on the example, which has no practical significance, this detailed investigation proves the potentiality of the paleotemperature method. Nevertheless, it is needless to say that its perspectives for practical geology are unusually broad. There was a fluctuation recorded in the isotopic composition of oxygen for various minerals. A. P. Vinogradov and E. I. Dontsova [64] discovered an enrichment of the isotope O^{18} in the minerals of scarn origin which were formed with the participation of carbon dioxide of the sedimentary rocks.[36] In the magmatic minerals the fluctuations of the ratio O^{18}/O^{16} are as high as 2.4 per cent [65, 63, p. 505].

Nitrogen of the natural gases and oils shows variations in the relative content of the isotope N^{15} which are greater than 1 per cent [181]. This effect is evidently due to different diffusion rates of nitrogen isotopes during their underground circulation.

The deviation of the isotopic composition of sulfur in natural objects is studied in terms of the ratio S^{32}/S^{34}. Trofimov [66] has found that sulfur of meteoritic origin (from troilites) does not differ from most of the sulfur samples of magmatic rocks and hydrothermal sulfides.[37] The origin of the individual fluctuations is not explained. By contrast, for organic sulfur a very clear regularity is observed. For the sedimentary pyrites (divalent sulfur), the ratio S^{32}/S^{34} changes from 23.05 for the young to 22.08 for the very old formations. On the other hand, the organic sulfates (hexavalent sulfur) are enriched in the heavy isotope. The ratio S^{32}/S^{34} is equal to 21.8 for the young sulfates and increases to 22.1 for the pre-Cambrian samples [67, 63, p. 624]. We come to the conclusion that the biogenic processes enrich the divalent sulfur in the light isotopes and the hexavalent sulfur in the heavy isotopes.

Especially interesting is the fact that the organic matter only relatively recently has "learned" how to fractionate isotopes. Significant

[36] More recently R. N. Clayton and S. Epstein (*Jour. Geol.,* **66:** 352–3, 1958) found O^{18}-enrichment in quartz in the co-genetic mineral pairs quartz and calcite and quartz and magnetite; and S. Epstein and R. P. Sharp (*Jour. Geol.,* **67:** 88–102, 1959) observed a small O^{18}-enrichment in ice relative to firn of the Saskatchewan Glacier, Canada.

[37] W. U. Ault (*Researches in Geochemistry,* ed. P. H. Abelson [New York, 1959], pp. 241–59) reports that Trofimov's results are of doubtful value because of disagreement with subsequent work. An extensive bibliography of that work is given in Ault's article.

changes are observed only in the post-Cambrian samples. The organogenic formations 700–800 million years old do not show this effect (see Fig. 2), even though life on the earth is known to have existed much

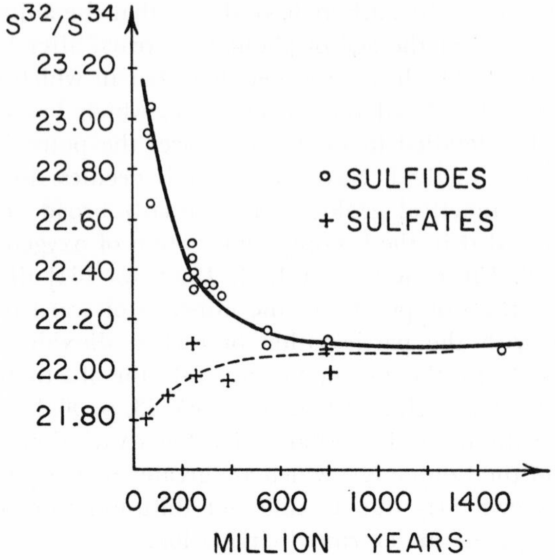

FIG. 2.—Change in the S^{32}/S^{34} ratio for biogenic sulfates and sulfides with their increasing age.

earlier, perhaps as far back as 2,700 million years. Evidently, the biochemical reaction of the fractionation of isotopes was developed in micro-organisms only at later stages in their evolution.[38]

At the present time, considerable material has been collected which confirms Vernadskii's guess concerning the fractionation of isotopes in the biosphere. However, the material is not yet sufficient for the substantiation of general laws for the interesting and little-known field of the physics of life's processes.

Detailed studies have been made of the isotopic composition of atmospheric gases up to the altitude of the order of 60 km. No detectable deviations were observed [69] in the composition of oxygen and nitrogen due to gravitational differentiation, although the theory of a static atmosphere for this altitude yields a decrease in the light isotopes by 20–30 per cent. Evidently, intense mixing of the gases is observed as high as the upper layers of the atmosphere.

For the elements which do not take part in the biogenic processes, the isotope fractionation takes place to a smaller extent, and, of course, the possibility of fractionation diminishes for the heavy ele-

[38] W. U. Ault and J. L. Kulp (*Geochim. et Cosmochim. Acta,* **16:** 201–35, 1959) have found no age effect upon S^{32}/S^{34} ratios for at least the last 2×10^9 years.

ments. Unfortunately, in spite of the high accuracy of modern measurements, enrichments of individual isotopes (by less than 1 per cent) cannot usually be considered trustworthy. The considerable material collected for the light elements is often conflicting and unreliable.

The greatest fractionation of isotopes should be expected for the elements which yield volatile compounds. However, boron—one of the most mobile lithophile elements—does not show, according to the latest data [182], noticeable fractionation under natural conditions. For silicon, fluctuations up to 1.4 per cent have been found. Very precise investigations of germanium showed variations up to 0.7 per cent [70]. The iron of terrestrial minerals and of meteorites has an identical isotopic composition, but for terrestrial iron there is apparently observed a slight increase in the Fe^{54}/Fe^{56} ratio down the series: native iron, 2.6; pyrite, 2.7; siderite, 2.77 [52]. An unexpected large variation (up to 4 per cent with an error of the order of 0.5 per cent) was found [58] for the Sr^{86}/Sr^{88} ratio of the non-radiogenic strontium isotopes:

Feldspars	From 0.116 to 0.119
Biotites	From 0.117 to 0.121
Celestites (strontium sulfate)	From 0.118 to 0.121
All studied minerals	From 0.116 to 0.121

A complete review of the extensive material accumulated by modern science is given in the compilation by Rankama *Isotope Geology* [71]. The most interesting papers published in journals have been included in the collected volume *Isotopy v Geologii* ("Isotopes in Geology") [63].

5. FORMATION OF ATOMIC NUCLEI IN THE PROCESS OF ARTIFICIAL TRANSMUTATION

It is convenient to classify the nuclear reactions of the universe into three types: thermonuclear reactions of the synthesis of the heavy nuclei from hydrogen; reactions of the disintegration of atomic nuclei with fast particles, including neutrons; and spontaneous radioactive decay. The area of the operation of these reactions is sharply limited. Thermonuclear reactions take place in the interior regions of stars at high environmental temperatures, with the environment approaching the condition of thermodynamic equilibrium. In this condition the probability of reactions resulting from collisions among nuclei is very small. However, a vast number of collisions in a medium at a high temperature and density can result in a large number of reacted nuclei. These are the reactions which supply the energy of the stars.

The processes of fission with fast particles and neutrons prevail in interstellar matter and on the surface of cosmic bodies, particularly on the earth's surface. The disintegrations are caused by the primary and secondary particles of cosmic rays with energies up to 10^{17} ev. The role of these processes in both the energetics of the universe and the change in its chemical composition is immeasurably smaller than in thermonuclear reactions. In the interiors of the solid cosmic bodies (for example, in the interior of the earth) the principal type of nuclear reaction is spontaneous radioactive decay, with the emission of particles with the energy of not more than 8.8 Mev. These particles can only very seldom induce artificial transmutation of atomic nuclei of the surrounding matter (on the average, one transmutation per several million particles).

Thermonuclear Processes in the Cosmos

The probability of thermonuclear reactions increases sharply with decreasing charge, and for this reason the most probable are the reactions of the lightest nucleus—the proton—with the lightest targets. A detailed consideration of this question will be given in Section 18 (p. 231). The collision of the proton with the principal isotope of helium, He^4, does not lead to transmutation because the nucleus with the atomic weight of 5 is unstable. The reactions of hydrogen capture by the nuclei of the light metals—lithium, beryllium, and boron—proceed according to the equations

$$\begin{aligned} Li^6 + H^1 &= He^4 + He^3, \\ Li^7 + H^1 &= 2He^4, \\ Be^9 + H^1 &= Li^6 + He^4, \\ B^{10} + H^1 &= C^{11}; \quad C^{11} \xrightarrow{\beta^+} B^{11}, \\ B^{11} + H^1 &= 3He^4, \end{aligned} \tag{5.1}$$

and ultimately lead to the destruction of these nuclei, with the formation of the stable helium nuclei. The time of burning of the light metals in the interiors of the ordinary stars—for example, the sun—ranges from fractions of 1 second to several hundred years, which is negligibly short in comparison with the time of the existence of cosmic systems. Therefore, the content of light metals in the stellar envelopes is very low. The small amounts of these light metals in the sun probably represent the remnants of the original content which did not have enough time to penetrate into the central zone because of the sluggishness of the transport processes.

A considerable portion of the energy of the majority of the hot stars is presently supplied by the so-called Bethe reaction. In the course of this reaction, the carbon nucleus C^{12} absorbs successively four protons. After passing through the intermediate stages according to the scheme

$$\begin{aligned} &C^{12} + H^1 = N^{13}; \quad N^{13} \xrightarrow{\beta^+} C^{13}, \\ &C^{13} + H^1 = N^{14}, \\ &N^{14} + H^1 = O^{15}; \quad O^{15} \xrightarrow{\beta^+} N^{15}, \\ &N^{15} + H^1 = O^{16} = C^{12} + He^4, \end{aligned} \tag{5.2}$$

the nucleus returns to its initial condition following the emission of an α-particle.

The net result of the reaction is the transformation of hydrogen into helium with a nearly unchanged amount of carbon, which appears here in the role of a unique catalyst. To the equilibrium of such a catalytic reaction there corresponds a definite state of the nitrogen and carbon isotopes, which apparently is close to this relationship for elements on the earth and in meteorites. This shows that the solar system was formed at the time that the sun had already attained the energy regimen in which the catalytic thermonuclear reaction played a dominant role.

In the process of the investigation of the isotopic composition of carbon of N-type red giants, G. A. Shain [72, 73] discovered considerable enrichment of the isotope C^{13}, with the ratio C^{13}/C^{12} varying from 1 to 19 for different stars. Probably, the mechanism of nuclear reactions in the interior of these stars is different from the catalytic reaction.

Among other nuclear reactions in the sun, the formation of heavy hydrogen may take place through the interaction of two protons:

$$H^1 + H^1 = D^2 + e^+. \tag{5.3}$$

The probability of this reaction is small because it requires a simultaneous emission of the positively charged electron (e^+) and is not merely limited to the collision between the two particles. However, hydrogen predominates in the composition of the stars, and the total energy of this reaction is high. At the same time, the reaction does not lead to the accumulation of deuterium, inasmuch as the opposite reaction of the destruction of deuterium,

$$D^2 + H^1 = {}_2He^3, \tag{5.4}$$

occurs almost instantaneously, so that the deuterium content of the stellar hydrogen should be negligibly small. Indeed, Class [74] has shown that the heavy hydrogen is present in the atmosphere of the sun to the extent of less than 2.5×10^{-6} per cent.[39]

Thus the isotopic composition of hydrogen in the sun differs sharply from that of the solar system (the earth and meteorites). It is difficult to understand why the light metals are found in the sun's atmosphere,

[39] More recent work dealing with the content of heavy hydrogen in the sun has been reported by C. De Jager (*Mem. 8°, Soc. Roy. Sci. Liège,* 4th ser., **13:** 460, 1953).

whereas deuterium is practically absent. Perhaps this is connected with the fact that thermonuclear reactions which destroy deuterium begin at temperatures that are considerably lower than those for the light metals, so that deuterium can be burned out even in the intermediate layers of the sun.

Thermonuclear reactions with the participation of the elements heavier than nitrogen are practically impossible in the sun. From the geochemical (or, more precisely, cosmochemical) side, the course of nuclear reactions in the sun stipulates a gradual decrease in hydrogen and a corresponding synthesis of helium, during which the amount and the ratio of the other light elements remain nearly constant. In the course of these reactions a new ratio of isotopes of the light elements is established, namely, that which is observed on the earth. During the existence of the sun, the total decrease in the content of hydrogen has not exceeded a few per cent, i.e., it is relatively small and lies within the limits of accuracy of modern methods of determination.

In spite of the importance of thermodynamic reactions which supply the energy of the sun and therefore support most of the processes on the earth's surface, the geochemical consequences of this process are comparatively small.

Artificial Splitting of Atomic Nuclei

The artificial transmutations of atomic nuclei under the action of fast particles occur in the cosmos on a still smaller scale because the total particle flux is usually small.

Under terrestrial conditions such transmutations are brought about by cosmic rays and α-particles from radioactive decay. As a result of the interaction of the primary cosmic rays with the atmosphere, neutrons—the unstable elementary particles with a lifetime of about 13 minutes—are produced. In nature, neutrons rarely die a "natural death." The absence of charge enables neutrons to penetrate freely into the interior of the atom and to react with the nucleus. In addition to the cosmic-ray neutrons, there exist in the earth's crust neutrons which are released during the spontaneous fission of uranium and thorium and also those generated in the course of the reactions of α-particles with light metals.

The change in the composition of the earth's matter as a result of artificial transmutations is not large, and the products of these reactions were detected only in recent years. These products are highly unique and merit detailed investigation, for in this example we study most of all the possibility of the alteration of the composition of atomic nuclei under the conditions of the external environment.

The detected reaction products are either some artificial radioactive nuclei (which consequently are determined from their radiations) or the stable isotopes of the rare gases. This is not connected with any special characteristics of the structure of the atoms of these gases but with the fact that the majority of these atoms was lost by the bodies of the solar system during its formation. For other elements, the reaction products merge with the background of the non-radiogenic isotopes. For the rare gases this background is absent, and it is possible to detect successfully the accumulation of the products of nuclear transmutations in quantities as small as 10^{-11} weight per cent of the sample investigated. In addition, the investigation of the rare gases is favored by the fact that, with modern laboratory techniques, they can easily be isolated from the mineral, freed of chemically active impurities, and measured in trace quantities.

The primary cosmic-ray particles produce bursts of atomic nuclei in the earth's crust, with the ejection of a large number of protons and neutrons. The immediate products of these reactions could not thus far be observed in the vast and mobile strata of the atmosphere, but the secondary neutrons, as we shall see later, are easily detected and lead to observable consequences.

The change in the isotopic composition of meteoritic matter.—The objects which are more suitable for investigation of the products of reactions involving the primary cosmic rays are meteorites—solid bodies with a very large specific surface area which have been exposed over the period of several billion years to the bombardment by cosmic rays.

Bauer [75] first showed that the helium content of iron meteorites increases, on the average, as their dimensions decrease; he explained this by the formation of helium in the surface layer of the mineral under the action of cosmic rays. Paneth and co-workers [23, 76] investigated the isotopic composition of helium in iron meteorites and found a strikingly high content of the light isotope (Table 7). The

TABLE 7

CONTENT AND ISOTOPIC COMPOSITION OF HELIUM IN IRON METEORITES [76]*

Meteorite	Helium Content (10^{-6} Cm^3/Gm)	$\frac{He^3}{He^4} \times 100$
Mount Ayliff	36.8	31.5
Carbo	22.0	28.6
Toluca	18.9	29.7
Bethany Amalia	3.4	27.8
Bethany	0.36	17.8

* The data in this table have been superseded by later work of K. H. Ebert and H. Wänke (*Zeitschr. f. Naturforsch.*, 12a: 766–73, 1957).

isotopic ratio He^3/He^4 reaches the value of 0.315, whereas for the earth's atmosphere $He^3/He^4 \approx 10^{-7}$.

According to calculations, He^3 is formed at the rate of 5×10^{-14} $cm^3/gm/year$ by bombarding iron with the primary cosmic-ray protons, so that the age of iron meteorites is probably of the order of 10^8–10^9 years.[40] Helium formed under the action of the primary particles is characterized by the ratio $He^3/He^4 = 0.4$, whereas the secondary particles produce helium with the ratio $He^3/He^4 = 0.25$.[41] For a number of meteorites the ratio $He^3/He^4 > 0.25$ has been obtained, so that in the opinion of the authors one may assume that He^3 was produced by the primary cosmic-ray component. A noticeable change in the composition of helium at the depth of 30 cm. in a meteorite section has not been found.[42]

E. K. Gerling [78] isolated helium and argon from several stony meteorites in the amount of about 10^{-7} weight per cent and neon in the amount of about 10^{-8} per cent, and determined their isotopic composition. The ratio He^3/He^4 ranges from 0.019 to 0.03, i.e., it is smaller than the corresponding ratio for iron meteorites. This should be expected, since the content of radioactive elements in stony meteorites is higher by two orders of magnitude and therefore the admixture of radiogenic helium may be quite large. According to Reynolds and Lipson [183], the ratio He^3/He^4 in the stony meteorite Nuevo Laredo is 0.0028. Begemann, Geiss, and Hess [184] isolated both He^3 and tritium from the achondrite Norton County. In the nuclear disintegrations the fragment with the atomic weight of 3 nearly always separates as tritium and not as helium, since the particle with a greater

[40] Calculations by H. C. Urey (*Jour. Geophys. Res.*, **64**: 1721–37, 1959) and by J. H. Hoffman and A. O. Nier (*Jour. Geophys. Res.*, **65**: 1063–68, 1960) based upon recent measurements of He^3 in a number of mostly smaller iron meteorites gave cosmic-ray ages ranging from 70 to 1,750 million years.

[41] J. H. Hoffman and A. O. Nier (*Phys. Rev.*, **112**: 2112–17, 1958) report the ratio He^3/He^4 of 0.50 for primary cosmic rays and of 0.14 for secondary rays, whereas O. A. Schaeffer and J. Zähringer (*Phys. Rev.*, **113**: 674–78, 1959) estimate He^3/He^4 production cross-section to be about 0.25 for proton energies of 6 Bev and give a measured value of 0.09 for this ratio at proton energies of 0.16 Bev.

[42] More recent studies of the changes with depth in the isotopic composition of helium (He^3/He^4) in iron meteorites were made by K. H. Ebert and H. Wänke (*Zeitschr. f. Naturforsch.*, **12a**: 766–73, 1957); E. L. Fireman and J. Zähringer (*Phys. Rev.*, **107**: 1695–98, 1957); E. L. Fireman (*Nature* [London], **181**: 1725, 158; *Planetary and Space Sci.*, **1**: 66–70, 1959); J. H. Hoffman and A. O. Nier (*Phys. Rev.*, **112**: 2112–17, 1958; *Geochim. et Cosmochim. Acta*, **17**: 32–36, 1959; *Jour. Geophys. Res.*, **65**: 1063–68, 1960). These investigators found that the ratio He^3/He^4 is approximately constant throughout small meteorites (and also in certain meteorites having distinctly non-spherical shape) but varies noticeably in very large iron meteorites in such a way that the minimum values of the ratios are near the center and the maximum values near the surface of these objects. The variations with depth in the absolute contents of He^3 and He^4 permitted interesting conclusions in regard to pre-atmospheric surface features, shapes, and sizes of the iron meteorites studied.

charge has more difficulty in leaving the nucleus.[43] Almost all He^3 accumulated in meteorites was formed during the decay of the short-lived tritium:

$$H^3 \xrightarrow{\beta} He^3, \quad T_{1/2} = 12.262 \text{ years.}$$

The specific activity of tritium for this achondrite is 0.25–0.28 disintegration per gm. per minute. Having determined He^3 and assuming that the accumulation took place at a constant rate, the authors found that the time of the existence of the system is 0.42–0.48 billion years, which is one order of magnitude lower than the age of 4.4 billion years obtained from the accumulation of Ar^{40}, the radioactive decay product of K^{40} (see Sec. 6).[44] The authors proposed two explanations for this discrepancy: (1) the cosmic-ray flux has undergone a drastic change in the course of the 4 billion years of the existence of the meteorite; (2) the meteorite was formed approximately 400 million years ago during the disintegration of a larger celestial body. The available fragment was first situated in a deep part of this body, where it was not subject to irradiation with fast cosmic-ray particles. The second explanation appears to me to be more probable, perhaps because it does not violate the customary idea regarding the constancy of the cosmic-ray flux. But any conclusion in this respect has great cosmogonic significance, and further investigations are exceedingly important.[45]

Exceptionally interesting is the isotopic composition of meteoritic neon and argon. For atmospheric neon, $Ne^{21}/Ne^{20} = 0.0028$ and $Ne^{22}/Ne^{20} = 0.097$. For neon from the stony meteorites these ratios increase to 0.5–1.2, according to Gerling [78], and for the achondrite Nuevo Laredo these ratios are $Ne^{21}/Ne^{20} \geqslant 0.58$ and $Ne^{22}/Ne^{20} \geqslant 0.60$, according to Reynolds and Lipson [183]. For neon from the iron meteorites, $Ne^{21}/Ne^{20} = 0.84$ and $Ne^{22}/Ne^{20} = 0.5$, according to Reasbeck and Mayne [80]. Particularly interesting is the increase in the content of the odd isotope. If for terrestrial neon the rare even isotope

[43] This statement is subject to correction in the light of recent measurements by O. A. Schaeffer and J. Zähringer (*Phys. Rev.*, **113:** 674–78, 1959), who found that He^3 yields from iron targets are higher than previously measured tritium values. Since the He^3/T is 2.4 at 3 Bev, most of He^3 in meteoritic iron is produced directly and the He^3-T ages reported in the literature for meteorites are too high by a factor of about 3.

[44] Actually, the authors said: ". . . The amount of He^3 accumulated and the tritium production rate combined give He^3-H^3 ages for irradiation of 420 and 480 million years respectively [for two different specimens of the meteorite]. If an assumption is made as to the direct production rate of He^3 by spallation, these ages reduce to 240 and 280 million years. The Ar^{40}-K^{40} age of this meteorite is 4400^{+640}_{-740} million years. . . ."

[45] See recent He^3 and He^4 investigations on 13 stony meteorites by P. Eberhardt and D. C. Hess (*Astrophys. Jour.*, **131:** 38–45, 1960).

Ne^{22} is more abundant than Ne^{21} by a factor of 35, then for meteoritic neon the content of these isotopes is of the same order of magnitude. Among the argon isotopes there are two non-radiogenic isotopes the ratio of which in the terrestrial atmosphere is $Ar^{36}/Ar^{38} = 5.3$. In the stony meteorites there is a preferential accumulation of the heavy isotope, so that, according to Gerling [78],[46] this ratio decreases to 0.8–2.4, and, according to Trofimov and Rik [79], to 1–4. For the iron meteorites, according to Gentner and Zähringer [185], the ratio Ar^{36}/Ar^{38} assumes values from 0.7 to 2.4.[47] At the same time, there is observed a proportional relation between the two products, Ar^{38} and He^3, of the artificial disintegration of nuclei.

The formation of the isotopes Ne^{21}, Ne^{22}, and Ar^{38} can take place during the following nuclear transmutations:

$$\left.\begin{array}{l} Mg^{24,25} + n^1 = Ne^{21,22} + He^4, \\ Mg^{24,25} + H^1 = Na^{21,22} + He^4; \quad Na^{21,22} \xrightarrow{\beta^+} Ne^{21,22}, \\ O^{18} + He^4 = Ne^{21} + n^1, \\ K^{39,41} + H^1 = Ar^{36,38} + He^4 \text{ and others.} \end{array}\right\} \quad (5.5)$$

The enrichment of stony meteorites in the isotopes of neon and argon can also occur in the spallation of heavy atomic nuclei—for example, of the iron nucleus—with the emission of many particles.[48] The isotopic composition of krypton from stony meteorites was investigated by Gerling and that of xenon by Wasserburg and Hayden [186] and Reynolds and Lipson [183]. These investigators found practical agreement with the composition of these gases in the earth's atmosphere.[49] This was expected, since meteorites contain very small amounts of the heavy elements from which, under cosmic-ray action, the heavy rare gases could be produced.

Reactions in the earth's atmosphere under the action of cosmic rays.—The charged particles of cosmic rays often possess enormous energy, sometimes sufficient for a complete breakup of the atomic nucleus into its individual nucleons. However, only the primary cosmic-ray particles and the short-lived π-mesons actively interact with atomic nuclei.

[46] See also E. K. Gerling (*Doklady Akad. Nauk S.S.S.R.*, **107**: 559–61, 1956); E. K. Gerling and L. K. Levskii (*ibid.*, **110**: 750–753, 1956); J. Geiss and D. C. Hess (*Astrophys. Jour.*, **127**: 224–36, 1958).

[47] Actually, the reported value of the Ar^{36}/Ar^{38} ratio is about 0.6. In more recent studies of this ratio in iron meteorites, H. Fechtig, W. Gentner, and G. Kistner (*Geochim. et Cosmochim. Acta,* **18**: 72–80, 1960) and O. A. Schaeffer and J. Zähringer (*Geochim. et Cosmochim. Acta,* **19**: 94–99, 1960) found values from 0.59 to 0.67.

[48] See R. E. Batzel, D. R. Miller, and G. T. Seaborg (*Phys. Rev.*, **84**: 671–83, 1951); and G. Friedlander, J. M. Miller, R. Wolfgang, J. Hudis, and E. Baker (*Phys. Rev.*, **94**: 727–28, 1954); O. A. Schaeffer and J. Zähringer (*Phys. Rev.*, **113**: 674–78, 1959).

[49] Lately J. H. Reynolds (*Phys. Rev. Letters,* **4**: 8–10, 351–54, 1960) reported the discovery of a strong enrichment of xenon isotopes in the chondritic meteorite Richardton and the carbonaceous chondrite Murray.

These particles operate primarily in the upper strata of the atmosphere. As a result of the splitting of atomic nuclei, neutrons are formed in the entire thickness of the atmosphere in the amount of 2.6 neutrons/cm²/sec. The neutron flux reaches its maximum at the altitude of 15 km. and falls almost to zero at the earth's surface. The neutrons are spent primarily in the splitting of the nitrogen nuclei, inasmuch as the probability of these reactions is relatively high and nitrogen predominates in the composition of the atmosphere. Reactions of the following types [80] are possible:

$$\left.\begin{aligned} N^{14} + n &= C^{14} + H^{1}, \\ N^{14} + n &= C^{12} + H^{3}, \\ N^{14} + n &= B^{11} + He^{4}, \\ O^{16} + n &= Be^{7} + Be^{10}, \end{aligned}\right\} \qquad (5.6)$$

the first of which takes place under the action of fast as well as slow (most effective) neutrons, whereas, for the splitting in which H^3 and He^4 are formed, neutrons of high energy are indispensable. As a result, there are produced in the earth's atmosphere the unstable isotopes radiocarbon C^{14} and tritium H^3, (see p. 51), of which the former decays according to the scheme

$$C^{14} \xrightarrow{\beta} N^{14} \quad (T_{1/2} = 5{,}568 \text{ years}), \qquad (5.7)$$

and both can be detected by means of their radioactive properties.

The larger fraction of the secondary cosmic-ray neutrons are slowed down upon collision with the atoms of the atmosphere, and, after traversing its layer about 200 meters thick, they are absorbed by nitrogen with the formation of C^{14}. The atoms of this radiocarbon are oxidized to the usual state of atmospheric carbon, i.e., to carbon dioxide, and enter the carbon cycle in exactly the same manner as do the stable carbon isotopes.

The total amount of radioactive carbon on the earth can be estimated by equating the mass of radiocarbon which is produced to the mass of C^{14} which decays during the same time:

$$i \times S = N \times \lambda_C, \qquad (5.8)$$

where $S = 5.1 \times 10^{18}$ cm² is the earth's surface, $i = 2.6/\text{cm}^2/\text{sec}$ is the number of the C^{14} atoms formed under the action of neutrons, and λ_C is the decay constant of C^{14}. The calculation shows that the total quantity of C^{14} on the earth is 80 tons. The production rate of radiocarbon is 10 kg/year.

According to the data of geochemistry, the quantity of carbon which participates in the material cycle of the biosphere is 8.3 gm/cm² of the earth's surface, or of the order of 4×10^{14} tons for the entire earth. Of this quantity, the larger part, about 7.84 gm/cm², is found in sea water in the form of dissolved carbonic acid and carbonate ions. Approximately 4 per cent of carbon is combined in the living matter of the biosphere, and 1.5 per cent is present in the atmosphere. The average content of C^{14} in the isotopic composition of carbon is, according to a theoretical estimate, 1.8×10^{-10} per cent. To this quantity there correspond about 18 disintegrations/gm/min. In reality, the activity of carbon in the biosphere is 15–16 disintegrations/gm/min, whence the carbon-14 content of the biosphere is 1.5×10^{-10} per cent.

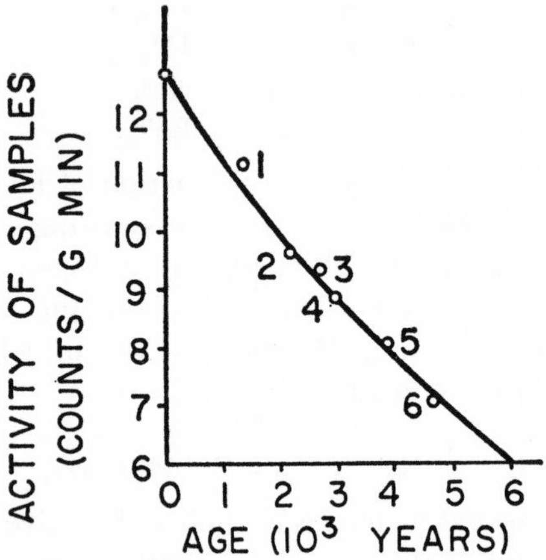

FIG. 3.—Decrease in the activity of radiocarbon in old wood samples. The continuous curve is the theoretical curve of the decay of C^{14}. The points represent the data for the samples described in Table 8.

The calculation presented illustrates the sufficient reliability of modern geochemical methods. The activity of the carbonaceous substances in the biosphere is relatively high. It approximates the activity produced by the heavy radioactive elements and their decay products in such rocks as granites; but the maximum energy of the β-rays from C^{14} and particularly from H^3 is so very small (155 and 18 kev., respectively) that even a determination of these isotopes presents a relatively difficult experimental problem.

It is known that cosmic rays show a sharply expressed geomagnetic effect, but the relative radiocarbon content of the plant samples does not depend on geomagnetic latitude [81]. This indicates rapid mixing of carbon in the biosphere. The average activity of plant carbon is 15.3 ± 0.1 disintegrations/gm/min. At the same time, carbon of animal origin (the shells of sea organisms) shows the considerably higher activity of 16.5–0.5 disintegrations/gm/min, i.e., the enrichment of C^{14} in animal carbon relative to that of plant carbon is 1.09–0.04. We have already pointed out in Section 4 that the heavy stable isotope C^{13}

predominates in the carbon of the calcitic skeletons by a factor of 1.03 in comparison with vegetable carbon. For the heavier C^{14} this ratio should be equal to 1.06, which agrees within the limits of error with the observed value.

For the old organogenic samples the activity of radiocarbon decreases according to the law of radioactive decay:

$$C^{14} = C_0{}^{14}e^{-\lambda ct}, \quad (5.9)$$

where $C_0{}^{14}$ is the initial activity. Libby [81] [50] proposed to utilize the decrease in the activity of C^{14} for the determination of the age of organic remains. The results of the investigation of some objects are shown in Table 8 and Figure 3.

TABLE 8

ACTIVITY OF RADIOCARBON IN ORGANIC SAMPLES*

Name	Activity of Radiocarbon (Counts/Gm/Min)	Age (Years): From Activity According to Equation (5.9)	Age (Years): According to Archeological Data
1. Fir tree from excavation of VI century	10.99 ± 0.15	1,042 ± 80	1,371
2. Egyptian mummiform coffin from Ptolemaic period	9.5 ± 0.45	2,190 ± 450	2,280
3. Wood from excavations of palace in Syria	9.18 ± 0.18	2,531 ± 150	2,625 ± 50
4. Interior part of sequoia wood	8.68 ± 0.17	2,710 ± 130	2,928 ± 51
5. Funerary ship in tomb of Sesostris III (Egypt, Middle Kingdom)	7.97 ± 0.30	3,621 ± 180	3,750
6. Tombs of Sneferu and Zoser (Egypt, Ancient Kingdom)	7.04 ± 0.20	4,802 ± 250	4,575 ± 75

* According to W. F. Libby and co-workers [81]. Some corrections have been made in the original table to bring its data into agreement with the results as reported in the work of W. F. Libby and co-workers [81].

The age determined by the radiocarbon method is in good agreement with the historical data. Aside from the importance of an objective estimate of the age of archeological materials, this investigation is of great significance to nuclear physics. We have already noted that the data on the tritium content of meteorites throw some doubt on the constancy of the cosmic-ray flux during hundreds of millions of years. However, in the course of the last five thousand years this flux was practically constant. This is supported by the suitability of the radiocarbon method for the given time interval. This fact, while of fundamental importance to cosmic-ray science, finds surprising proof in archeological material. The science of the abundance of atomic nuclei

[50] See also W. F. Libby, *Radiocarbon Dating* (2d ed.; Chicago: University of Chicago Press, 1955).

encompasses a vast amount of material from diverse scientific disciplines and discloses internal connections among them.

The next stage in the work was, of course, the application of the radiocarbon method to the determination of the absolute age of the objects for which historical chronology was not available. Thus the age of the Iranian mezolite and of the ancient cultures of America, which were isolated from the Old World, was determined. This age cannot be successfully estimated by the common methods of comparison of material monuments.

The radiocarbon method in the present state of experimental techniques is theoretically suitable for the determination of the age of objects up to 45 thousand years old [82]. However, many samples with a true age of 5–10 thousand years already yield lower age values by this method. The younger ages are probably caused by the admixture of modern radiocarbon due to the interaction of the object with the surrounding medium. For the monuments of the Upper Paleolithic age in France (Saint-Marseille), the values obtained range from 11 to 16 thousand years [81]. At the same time, according to the accumulation of thorium isotopes, the age of the Upper Paleolithic in the U.S.S.R., as we shall see in Section 9 (p. 94), was found to be 40–90 thousand years.[51] However, considering the characteristics of the method, these results are more likely too low than too high.

A large number of works are devoted to the behavior of tritium in the atmosphere (for reviews see [187, 188]). In rain water the ratio H^3/H^1 is 6.6×10^{-17}. For river waters it decreases to $n \times 10^{-18}$ [83]. The tritium content of hot springs permits an estimation of their "age," i.e., the time of their underground circulation [187].

The total amount of tritium on the earth is small, of the order of kilograms, so that nuclear weapons tests can sharply increase (by hundreds of times) the tritium content of atmospheric hydrogen. The investigated tritium balance in the turnover of terrestrial matter permits a calculation which shows that the total rate of tritium production is 0.5–2.5 atoms/cm^2/sec. The cosmic-ray neutrons [see eq. (5.6)] produce only 0.1–0.3 atom. It is necessary to look for other mechanisms of tritium production. It is possible that tritium is formed by the cosmic-ray protons of intermediate energy. The problem of tritium emission by the sun is discussed by H. Craig [189].

In respect to other products of cosmic-ray reactions with the matter of the atmosphere, there are only sporadic, insufficiently verified indications. Arnold and Al-Salih [190] detected traces of Be^7 in rain water, and Winsberg [191] found traces of Cl^{39}. The latter can be formed

[51] Most experts in the field will agree that the radiocarbon method of age dating is more reliable than the thorium method.

under the impact of negative mesons upon Ar^{40} with the emission of a neutron.

It is not difficult to show that the products of other reactions of the type (μ^-, n) with the atmosphere either are stable, are formed in negligible amounts, or are the isotopes of gaseous substances which do not fall onto the surface of the earth. The radiocarbon formed in the reaction $N^{15}(\mu^-, n)C^{14}$ is masked by the isotope of a different origin.

The neutron flux of cosmic rays decreases toward the earth's surface according to the exponential law, $e^{-x/L}$, where the mean-free path $L \approx 140$ gm/cm^2 corresponds to the path of the nuclearly active cosmic-ray particles in the matter. At the earth's surface (with the exception of individual high-altitude regions) the flux decreases hundreds of times in relation to a maximum value and drops to zero in the surface layer several meters thick. The μ-meson flux penetrates to a considerably greater depth, but the probability of its interaction with atomic nuclei is negligibly small. Any observable accumulation of the products of nuclear reactions caused by cosmic rays in the earth's crust can be expected in the surface layer of mountainous, glaciation-free regions.

Recently Davis and Schaeffer [123] investigated the Cl^{36}-content of some natural materials. This isotope is formed by the action of neutrons on Cl^{35}:

$$Cl^{35} + n = Cl^{36} \xrightarrow{\beta} Ar^{36}.$$

The thermal neutron cross-section of this reaction is fairly large (2 barns), and the half-life of Cl^{36} is long ($T_{1/2} = 3.1 \times 10^5$ years). This radioisotope was discovered in the element isolated from a chlorine-rich rock (phonolite) which occurs at the altitude of about 3,300 meters above sea level and has not undergone glaciation during the last millennia. The activity of Cl^{36} was 0.12 ± 0.02 counts/gm/min. A similar rock outcrop at a lower altitude did not show measurable activity. According to the estimate of the authors, the high-altitude phonolite accumulated Cl^{36} during the period of about 24 thousand years, which perhaps corresponds to the time of the last glaciation in that region. We have detected Cl^{36} in chlorine isolated from waters of high-altitude salt lakes of East Pamir.

Artificial transformation of atomic nuclei in the lithosphere.—Even the most effective reactions of splitting of atomic nuclei by cosmic rays are only slightly reflected in the change of the over-all composition of the earth's surface.

Weaker yet is the manifestation of nuclear transmutations in the earth's crust which are caused by radioactive emission (α-particles and neutrons from spontaneous fission) and the residual flux of secondary cosmic-ray particles. However, a number of cases have been found in which the accumulation of the individual isotopes in the lithosphere takes place at the expense of nuclear reactions.

The He^3 content of the atmosphere is insignificant, with the ratio He^3/He^4 equal to $(1.2–1.3) \times 10^{-6}$ [84]. It is smaller still for the subterranean gases, where its value ranges from 5×10^{-8} to 5×10^{-7}. The ratio drops almost to zero for helium from the radioactive minerals. M. G. Meshcheryakov has shown that in this case it is less than 10^{-10}. This should be expected, since helium in radioactive minerals accumulates at the expense of α-particles (quoted from [85]). In helium isolated from beryl, the ratio He^3/He^4 varies from 0.5×10^{-7} to 12×10^{-7} [84]. At the same time, for helium from the mineral spodumene (alumosilicate of lithium) values of $He^3/He^4 = 2.4 \times 10^{-6}$ and even $He^3/He^4 = 1.2 \times 10^{-5}$ were obtained, comprising maximum enrichment of the light helium isotope that was found under terrestrial conditions. Probably the accumulation of helium in spodumenes takes place during the splitting of lithium by neutrons:

$$Li^6 + n = He^4 + H^3; \quad H^3 \xrightarrow{\beta} He^3. \tag{5.10}$$

The weight content of He^3 in minerals is of the order of 10^{-11} per cent.

Wetherill [86] found considerable enrichment (by factors of tens and hundreds) of the heavy isotopes in neon isolated from radioactive minerals. Thus in neon from euxenite (nibo-tantalate of the rare earths) the ratios are $Ne^{22}/Ne^{20} = 4.72$ and $Ne^{21}/Ne^{20} = 1.05$, and in neon from monazite $Ne^{22}/Ne^{20} = 0.095$ and $Ne^{21}/Ne^{20} = 0.40$, whereas in atmospheric neon these ratios are 0.097 and 0.0028, respectively. The fluctuation in the ratio of the heavy isotopes for different minerals indicates that the formation of Ne^{21} and Ne^{20} is due to nuclear transmutations. Wetherill assumes that the most probable are the reactions of the capture of α-particles from radioactive elements by oxygen and fluorine:

$$\left.\begin{array}{l} O^{18} + He^4 = Ne^{21} + n^1, \\ F^{19} + He^4 = Na^{22} + n^1; \quad Na^{22} \xrightarrow{\beta^+} Ne^{22}. \end{array}\right\} \tag{5.11}$$

However, the intensity of these reactions is evidently low.

The ratio of argon isotopes from uraninites [86, 87] has been studied more fully. If in the atmosphere $Ar^{36}/Ar^{38} = 5.35$, then for argon from uraninites [87] this ratio is of the order of unity and even decreases to as low a value as 0.02 [71], with the Ar^{38} content of the mineral being of the order of 10^{-10} weight per cent.

It can undoubtedly be maintained that Ar^{38} is formed in a certain nuclear process. The following reactions have been proposed:

$$\left.\begin{array}{l} Cl^{35} + He^4 = Ar^{38} + n^1, \\ Cl^{35} + He^4 = K^{38} + H^1; \quad K^{38} \xrightarrow{\beta^+} Ar^{38}. \end{array}\right\} \quad (5.12)$$

But it is not understood why chlorine, which is contained in uraninites in negligible traces, proves so effective. In order to explain this important and interesting process, it is obviously necessary to investigate argon from other old minerals, since the connection of Ar^{38} with uranium is not clear. Against this connection is the fact that the ratio Ar^{36}/Ar^{38} for argon from various natural samples of uraninite is subject to considerable fluctuation, ranging from 0.02 to 5.2.[52]

We shall turn to the isotopic composition of krypton and xenon from terrestrial minerals. Inghram and Reynolds [88] isolated xenon from an old sample of the rare mineral telluro-bismuthite, Bi_2Te_3. The objective of the work was a search for Xe^{130}, the assumed product of a double β-decay of Te^{130}. From 370 gm. of the mineral the authors succeeded in obtaining a fraction of rare gases which contained 0.024 cm.^{3} of argon and only 2.6×10^{-7} cm.^{3} of xenon, the isotopic composition of which could, however, be determined (Table 9).

TABLE 9

ISOTOPIC COMPOSITION OF XENON ISOLATED FROM TELLURO-BISMUTHITE

Atomic Weight	Isotopic Composition of Xenon*		Difference	Per Cent Difference
	From Mineral	From Atmosphere		
124.........	<0.004	0.0005	<0.0035	<0.29
126.........	<0.005	.0005	<.0035	<0.38
128.........	<0.014	.011	<.003	<0.25
129.........	1.00†	.1525	.8475	71.66 ± 0.7
130.........	0.0652	.0236	.0416	3.52 ± 0.17
131.........	0.4088	.1235	.2853	24.12 ± 0.3
132.........	0.1566	.1566	.0000	0.00
134.........	0.0651	.0611	.0040	0.34 ± 0.25
136.........	0.0562	0.0519	0.0043	0.36 ± 0.16

* Normalized to Xe^{132}. [Author's footnote.]
† Accepted as standard. [Author's footnote.]

Some accumulation of Xe^{130} does indeed take place, but much more enrichment of isotopes Xe^{129} and Xe^{131} is observed. The authors suppose that these isotopes were formed during the irradiation of tellu-

[52] E. K. Gerling and Yu. A. Shukuliukov (*Geokhimiya* ["Geochemistry"], 7: 608–18, 1959) found that the Ar^{38} content of uranium minerals depends on the age of these minerals, their uranium content, and the ratio Xe(neutr. fiss.)/Xe(neutr. fiss.) +Xe(spon. fiss.), but cannot be explained in terms of reactions (5.12). The authors propose that Ar^{38} is formed in the spontaneous fission of U^{238} as well as in the neutron fission of U^{235}.

rium with neutrons from radioactive inclusions of thucholite found in the same pegmatitic vein from which this mineral was obtained:

$$\left.\begin{aligned} Te^{128} + n^1 &= Te^{129}; \quad Te^{129} \xrightarrow{\beta} I^{129} \xrightarrow{\beta} Xe^{129}, \\ Te^{130} + n^1 &= Te^{131}; \quad Te^{131} \xrightarrow{\beta} I^{131} \xrightarrow{\beta} Xe^{131}. \end{aligned}\right\} \qquad (5.13)$$

Interesting is the ratio of krypton and xenon isotopes in uraninites. V. G. Khlopin and co-workers [89] first detected xenon—the product of the spontaneous fission of uranium—in old uranium minerals. Later Macnamara and Thode [90] isolated from uraninites both xenon and krypton. These investigators found that the isotopic composition of these gases was different from the isotope ratio produced in an artificial slow-neutron fission of uranium and was completely unlike the ratio of the isotopes of these rare gases observed in the earth's atmosphere.

Further investigations of Fleming and Thode [91] and those of Wetherill [86] showed that the isotopic composition of xenon and krypton from uranium minerals is subject to significant fluctuations. Admixtures of atmospheric xenon were practically absent, as could be concluded from the absence of Xe^{130}, which is not produced in the fission of uranium. The authors believe that the diversity is caused by the overlap of two processes: the spontaneous fission of U^{238} and the artificial fission of AcU^{235} with neutrons. The probabilities of these processes are comparable, but their ratio changes depend on local conditions, such as the uranium content of the mineral, the presence of impurities, particularly of some rare-earth elements which are known for their intense neutron absorption, etc. The results of the measurements are given in Table 10.[53]

Comparing the ratios of the xenon isotopes from uranium minerals with those in a slow-neutron fission of actinouranium, it is possible to show that the content of isotopes—the products of artificial fission —in some minerals is as high as 35 per cent. The smallest amount (not greater than 5 per cent) of the artificial fission products is present in uraninite, which contains the rare-earth elements. The amount of krypton and xenon produced in uraninite at the expense of nuclear processes is 10^{-10} cm³/gm, or 10^{-13}–10^{-12} weight per cent.

Of particular interest is the investigation of transuranium elements, which can be formed in radioactive minerals under the action of neutrons [92]:

[53] More recent results on the isotopic composition of xenon from uranium minerals, which essentially confirm Wetherill's results, have been reported by E. K. Gerling and Yu. A. Shukoliukov (*Radiokhimiya* ["Radiochemistry"], 1: 212–22, 1959). The authors also report the age-dependent xenon retention in uranium minerals which ranges from as high as 100 to as low as 1 per cent.

TABLE 10

FISSION YIELD OF ISOTOPES OF XENON AND KRYPTON

Description of Samples	U_3O_8 (Per Cent)	Relative Content of Isotopes*								
		Kr^{83}	Kr^{84}	Kr^{86}	Xe^{129}	Xe^{131}	Xe^{132}	Xe^{134}	Xe^{136}	Xe/Kr
				Products of the Spontaneous Fission in Minerals						
Pitchblendes:										
Katanga, Belgian Congo [91]	65.21	0.30	0.50	1.62	0.22	1.27	3.91	6.03	6.5	7.4
Katanga, Belgian Congo [86]	...	...	...	...	.21	1.28	4.00	6.09	6.5	...
Eagle Mine, Canada [91]	45.5	...	...	...	.22	1.16	3.91	5.93	6.5	...
Ace Mine [91]	17.0	...	...	...	.23	1.07	3.89	5.79	6.5	...
Lake Athabaska [91]	14.0	...	...	...	.09	0.80	3.79	5.58	6.5	...
Nesbitt Labine [91]	27.6	...	...	...	.11	0.83	3.80	5.56	6.5	...
Great Bear Lake [91]	36.5	0.073	0.34	1.19	.10	0.80	3.73	5.54	6.5	10.3
Uraninite, Ontario [91]	60	...	...	...	0.03	0.61	3.74	5.41	6.5	...
Fission of AcU^{235} with slow neutrons	...	0.61	1.16	2.24	...	3.00	4.57	7.91	6.5	6.7

* The Xe^{136} content is taken as 6.5.

$$U^{238} + n^1 = U^{239}; \quad U^{239} \xrightarrow[23.5\text{ min.}]{\beta} Np^{239} \xrightarrow[2.33\text{ days}]{\beta} Pu^{239}. \qquad (5.14)$$

The long-lived Pu^{239} ($T_{1/2} = 2.4 \times 10^4$ years) is transmuted into AcU^{235} by α-particle emission. Reaction (5.14) is feasible under the action of slow neutrons and attains an exceptionally high efficiency at the intermediate values of the energy of neutrons of about 25 ev.

On bombarding the uranium nuclei with fast neutrons, the splitting can take place with the expulsion of two neutrons and the formation of the principal neptunium isotope, Np^{237}:

$$U^{238} + n^1 = U^{237} + 2n^1; \quad U^{237} \xrightarrow[6.75\text{ days}]{\beta} Np^{237}. \qquad (5.15)$$

Np^{237} gives rise to the so-called neptunium decay series, which is unknown among natural radioactive elements:

$$Np^{237} \xrightarrow[2.2 \times 10^6\text{ years}]{\alpha} Pa^{233} \xrightarrow[27.4\text{ days}]{\beta} U^{233} \xrightarrow[1.62 \times 10^5\text{ years}]{\alpha} Th^{229} \xrightarrow[7{,}340\text{ years}]{\alpha} \text{etc.} \qquad (5.16)$$

Thorium, by capturing neutrons, is also transformed into a member, U^{233}, of the neptunium series:

$$Th^{232} + n^1 = Th^{233}; \quad Th^{233} \xrightarrow[23.3\text{ min.}]{\beta} Pa^{233} \xrightarrow{\beta} U^{233}. \qquad (5.17)$$

We shall consider the accumulation of transuranium elements under the action of neutrons from spontaneous fission. The Pu^{239} content corresponds to an equilibrium condition of reaction (5.14), in which the number of atoms of the disintegrating plutonium is equal to the number of atoms being produced. Under the conditions of full utilization of neutrons for the formation of plutonium, the contents of uranium, U, and plutonium, Pu, are connected by means of the expression

$$\eta \mathrm{U} \lambda_f = \mathrm{Pu}\, \lambda_\alpha, \qquad (5.18)$$

where λ_f is the probability of the uranium fission ($T_f = 8 \times 10^{15}$ years),[54] λ_α is the α-decay probability of plutonium ($T = 24{,}360$ years), $\eta = 2.4$ is the number of neutrons emitted during one fission event [53]. The relative plutonium content is

$$\frac{\mathrm{Pu}}{\mathrm{U}} = \eta \frac{\lambda_f}{\lambda_\alpha} = \eta \frac{T}{T_f} \approx 7.5 \times 10^{-2}. \qquad (5.19)$$

Naturally, the true content of plutonium should be considerably less, since the larger fraction of neutrons leaks out of the mineral without having had time to react with uranium atoms. However,

[54] According to new determinations by E. K. Gerling, Yu. A. Shukuliukov, and B. A. Makarochkin (*Radiokhimiya*, 1: 223–26, 1959) the value is $T_f = 5.8 \pm 0.5 \times 10^{15}$ years.

Levine and Seaborg [93], as well as Peppard and co-workers [94], found that in a number of cases the relative content of plutonium exceeded the limiting content (5.19), as shown in Table 11. This indicates that,

TABLE 11

PLUTONIUM CONTENT OF RADIOACTIVE MINERALS [71]

Mineral	U Content (Per Cent)	$\frac{Pu^{239}}{U} \times 10^{12}$
Pitchblendes:		
Colorado	50	7.7
U.S.S.R. [193]	43.5	20
Belgian Congo	38	12
Great Bear Lake	13.5	7.1
Uranium ore, Belgian Congo	45.3	15
Carnotite, Colorado	10	<0.4
Monazite, North Carolina	1.64	3.6
Fergusonite, Colorado	0.25	<4
Monazite, Brazil	0.24	8.3

in addition to spontaneous fission neutrons, there acts a neutron flux of another origin, perhaps from the reactions of the type (α, n), that is, from the splitting of atomic nuclei by α-particles with the emission of neutrons. Very interesting is the fact that there is no direct relationship between the content of uranium and the enrichment of plutonium. For example, plutonium isolated from a Brazilian monazite with a relatively low uranium content (0.24 per cent) has the ratio Pu/U, which is higher than the limiting ratio.

From a ratio similar to (5.18) we find that, during the formation of neptunium,

$$\frac{\text{Np}}{\text{U}} = \eta \frac{\lambda_f}{\lambda_\alpha} \approx 7 \times 10^{-10}, \tag{5.20}$$

where λ_α is the α-decay constant of neptunium. Neptunium is formed only at a very high energy of the incident neutrons. The probability of the reaction is small, so that the true value of the ratio Np/U should be lower than that shown in reaction (5.20). Indeed, it has been found for pitchblende from the Belgian Congo [95] that $Np^{237}/U^{238} = 1.8 \times 10^{-12}$ and $Pu^{239}/U^{238} = 1.5 \times 10^{-11}$. It can be concluded from reactions (5.19) and (5.20) that the formation of neptunium by neutrons under given conditions is approximately one thousand times less probable than the formation of plutonium. However, the accumulation of Np indicates that under natural conditions there exists a sufficiently intense neutron flux of high energy.

In addition, Th^{229} and U^{233}—the components of the neptunium series [95]—were isolated from pitchblende and monazite. U^{233} can be formed during the decay of neptunium and by means of reaction (5.17), whereas Th^{229} is probably produced only during the decay of U^{233}.

The preliminary experiments by Alperovitch and Miller [118, 119] led to the detection in some minerals of the unstable technetium isotope, Tc^{98}, which, in the opinion of the authors, is produced in the process of neutron capture by molybdenum.[55] Merrill [193] detected spectral lines of technetium in the atmosphere of type-S cold stars. It is possible that technetium is present in the sun. If these data are verified, they will provide valuable information for nuclear astrophysics.

Kuroda and others [194] found radioactive chlorine in pitchblende from Great Bear Lake. The mineral contained 0.02 per cent chlorine. Radioactive chlorine is evidently formed by the action of neutrons on chlorine, according to the equation on page 57. Calculations show that the neutron flux in the given environment comprised 430 ± 110 neutrons/cm^2/hour.

Thus, in the minerals of the lithosphere, diverse processes of artificial transformation of atomic nuclei take place. The content of the decay products for a number of isotopes of the rare gases approaches 10^{-9} per cent by weight. Apparently, within the amounts of this order, all isotopes of light elements can be formed as decay products. The principal agents of nuclear reactions are neutrons.

Neutrons are emitted in the reactions of light nuclei with α-particles from naturally occurring radioactive elements:

$$\left.\begin{array}{l} Be^9 + He^4 = C^{12} + n^1, \\ O^{18} + He^4 = Ne^{21} + n^1, \\ F^{19} + He^4 = Na^{22} + n^1; \quad Na^{22} \xrightarrow{\beta^+} Ne^{22}. \end{array}\right\} \qquad (5.21)$$

In addition, neutrons are emitted during the spontaneous fission of uranium. Approximate calculations by Morrison and Pine [96] give a yield of 2.5 ± 1 neutrons per 10^6 α-particles. The experiments performed by these authors have shown that the true yield of neutrons is smaller: for uraninites, 0.3 neutron per 10^6 α-particles or 1.9 neutrons per gram of uranium; and for thorite, 0.27 neutron per 10^6 α-particles or 0.4 neutrons per gram of thorium. According to the data of Kashkarov and Cherdyntsev [198], the neutron yield per 10^6 α-par-

[55] Actually, the authors said: "The most plausible explanation of the internal consistency of the result suggests the presence of a long-lived technetium-98." They indicated, however, that this conclusion was tentative. The probability of the occurrence of such an isotope has been reduced by the discovery of 1.5×10^6-year Tc^{98} by S. Katcoff (*Phys. Rev.*, **99**: 1618–19, 1955) and G. E. Boyd, J. R. Sites, Q. V. Larson, and C. R. Baldock (*Phys. Rev.*, **99**: 1030–32, 1955).

ticles for uranium ores comprises, on the average, 0.4 neutron and for ferrithorites (enriched in fluorine) 0.9 neutron. The pure thorium oxide liberates only 0.2 neutron. For uranium minerals, about half the neutrons are generated during spontaneous fission. For thorium minerals, the number of such neutrons is negligibly small. A considerable number of neutrons (0.2–0.3 per 10^6 α-particles) is emitted by radioactive elements at the expense of reaction (5.21) involving oxygen. The presence in the mineral of beryllium, fluorine, magnesium, and aluminum increases the yield of neutrons. Thus the varieties of ferrithorite especially rich in fluorine emit up to 7.5 neutrons per 10^6 α-particles.

Direct measurements of the neutron flux of the earth by means of nuclear emulsions were conducted by Mather [195] in the deep mines of polymetallic deposits in Australia. The experiments produced a negative result (less than 20 neutrons/cm^2/day). Cherdyntsev and Suyarova [196] detected 500 neutrons/cm^2/day in the beryllium mines of Central Kazakhstan. Further experiments [197] using neutron counters showed that the slow-neutron flux in the inactive zones of the lithosphere comprises about 5 neutrons/cm^2/day and increases, on the average, by 0.006 neutron/cm^2 with increase in the γ-activity of the surrounding rocks by 1 microroentgen. The fast-neutron flux is somewhat more intense than the slow-neutron flux, but the absolute number of fast neutrons may be neglected, inasmuch as, roughly speaking, the concentration is proportional to the flux and inversely proportional to the velocity.

If one speaks of the neutron as the zero element of Mendeleyev's table, then its content in the lithosphere is of the order of 10^{-30} weight per cent. The radioactive elements of the earth's crust are always present as simple or complex compounds of oxygen, so that the principal and ubiquitous reaction of neutron liberation in the lithosphere is the $O^{18}(\alpha, n)Ne^{21}$ reaction. The neutron yield in the spontaneous fission of uranium is approximately three times smaller. If one assumes that neon is lost by minerals to the same extent as argon (actually, the losses of the lighter neon should be greater), then not less than one-fourth of Ne^{21} in the earth's atmosphere is of radiogenic origin [198]. The accumulation of Ne^{22} and of other products of reaction (5.21) is appreciable in the specific minerals that are rich in both radioactive and light elements (fluorine, beryllium, and others). The accumulation of the heavy neon isotopes in radioactive minerals was actually detected by Wetherill [86] (see p. 58).

Ne^{21} and the decay product of tritium, He^3, are the only stable isotopes in the earth's crust that have been formed in appreciable amounts through the artificial disintegration of atomic nuclei.

6. RADIOACTIVE ELEMENTS IN NATURE

All cosmic bodies contain a large number of radioactive isotopes which have entered the systems since the time of their formation in the same manner as the stable isotopes. The geochemical consequences of radioactivity are a decrease in the content of the radioactive element and an accumulation of its decay products. As will be shown in chapter ii, the instability of radioactive elements is brought about by completely dissimilar causes. According to the type of decay, the known unstable isotopes can be divided into the following groups:

1. The heavy radioactive elements at the end of the periodic table, capable of α-decay and, to a small extent, of spontaneous fission. The independent isotopes of this type are Bi^{209}, Th^{232}, AcU^{235}, and U^{238}. The last three are the progenitors of the radioactive-decay series.

2. The α-emitters of the central part of the table belonging to the nuclear shell region, which contains 82 neutrons (Sec. 10, p. 114)—Nd^{144} and Sm^{147}.

3. The unstable isotopes with an even atomic weight and odd atomic number. These atomic nuclei contain odd numbers of both neutrons and protons and are known conventionally as "odd-odd nuclei." In nature several isotopes of this type have been preserved: K^{40}, V^{50}, La^{138}, Lu^{176}, and Ta^{180}; here also belong the artificially radioactive C^{14} and Cl^{36}. The odd-odd nuclei, in general, can decay by electron emission (β-decay) as well as by electron capture (K-capture).

4. The β-emitters forming odd isobar (nuclei of the same weight) pairs—Rb^{87}, In^{115}, Re^{187}—and also the artificially radioactive H^3.

5. The components of the so-called even isobars. As will be shown in Section 12 (p. 138), a considerable group of these nuclei is energetically capable of a decay in which two electrons are simultaneously emitted. Such double β-decay is actually assumed for Te^{130}.

The largest radioactive-decay energy is released by uranium and thorium, together with their decay products, and also by potassium. Next follows actinouranium and its decay products and rubidium. The energy contributed by other radioactive elements is so small that it may be ignored in the study of the heat regimen of the earth.

From the standpoint of activity in the earth's crust, potassium occupies the first place. Its activity is greater than that of all other radioactive elements combined.[56] It is followed by rubidium, uranium, and

[56] This statement about the activity of potassium in the earth's crust contradicts the statement about the decay energy of potassium in the preceding paragraph. One should distinguish between the decay energy per atom and the total heating rate due to a particular radionuclide.

thorium. By weight, the most abundant radioactive elements are Rb^{87}, Ca^{48}, and Th^{232}. However, in spite of their high abundance and considerable activity, Rb^{87} and K^{40} possess small decay energy compared with the heavy radioactive elements.

The fundamental law of natural radioactive decay states that, for all modes of nuclear transmutation, the activity of a radioactive element, that is, the number of atoms disintegrating per unit time, depends only on the number of atoms present and does not depend on the conditions of the external environment:

$$\frac{dn}{dt} = -\lambda n, \tag{6.1}$$

where n is the number of atoms and λ is the radioactive-decay constant. This constant is connected with the half-life $T_{1/2}$ (the time in which n decreases to one-half of its initial value) by means of the simple relationship

$$\lambda = \frac{\ln 2}{T_{1/2}} \approx \frac{0.693}{T_{1/2}}. \tag{6.2}$$

From equation (6.1) we readily find

$$n = n_0 e^{-\lambda t}, \tag{6.3}$$

where n_0 is the initial content of the radioactive element. If, as a result of the decay, a series of radioactive-decay products is formed, then the formation of each of them is described by a more complex equation. This, however, is a linear combination of expressions of type (6.3).

The accumulation of decay products is described in the following manner:

$$m = n_0 - n = n(e^{\lambda t} - 1). \tag{6.4}$$

In the absence of migration of both the radioactive element and its decay product, the ratio of the number of their atoms is only a function of time:

$$\frac{m}{n} = e^{\lambda t} - 1.$$

Hence

$$t = \frac{1}{\lambda} \ln \left(1 + \frac{m}{n}\right), \tag{6.5}$$

or, for small values of the age,

$$t = \frac{1}{\lambda} \frac{m}{n}. \tag{6.6}$$

Radioactive decay is used in successful dating of cosmogonic, geologic, and archeologic processes, inasmuch as the decay constant is practically independent of the condition of the external environment. The first ideas concerning the application of radioactive decay to the determination of absolute age[57] were expressed by P. Curie in 1902. From this date on, there began the accumulation of data on the absolute geochronology. But only in the 1930's did data of radiologists begin to receive recognition from geologists. Much work in substantiation of radioactive methods of geochronology in the Soviet Union was performed by the academicians V. I. Vernadskii [97] and V. G. Khlopin [98].[58]

It is difficult to overestimate the significance of radioactive methods in establishing the absolute scale of geochronology. Prior to the discovery of radioactivity, geology used a relative time scale based essentially on the data from the realm of fauna. Paleontology invented accurate and ingenious methods of dating, but they cannot answer the question of the duration of geologic epochs in absolute units. These methods encompass only the period following the evolution of vertebrate organisms—the period which constitutes the shorter interval in the history of the earth. Besides, using the methods of paleontology and stratigraphy, it is generally impossible to establish the age of igneous rocks as well as that of the "mute" sedimentary strata which do not contain relics of organic life.

The fundamental and decisive difficulty of all efforts aiming at determining absolute age is the possibility of the migration of elements which displaces the isotopic ratios established in the system as a result of radioactive decay.

Table IV of the Appendix (p. 280) contains fundamental information on the known radioactive isotopes [50, 51, 99–102]. We shall examine the behavior of these isotopes in nature (with the exception of those for which radioactive decay is assumed but not as yet discovered).

Potassium

The radioactive isotope K^{40} decays by β-emission into Ca^{40} and by electron capture into Ar^{40}. The first process is approximately eight times more probable than the second one, and the β-ray energy is high. Therefore, β-activity is easily detected; and this was done as early as 1905, immediately following the discovery of the radioactivity of uranium and thorium. Modern laboratory β-counters permit the

[57] By "absolute age" is understood the determination of the age in absolute units (for example, in years) and not the determination with absolute accuracy. [Author's footnote.]

[58] Among Western authors, pioneering work in this field was done by E. Rutherford and his group and by O. Hahn.

determination of potassium at concentration levels as low as fractions of 1 per cent.

The greater part of the β-activity of rocks is due to potassium. However, the geochemical manifestation of this activity is small, since K^{40} is a rare isotope of potassium and Ca^{40} predominates in the composition of calcium. The abundance of the two elements is of the same order of magnitude. Their geochemical properties are also similar. Both are lithophile elements which gravitate toward the acidic rocks of the earth's crust. Small admixtures of radiogenic calcium can be detected only in minerals relatively rich in alkali metals, such as the minerals of pegmatitic veins. Ahrens and Evans [103] investigated the calcium content of old potassium minerals from pegmatites. Lepidolite and muscovite were found to contain a considerable concentration of potassium and other alkali metals (rubidium, cesium, lithium), with the content of alkaline-earth metals (calcium, strontium, barium) very low. An increased content of calcium was detected for a group of old lepidolites. Later work confirmed the accumulation of Ca^{40}.

The effect of electron capture, experimentally, is much more difficult to investigate than the effect of β-emission, and, besides, the probability of K-capture in potassium is small. This process was discovered only in 1943 [104], but conclusive geochemical data favoring the possibility of the formation of Ar^{40}, as a result of disintegration of potassium [105], were available much earlier.

Like the other rare gases, argon was lost to a considerable extent by the earth. The content of the light argon isotopes, Ar^{36} and Ar^{38}, is approximately one million times lower than the content of the even isotopes of the neighboring elements. The content of Ar^{40} is much higher, so that argon turns out to be the most abundant element among the gases of the zero group. Its concentration in the atmosphere amounts to 0.93 atom per cent. Atmospheric argon is characterized by two anomalies: an exceptionally high abundance and an isotopic composition that is unusual for the light elements, in that the heaviest isotope is a dominant constituent, comprising 99.6 per cent of the total composition of argon. In addition, argon constitutes one of the violations of Mendeleyev's table. Its atomic weight is greater than that of potassium, which follows it. If one considers the fact that the heavy isotope of argon is of radiogenic origin, then the abundance and ratio of the other argon isotopes appear to be normal. In the same manner is explained the exceptional position of the element in the periodic system. From the content of the light argon isotopes it is possible to estimate that atmospheric argon is enriched in Ar^{40} by nearly ten thousand times relative to primeval argon. Also, evidently, unlike the majority of the elements, the isotopic composition of atmospheric argon is entirely different from that of cosmic argon.

Even argon extracted from stony meteorites, i.e., from objects relatively rich in potassium and radiogenic argon, shows a relative content of Ar^{40} which in some instances is tens of times lower than that shown by the earth's atmosphere.

Page [106] demonstrated that in the planetary nebulae the abundance of rare gases—argon and neon—is close to that of the neighboring even elements. From this it is possible to find that the argon-neon ratio for the earth is thousands of times greater than for the matter of the gaseous envelopes of the nebulae. In these systems there was no specific loss of the rare gases, or, more precisely, these gases were dissipated to an equal degree, just like the other elements of the gaseous envelopes. Therefore, the ratio of the rare gases is close to the primeval ratio. One may assume that the isotopic composition of argon of the gaseous nebulae is quite different from that of terrestrial argon.

In weight units, argon in the earth's atmosphere (6.5×10^{19} gm) is somewhat more abundant than K^{40} is in the earth's crust down to the depth of 15 km. and approximately five times more abundant than it is in the entire earth. Starting with these values, repeated attempts were made to estimate the age of the earth from the accumulation of Ar^{40}. The accuracy of these estimates cannot be high. If we have information on the liberation of argon from the surface minerals, then our knowledge of the conditions of its migration in the deep zones is insufficient. Knowing the age of the earth from other sources, it is possible to estimate that in the course of the earth's existence its content of K^{40} decreased by approximately ten times.

Direct determination of the probability of *K*-capture for potassium is not very accurate. For its determination E. K. Gerling and co-workers proposed to utilize the geochemical data on the accumulation of argon in the naturally occurring minerals [107]. Gerling and also Aldrich and Nier [84] have shown that the principal content of argon in potassium minerals is associated with the decay of K^{40}.

The insignificant admixtures of atmospheric argon can be estimated from the content of non-radiogenic Ar^{36}. Denoting the modern content of potassium by the symbol K^{40} and the initial content by K_0^{40}, we find that the amount of potassium decayed during the lifetime of the mineral is

$$K_0^{40} - K^{40} = K^{40}(e^{\lambda t} - 1),$$

where $\lambda = \lambda_\beta + \lambda_K$ is the total decay probability of potassium, equal to the sum of the probabilities of β-decay and *K*-capture. Provided that the argon produced does not migrate, the quantity of argon accumulated in the mineral will be

$$Ar^{40} = \frac{\lambda_K}{\lambda_\beta + \lambda_K} K^{40}(e^{\lambda t} - 1). \quad (6.8)$$

Gerling investigated a number of potassium minerals, predominantly of the pegmatitic phase (amazonite, microline, lepidolite), from deposits whose age had been previously determined by the method based on the accumulation of helium or lead from the radioactive elements. It turned out that the age calculated on the basis of equation (6.8), i.e., according to the "argon method," is close to the true age (Table 12).

TABLE 12

Data on Argon Content of Some Minerals [107]*

Mineral	K^{40} (10^{-5} Per Cent)	Ar (10^{-4} Cm³/Gm)	Age (Million Years)		Content of Atmospheric Argon (10^{-4} Cm³/Gm)
			According to Equation (6.8)	According to Other Methods	
Lepidolite.....	0.98	0.987	228	230	0.177
Amazonite....	1.19	7.42	1290	....	.66
Microline.....	1.19	9.61	1485	1720	0.34

* The electron-capture constant used in preparing this table was the geologically determined value $\lambda_K = (6.1 \pm 1.2) \times 10^{-11}$ year^{-1}. The constant for β decay was $\lambda_\beta = 4.9 \times 10^{-10}$ year^{-1}. The geological value for λ_K reported more recently by G. W. Wetherill and co-workers (*Phys. Rev.*, **103:** 987–89, 1956) is 5.57×10^{-11} (using $\lambda_\beta = 4.72 \times 10^{-10}$ year^{-1}). G. W. Wetherill (*Science*, **126:** 545–49, 1957) from a new gamma measurement obtained $\lambda_K = 5.83 \times 10^{-11}$ year^{-1}.

The content of atmospheric argon (determined on the basis of Ar^{36}) of the minerals investigated ranged from 3 to 18 per cent of the amount of radiogenic argon. Later, Mousuf [108] found that argon isolated from microlines contained from 0 to 7 per cent argon of atmospheric origin.

Very significant is the fact discovered by Soviet geochemists [107]. They observed good retentivity of argon in naturally occurring minerals. The atomic radius (1.92 Å) of argon is larger than the radius of all cations which compose the natural minerals. As a result, argon can be retained even in minerals with an unstable structure and perfect cleavage, such as lepidolite and muscovite. This allows the application of the argon method to a large number of minerals of the earth's crust. The task is facilitated by the fact that many potassium minerals (in particular, potassium feldspars) are the common rock-forming minerals, so that, in practically all geologic formations, objects can be found that are suitable for age determination by the argon method.[59]

[59] The suitability of feldspars for age-dating purposes is now open to doubt, since they have been shown to be subject to diffusion losses of argon (see, for example, G. W. Wetherill, L. T. Aldrich, and G. L. Davis, *Geochim. et Cosmochim. Acta,* **8:** 171–72, 1955; J. H. Reynolds, *Geochim. et Cosmochim. Acta,* **12:** 177–84, 1957).

Of special interest is the determination of the age of meteorites.[60] A study of two stony meteorites of the chondritic type carried out by E. K. Gerling and T. N. Pavlova showed an age of 3.00 and 3.03 billion years [109]. Later E. K. Gerling and K. G. Rik found objects with an age up to 4.5 billion years [110]. Wasserburg and Hayden [111] determined the age of two chondrites and found for them 4.6 and 4.8 billion years;[61] Thomson and Mayne [112] found ages of 3.5 and 3.8 billion years.[62]

Gerling and co-workers [199] found that argon from old potassium minerals contained an excess of Ar^{38}. The ratio Ar^{38}/K was constant for the minerals of the same age, but it increased for the old minerals. Gerling[63] expressed the hypothesis that the accumulation of Ar^{38} in this case is explained by the presence in potassium of a very rare isomer, K^{38},[64] which decays to Ar^{38} by K-capture with a half-life of about 1 billion years. In the ground state, K^{38} is a short-lived β^+-emitter.

Rubidium

The abundance of the β-active isotope of rubidium, Rb^{87}, is relatively high (28 per cent), and in the earth's crust rubidium is the most abundant of all heavy, odd ($Z > 25$) elements. Together with strontium and zirconium, rubidium comprises a group of isotopes with an exceptionally high abundance in the region of atomic nuclei with a 50-neutron shell (see Sec. 10, p. 114).

In its geochemical properties, rubidium is a typical element of acidic magma. Its relative abundance in the earth's crust is tens of times higher than in meteorites and hundreds of times higher than in

[60] The K-Ar ages of meteorites are lower than the Rb-Sr and Pb-Pb ages because of the possible diffusion losses of argon (R. W. Stoenner and J. Zähringer, *Geochim. et Cosmochim. Acta,* **15**: 40–50, 1958). G. G. Goles, R. A. Fish, and E. Anders (*Geochim. et Cosmochim. Acta,* **19**: 149–95, 1960) derived an equation that gives the measured K-Ar age as a function of the "true" age and the parameter D/a^2, the diffusion constant of Ar^{40} divided by the square of the radius of potassium-bearing grains.

[61] These ages have been recalculated using a branching ratio of 0.124 for the K^{40} decay. The ages lie between 4.15×10^9 and 4.35×10^9 years (J. Geiss and D. C. Hess, *Astrophys. Jour.,* **127**: 224–35, 1958).

[62] Most recent determinations of K-Ar ages of stony meteorites were made by J. Geiss and D. C. Hess (*Astrophys. Jour.,* **127**: 224–35, 1958). The seven chondrites measured gave ages between 4.4×10^9 and 4.0×10^9 years. The ages of six achondrites extended from 4.4×10^9 to 0.7×10^9 years.

[63] Investigations by G. J. Wasserburg and R. Bieri (*Geochim. et Cosmochim. Acta,* **15**: 157–59, 1958) and by P. Signer and A. O. Nier (*Geochim. et Cosmochim. Acta,* **16**: 302–3, 1959) did not confirm the accumulation of Ar^{38} in old potassium minerals.

[64] For potassium of two iron meteorites H. Voshage and H. Hinterberger (*Zeitschr. f. Naturforsch.,* **14a**: 828–38, 1959) give a limiting ratio $K^{38}/K^{40} < 3 \times 10^{-3}$.

the sun's atmosphere. However, a low decay energy (0.27 Mev) is the cause of the small significance of rubidium in the energetics of the earth. The geochemical consequences of its decay are also insignificant. In the earth's crust rubidium does not form a single mineral but substitutes isomorphically for potassium and other alkali metals. The ionic radius of rubidium (1.49 Å) is considerably larger than that of potassium (1.33 Å). Rubidium contributes to the crystalline lattice of minerals a smaller energy than potassium and therefore crystallizes during a late stage of the magmatic process, namely, in the minerals of low-temperature pegmatites and pneumatolites. These minerals are impoverished in alkaline-earth metals, particularly in strontium. This fact favors the detection of the decay product of rubidium—the radiogenic isotope Sr^{87}.

The radioactivity of rubidium was discovered as early as 1905, but the fact that it was due to the isotope Rb^{87} was shown only in 1937 from the accumulation of Sr^{87} in a sample of an old lithium mica which contained up to 3 per cent rubidium and was almost completely free of the other alkaline-earth elements [113]. It is interesting to note that for rubidium, just as for calcium, the decay probability was first determined with sufficient accuracy by using geochemical material of a known absolute age.[65]

The average abundance of Rb^{87} is somewhat higher than that of Sr^{87}. During the existence of the earth's crust, the isotopic composition of rubidium and strontium changed by a few per cent. The concentration ratio of Sr^{87} and Rb^{87} can be used in determining the absolute age of some minerals of pegmatite veins enriched in rubidium. The "rubidium age" of lepidolites from Manitoba and Rhodesia approaches the age determined for these same pegmatite veins by the "lead method" [114, 115].[66] The age determination by the rubidium method is applicable to a limited group of minerals, essentially to old minerals, because the accumulation of radiogenic strontium is a fairly slow process. Nevertheless, this method is quite simple and reliable, since significant migration of rubidium and strontium could hardly be expected during the time of the existence of the mineral.

Indium

The radioactive isotope of indium has a very long half-life, and the geochemical consequences of its decay are not known. In the course of

[65] Recent geological determination of the half-life of Rb^{87} by L. T. Aldrich, G. W. Wetherill, G. R. Tilton, and G. S. Davis (*Phys. Rev.*, **103**: 1045–47, 1956) gives a decay probability of Rb^{87} of 1.39×10^{-11} year^{-1}.

[66] For other important examples of age comparisons involving the "rubidium age" see papers by L. T. Aldrich, G. L. Davis, G. R. Tilton, and G. W. Wetherill (*Jour. Geophys. Res.*, **61**: 215–32, 1956) and by G. R. Tilton, G. L. Davis, G. W. Wetherill, and L. T. Aldrich (*Trans. Amer. Geophys. Union,* **38**: 360–71, 1957).

the existence of the old minerals of the earth's crust, about one-millionth of the available indium has disintegrated. The element forms no minerals of its own and ordinarily enters the sulfide minerals as an isomorphic substitute for cadmium, zinc, tin, lead, and other elements of the sulfide field. Only in exceptional cases does the indium content of minerals approach 1 per cent. Considering this fact as well as the geochemical affinity of indium and tin, it can hardly be hoped that it will presently be possible to detect the admixture of the decay product of In^{115} in naturally occurring tin.

Tellurium

Tellurium is the only element whose radioactivity is indicated merely geochemically (accumulation of Xe^{130} in old tellurium minerals). Earlier in this chapter (Sec. 5) we reported the data on the isotopic composition of xenon from an old telluro-bismuthite. The probability of a double β-decay of tellurium is exceptionally small, approximately one disintegration per year in 1 gm. of tellurium. The detection of such a weak effect is possible only because during the decay of tellurium an isotope of xenon is formed—the rare gas which is present in the mineral only in negligible traces (about 10^{-9} weight per cent.)

Lanthanum

The geochemical effects of the radioactivity of the rare and long-lived isotope of lanthanum have not been detected. During its decay there is formed essentially the principal isotope of barium, Ba^{138}. Ce^{138}, in small quantities, is also produced. In the course of the earth's history the abundance of La^{138} decreased by 2–3 per cent. At the expense of this decrease the abundance of Ba^{138} increased by only 10^{-5} per cent and that of Ce^{138} by 10^{-2} per cent, i.e., by so little that, with present measurement techniques, this effect cannot be detected.

Neodymium

The decay probability of neodymium is small [99].[67] As a result of this decay the dominant isotope of cerium is produced. Taking into account the geochemical similarity of these elements, it is difficult to hope for a successful search for radiogenic cerium.

Samarium

Because of their position in the 82-neutron shell region (see Sec. 10 and 13, pp. 114 and 151), some samarium isotopes are α-active. The

[67] The mass number of the radioactive neodymium isotope is 144.

short-lived isotope with the atomic weight of 146 decayed completely and now forms a gap in the series of samarium isotopes. Sm^{147} possesses observable α-activity. It transforms into Nd^{143}. The abundance of this isotope increased during the existence of the earth by only fractions of 1 per cent.

Under natural conditions the presence of an α-active samarium isotope is manifested in the following manner. If in a transparent mineral—for example, mica—there is a microscopic inclusion of a radioactive mineral, then under the impact of α-radiation there are formed colored zones around the radioactive grain, the so-called pleochroic halos. A series of such zones is observed, each having a radius which corresponds to the α-particle range of a certain emitter in the given mineral. In the rare-earth minerals, which usually contain traces of heavy radioactive elements, there are present halos having a normal radius. It has long been observed that these minerals exhibit, in addition, halos which correspond to the α-particle range in the air, of the order of 1 cm. This was explained after the discovery of the radioactivity of samarium, which emits α-particles of a comparatively low energy.

Lutecium

During the β-decay[68] of Lu^{176}, a hafnium isotope is produced, i.e., in distinction from samarium, the decay product of this rare-earth element does not belong to the group of the rare-earth elements. In the course of the existence of the earth's crust, the average abundance of Hf^{176} increased by approximately 1 per cent. Probably it will be possible to detect the accumulation of this isotope by comparing hafnium isolated from old rare-earth minerals with the common hafnium.

Rhenium

Rhenium is one of the least abundant elements of the earth's crust. It is not a mineral-forming element. The largest concentrations of rhenium (up to 0.1 per cent) are observed in molybdenites, where it substitutes for tetravalent molybdenum according to the principle of the diagonal isomorphium of Fersman. In the course of β-decay, rhenium is transformed into Os^{187}. Non-radiogenic osmium, like the other elements of the platinum group, prefers minerals of the proto-crystallization stage and is almost absent from the hydrothermal

[68] W. Herr, E. Merz, P. Eberhardt, and P. Signer (*Zeitschr. f. Naturforsch.*, **13a**: 268–73, 1958) report for Lu^{176} a half-life of $(2.17 \pm 0.35) \times 10^{10}$ years, based on measurement of Hf^{176} in a gadolinium mineral.

geophase, where molybdenites are formed. Hinterberger, Herr, and Voshage [116] isolated from molybdenite, containing 0.32 per cent Re, 2.11 mg. Os, which turned out to be almost a pure Os^{187}.[69] This geochemical determination, for the first time, permitted the estimation of the half-life of rhenium.[70]

Bismuth

Even in the oldest minerals of bismuth, no more than 10^{-6} per cent of its decay product, Tl^{205}, has been accumulated.[71] The geochemical similarity of these two elements, which, according to Fersman, belong to the sulfide field, makes a search for radiogenic thallium difficult.

Thorium and Uranium

The most important of all natural radioactive isotopes, from the standpoint of both practical significance and energy liberation in the subcrustal material, are the isotopes of uranium and thorium. Under terrestrial conditions these elements have a high affinity for the late crystallization stages. It is possible that this is associated with their ability to form volatile compounds with halogens. The geochemical properties of uranium and thorium are similar, even as late as the final crystallization stage—the pegmatite phase. Here the behavior of these elements becomes sharply divided.

Thorium gravitates toward the granitic magma and its pegmatites. It usually enters, as a major constituent, the composition of the abundant accessory mineral monazite—a phosphate of the rare-earth elements. Here thorium substitutes isomorphically a molecule of thorium silicate, $ThSiO_4$, for a $CePO_4$ molecule. As shown by the founder of the geochemistry of radioelements, V. I. Vernadskii [3], thorium forms no soluble minerals and does not escape into the volatile fractions of magma.

Uranium enriches pneumatolites to a considerable extent, particularly the hydrothermal veins, where it precipitates in the low-temperature phases together with sulfides of copper, cobalt, silver, and other elements of the sulfide field. It is not known in what form

[69] J. Geiss, B. Hirt, P. Signer, W. Herr, and E. Merz (*Helvet. Phys. Acta,* **31:** 324–25, 1958) found Os^{187}-enrichment in the Henbury iron meteorite, which contains 1.4 ppm Re (E. Goldberg and H. Brown, *Phys. Rev.,* **76:** 1260, 1949). The ratio Os^{187}/Os^{186} is 1.128 ± 0.03 compared with 0.971 ± 0.035 for the common osmium.

[70] A new geochemical determination of the half-life of Re^{187} by W. Herr and E. Merz (*Zeitschr. f. Naturforsch.,* **13a:** 231–33, 1958) gave the limits of $5.5 \times 10^{10} < T_{1/2} < 6.8 \times 10^{10}$ years.

[71] See n. 6, p. 165.

uranium is transported into this field, but its minerals are always oxides—essentially uraninite, UO_2, and low-temperature pitchblende, U_3O_8. The fundamental property of uranium is its easy solubility in the sulfate-bearing waters of the oxidation zone of the sulfide deposits. Along with the magmatic and hydrothermal uranium deposits, there are developed deposits of secondary minerals which have precipitated from sulfate solutions. These minerals—the so-called uranium micas—ordinarily belong to the group of complex uranium vanadates and phosphates.

The decay of thorium and of the isotopes of uranium gives rise to a series of short-lived decay products (Figs. 4–6) which can migrate independently, thus rendering the geochemistry of the heavy radioelements complex and varied. The migration of the intermediate as well as of the end products of radioactive decay will be considered in later sections.

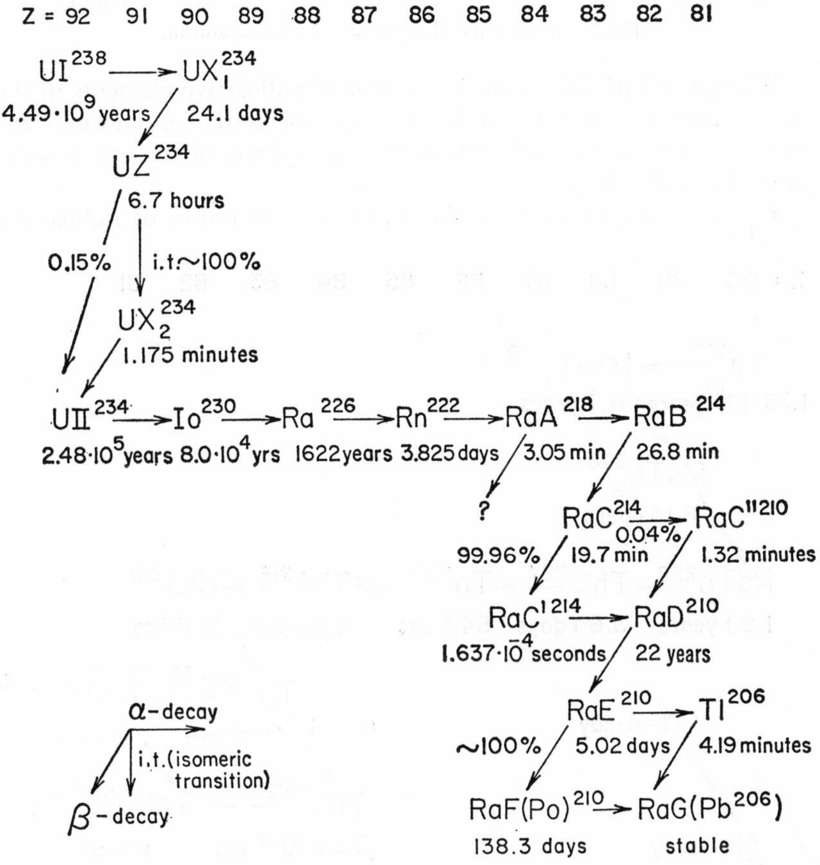

FIG. 4.—Radioactive-decay series of uranium.

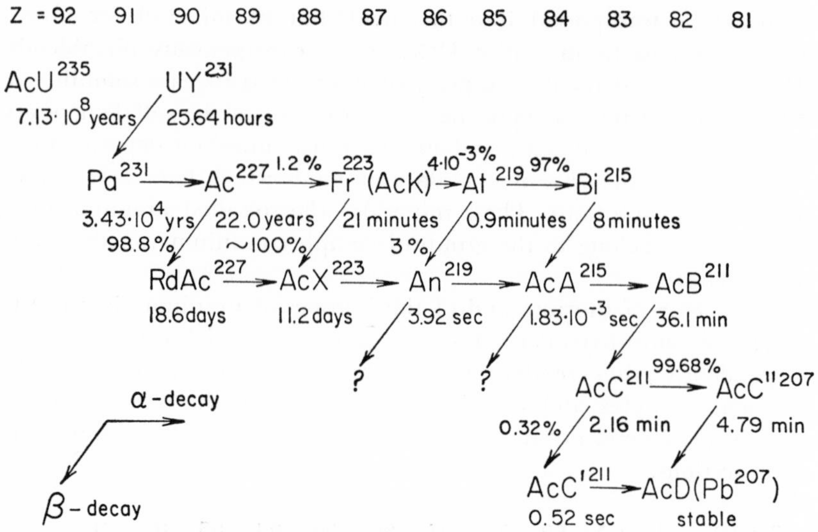

FIG. 5.—Radioactive-decay series of actinouranium.

The quantitative data on the content of radioactive elements in the atmospheres of the sun and the stars are not available. Thorium was detected in negligible amounts in the atmospheres of the sun and the star α Herculis [117].

On the earth, as we have shown, the concentration of radioactive

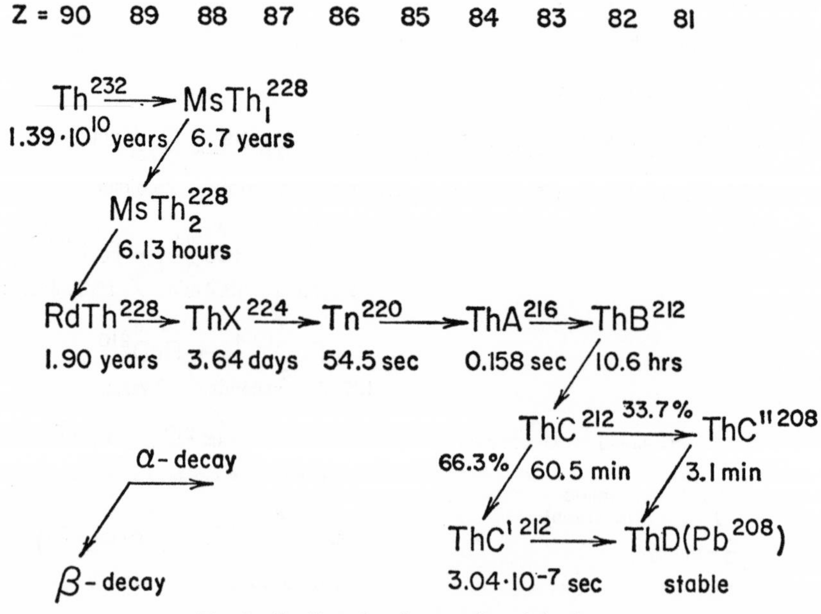

FIG. 6.—Radioactive-decay series of thorium.

elements increases uniformly from the deep-seated material toward the acidic rocks that prevail in the surface layers of the earth's crust. An incidental combination of the geochemical properties results in the earth's crust being enriched in the heavy α-emitters—thorium and uranium—as well as in other radioactive elements of highest activity —potassium and rubidium. This leads to important energetic consequences. The active processes of terrestrial matter take place primarily in the outer layers of the earth—the earth's crust and the adjacent subcrustal matter. The relative concentration of radioactive elements in the earth's crust is higher than in the sun's atmosphere and in stony meteorites. The difference is probably not less than thousands of times for the former and tens of thousands of times for the latter. As we have seen in Section 3, iron meteorites, with respect to the heavy-element composition, are closer to the earth's crust than they are to the sun. But an increased content of radioactive elements is a fortuitous feature of the earth's crust only.

However, the striking discrepancy between the abundance of thorium and uranium in the earth and in these objects is apparently caused not only by the enrichment of the earth's crust in radioactive elements but also by a relative decrease in their amount in the sun's atmosphere and the iron meteorites. The causes of this are probably diverse. In the sun's atmosphere the abundance of the heavy radioelements decreases in the general process of impoverishment of the heavy elements, possibly as a result of the gravitational differentiation of matter. For iron meteorites, however, a process of selective impoverishment of thorium and uranium is most likely. During the distribution of the matter of a hypothetical planet[72]—the starting material of meteorites—the natural radioactive elements were evidently transported into its outer regions, similar to those of the earth's lithosphere, in the form of volatile compounds. If the scheme presented is correct, then the closest to the average cosmic abundance of radioactive elements is their concentration in the stony meteorites, which is approximately one hundred times lower than the concentration of these elements in the earth's crust. It is possible that the abundance of radioactive elements in the surface layers of large planets is as high as in the earth's crust [20, p. 68].

The decay of all three heavy radioactive elements leads to the formation of the stable isotopes of lead:

$$\left.\begin{aligned} U^{238} &= Pb^{206} + 8He, \\ AcU^{235} &= Pb^{207} + 7He, \\ Th^{232} &= Pb^{208} + 6He. \end{aligned}\right\} \qquad (6.9)$$

In addition, uranium and thorium are capable of spontaneous fission,

[72] See n. 14, p. 27.

but the ratio of the probability of this process to that of α-decay is very small (5.5×10^{-7} for uranium and 7×10^{-9} for thorium). Thus, for example, in the course of 1 billion years a mineral with a maximum content of uranium will accumulate all elements combined—the fission products—in quantities not greater than 10^{-5} per cent. As already indicated in Section 5, it was possible to detect xenon and krypton among the fission products of radioactive minerals. V. G. Khlopin and co-workers [89] extracted, for the first time, 5×10^{-4} cm^3 of xenon from 1 kg. of an old uraninite. This is in agreement with the calculated quantity of the accumulated radiogenic xenon.

The heavy radioactive elements (also K^{40}) are the shortest-lived independent elements of the earth's crust. In the course of the existence of the earth, its content of Th^{232} decreased by approximately 10 per cent, that of U^{238} by almost half, and that of AcU^{235} by tens of times. Three and a half[73] billion years ago (this figure appears in many geological works as the approximate age of the earth's crust) there was liberated in the earth's crust a radioactive-decay energy that was twice the amount of the energy being released today. At that time the most active of all radioactive elements was actinouranium. A very great share of the energy was contributed by K^{40}. The role of these short-lived isotopes was exceptionally large in the energetics of the early geologic epochs. It is possible that the intensity of magmatic processes, the poor preservation of rocks, and the development of metamorphism in the pre-Cambrian rocks of the earth's crust are all due to extensive release of radioactive heat. From the Cambrian to the present, the radioactive energy supply decreased by only 4–5 per cent. This apparently could not substantially alter the thermal regimen and the climatic conditions of the earth.

The question of unstable radioactive elements is closely connected with the problem of the earth's energy, just as the problem of stellar energy is connected with the question of the transmutation of light elements in the interior regions of stars.

"Extinct" Elements

It is admissible to ask the question as to the existence of elements in the earth's crust which are products of the short-lived radioactive nuclei that have decayed in the course of the earth's existence. It is possible that some isotopes of this type existed at the time of the formation of the solar system.

The longest-lived isotopes that have been obtained artificially are

[73] The accepted age of the solid crust of the earth is now 4.5 billion years (F. G. Houtermans, *Nuovo Cimento,* **10:** Ser. 9, 1623–33, 1953; C. Patterson, G. Tilton, and M. Inghram, *Science,* **121:** 69–75, 1955).

the α-emitters Sm^{146} ($T_{1/2} = 1.5 \times 10^7$ years) [238], Cm^{247} ($T > 4 \times 10^7$ years), U^{236} ($T = 2.4 \times 10^7$ years) [121], Pu^{244} ($T = 7.6 \times 10^7$ years), the β-emitter I^{129} ($T = 1.72 \times 10^7$ years), and Pb^{205} ($T = 5 \times 10^7$ years) [200].[74] The last isotope is remarkable in that it does not decay by K-capture as is customary or a neutron-deficient isotope but, instead, captures electrons only from the L-shell of the atom. The decay product of iodine is xenon—the rare gas which was lost by the earth. This makes it the most favorable case to check the assumption concerning the "extinct" isotopes.

Indeed, Xe^{129} is the only odd isotope whose abundance is higher than the sum of the abundances of the neighboring even isotopes (for details see Sec. 17, p. 212). On the other hand, iodine in Mendeleyev's table represents one of the exceptions from the general rule of the increase of atomic weight with increasing atomic number of the element. Tellurium ($Z = 52$) has the atomic weight of 127.01, and iodine ($Z = 53$) 126.92. A similar reversal of the order among the stable elements is observed only at the argon-potassium and cobalt-nickel positions. The anomalous atomic weight of argon, as we have seen, is caused by the accumulation on the earth of its radiogenic isotope. It is possible that primordial iodine contained the two isotopes in approximately equal amounts and thus possessed an atomic weight which was normal in relation to tellurium, while primordial xenon also had the usual isotopic composition [120].[75]

The enrichment of terrestrial xenon in Xe^{129} constitutes the sole example by which one can postulate, with a sufficient degree of probability, the presence of a decay product of an extinct atomic nucleus. The considerations of other radio activities in scientific literature are speculative.[76]

7. HELIUM IN THE EARTH'S CRUST

The geochemistry of helium is unique. It is one of the dominant elements of the cosmos which is present in both the sun's atmosphere and the cosmic primaries to the extent of about 10 per cent of the total number of particles. At the same time, helium almost completely escaped from the earth, together with other gases of the zero group. He^4 is the lightest nucleus with a closed shell. Therefore, in nuclear reactions an α-particle, i.e., helium nucleus, is often emitted. The

[74] According to a later work by J. Wing, C. M. Stevens, and J. R. Huizenga (*Phys. Rev.*, **111**: 590–92, 1958), the partial half-life of Pb^{205} for L-electron capture is $(3 \pm 0.5) \times 10^7$ years. An attempt to measure M X-rays of Pb^{205} was unsuccessful.

[75] See also paper by H. E. Suess and H. Brown (*Phys. Rev.*, **83**: 1254–55, 1951).

[76] A critical examination of previous studies dealing with extinct natural radioactivities and their potentialities was published by T. P. Kohman (*Ann. New York Acad. Sci.*, **62**: 503–42, 1956).

formation of helium takes place in the course of thermonuclear reactions in the sun, but the quantity of radiogenic helium at the present stage is evidently much smaller than was the quantity of primeval helium. In the bodies of the solar system, helium is produced continuously during spontaneous α-decay of the natural radioelements and during artificial transmutation of atomic nuclei. On the earth, the former process unquestionably prevails.

In nature there is no other element whose isotopic composition varies within such broad limits (the ratio He^3/He^4 varies by more than nine orders of magnitude). Apparently, it is hopeless at the present time to attempt the establishment of the true primeval isotopic composition of helium.[77]

The earth's crust contains He^3 of the following origins:

1. The primordial isotope, partially preserved along with the other isotopes of the rare gases.

2. The decay of tritium. Probably the enrichment of atmospheric helium in the light isotope is connected with this source.

3. The neutron-induced nuclear reactions in the earth's crust, as shown by the accumulation of He^3 in spodumenes.

4. The possible capture of He^3 by the earth from cosmic space, for example, together with cosmic dust, whose content of this isotope should be even higher than the corresponding content in meteorites, owing to the small size of the dust particles.[78]

The reverse process—the loss of helium by the earth—most certainly takes place. There is observed a dynamic equilibrium during which the supply of He^3, produced at the expense of the decay of H^3, is offset by its escape from the earth's gravitational field. It is readily found that the average lifetime of He^3 in the earth's atmosphere is only 1.4 million years, a period which is negligible in the history of the earth.

Using these values and the most probable ideas on the thermodynamic cycle of the atmosphere, Damon and Kulp [188] obtained 50 million years for the average lifetime of He^4. Much earlier, V. G. Khlopin [122] had pointed out that the atmosphere contained only a small fraction of helium released by the earth's crust in the course of its geologic history.

Long before the discovery of radioactivity, Hillebrand established that during the heating of some uranium and thorium minerals

[77] Some information on the primordial isotopic composition of helium has recently become available. For example, J. H. Reynolds (*Phys. Rev. Letters,* 4: 351–54, 1960), assuming a constant uranium content for chondrites (0.01 ppm), attributed a large difference in the He^4 content between the Murray (142×10^{-6} cc STP/gm) and Richardton (12.0×10^{-6} cc STP/gm) chondrites to primordial helium in the former.

[78] The He^3 content of cosmic dust is expected to be lower than that of meteorites, inasmuch as the helium atom is likely to recoil out of the dust particles.

(uraninite, cleveite, monazite, aeschynite, fergusonite, and others) a large quantity of inert gases—which he believed to be nitrogen—is liberated. Later Ramsay proved that the gas consisted essentially of helium, which heretofore had been known only from the spectral lines of astronomical bodies.

In *Principles of Chemistry* Mendeleyev wrote:

> In what compound or condition . . . helium and the similar gases are present in cleveite, aeschynite and other minerals of this kind, is until now unknown. It is even unknown whether these gases constitute a substantial part of minerals or originate from their content of some peculiar admixture. In this area . . . there are many things over which a long work will be required, and one can hope that many most interesting data and conclusions will result.

The future bore out this anticipation. The "peculiar admixture" which determines the accumulation of helium turned out to be the radioactive elements. The helium content of uranium minerals amounts to several cubic centimeters per gram, i.e., the partial pressure of helium in the crystalline lattice of the mineral approaches 10 atmospheres. The atomic radius of helium is small, and minerals naturally lose a considerable fraction of their helium.

In the gas phase of the lithosphere, accumulation of helium is observed in the gas streams associated with magmatic intrusions and in the gas accumulators of sedimentary rocks. The gas streams of the former type are found in many mineral springs, the last manifestations of subsiding volcanic activity. Their helium is apparently a residual helium which was released during the remelting of the given intrusion. The helium content of the gas may be exceptionally high (up to 10.2 volume per cent of the gas from the Santoney spring in France), but the volume of the gas phase is usually small, and this type of spring has no practical significance. The gas accumulators in sedimentary rocks are formed beneath the anticlinal folds of the gas-impermeable halogenous strata. As shown by V. V. Belousov [124], the accumulation of helium in these strata is especially favored by the proximity of granitic bodies. Granite is distinguished by an increased content of radioactive elements and therefore also by an increased content of helium of radiogenic origin. The concentration of helium in these gases is not so high as in the streams of granitic intrusions, but large reserves of the gas render these occurrences industrially valuable. The anticlinal folds of the halogenous strata are also favorable for the accumulation of petroleum. Because of this, helium is usually associated with petroleum gases, regardless of the fact that the origin and history of these substances in the earth's crust are very different.

After the discovery of radioactivity, helium was used for the determination of the absolute age of geologic objects. The accumulation of helium from uranium, thorium, and actinouranium proceeds according to the law

$$\mathrm{He} = c_1\mathrm{U}(e^{\lambda_{\mathrm{U}}t} - 1) + c_2\mathrm{AcU}(e^{\lambda_{\mathrm{AcU}}t} - 1) + c_3\mathrm{Th}(e^{\lambda_{\mathrm{Th}}t} - 1), \quad (7.1)$$

where c with subscripts represents certain numerical constants. If, for the comparatively young minerals, the decrease in the content of the parent radioelements during the existence of the object is neglected, we find

$$t = \frac{846\mathrm{He}}{\mathrm{U} + 0.246\mathrm{Th}} \text{ million years.} \quad (7.2)$$

Here the helium content is expressed in cubic centimeters per gram, and uranium and thorium content in per cent.

Investigations have shown that the helium content generally increases for old radioactive minerals. However, it is subject to considerable fluctuation. The helium age is usually much lower than the lead age. Thus V. G. Khlopin found that three uraninites from North Karelia with a true age of 1,600–1,700 million years have a helium age of 6.1, 51.8, and 64.2 million years [125]. The discrepancy is explained by the considerable possibility of helium losses from the minerals. I. E. Starik in 1932 first showed, using the mineral khlopinite (niobo-tantalate of yttrium and titanium), that the age obtained by the helium method can approach the lead age. This is due to the good retentivity of helium in khlopinite [126]. Indeed, Khlopin, Gerling, and Yoffe [127] discovered that khlopinite releases in vacuum, even at the temperature of 985° C, only 12.6 per cent helium.

Systematic studies on the retentivity of helium in minerals and of their suitability for age determinations were made by E. K. Gerling [128]. According to him, the loss of helium is caused by its diffusion through the intercrystalline spaces of the mineral lattice. If in the lattice the volume of the space unoccupied by ions is large, the diffusion of helium in such a lattice takes place more readily than in the lattice with a close-packed structure. As a measure of the close packing of a crystalline structure, Gerling accepts the lattice volume per atom of oxygen. In the most compact packing, this volume is equal to 13.9 $Å^3$. The majority of the rock-forming minerals do not possess a close-packed structure and therefore lose their helium easily. In fact, Gerling showed that feldspars lose about 75–80 per cent of their helium. Nearly all important alumo-silicates and also quartz do not retain helium. Among the abundant minerals, some garnets and magnetite and, among the rarer minerals, spinels, columbite, and other niobo-tantalates retain helium quite well [129].

The helium method of age determination has been neglected for a long time because of the possibility of helium losses by minerals. The Soviet school of radiologists worked out theoretically and substantiated experimentally the criteria which determine the retentivity of helium in minerals and also their suitability for age determination.

Along with the minerals which lose helium, one finds in nature minerals with an increased helium content that cannot be explained by accumulation during the decay of the known radioactive elements. Such "excess" helium was first detected by Strutt [130] in 1908 in beryls and, in smaller quantities, in potassium minerals of the sedimentary stratum—sylvites and carnallites. Other beryllium minerals do not contain large quantities of excess helium. Later Strutt [131] determined the helium content of beryls of different ages and found that there is a tendency toward an increase in the average helium content of the old beryls. For the beryls of the pre-Cambrian age this content approaches 0.078 cm^3/gm. The effective age for these minerals calculated from their helium and radioactive-element contents, using equation (7.1), may attain absurd values of the order of tens of billions of years.

Subsequent studies demonstrated wide occurrence of excess helium. V. G. Khlopin [132] discovered its presence in certain minerals of light metals, and Keevil with co-workers in titanium minerals and hornblende [133, 134]. V. V. Cherdyntsev and L. V. Kozak made a study of the helium content of beryls from various geophases and of the paragenetically associated minerals [135]. As Table 13 shows, the he-

TABLE 13

HELIUM CONTENT OF BERYLS AS FUNCTION OF TEMPERATURE OF FORMATION [135]

Phase	No. of Samples	Helium Content (10^{-3} Cm³/Gm)		
		From	To	Average
Pegmatites:				
I. High temperature	17	0.13	5.35	2.31
II. Intermediate temperature	8	.65	1.7	1.12
III. Low temperature				
a) Albite veins	5	.05	0.74	0.35
b) *Zanorysh**	7	0.02	0.64	0.23
Pneumatolites	3	0.61	1.5	1.03

* This is a transliteration of the original term.

lium content decreases by approximately ten times on going from high- to low-temperature beryls. Among the paragenetic minerals, those have been investigated which have close packing of ions and are able to retain helium (cassiterite, garnet, ilmenite). During the simultaneous formation of beryl and of a given mineral, the excess helium content of both minerals is nearly the same [135]. The early minerals contain more excess helium than do beryls, and vice versa. Thus excess helium seems to be a common property of the high-temperature mineral derivatives of magma, provided that they have the capacity to retain helium.

Obviously, the excess helium can affect the age determination. The true age, t_0, of a mineral is related to its effective age t' (obtained from the determination of its content of helium and of the radioactive elements) by means of a simple equation:

$$t' = t_0 \frac{\text{He}}{\text{He} - \delta\text{He}}, \tag{7.3}$$

where δHe is the content of excess helium.

In the course of the investigation of tantalites from the same deposit, an increase was observed [77] in the effective age of the faintly radioactive varieties of the mineral. If one sets $\delta\text{He} = 0.76 \times 10^{-3}$ cm^3/gm, the obtained values of t' (Fig. 7) show good agreement with

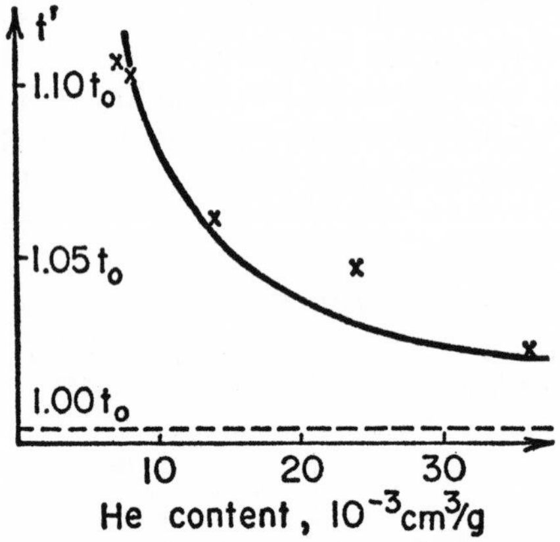

FIG. 7.—Decrease in the effective age t' with increasing helium content of the mineral (t_0 = the true age).

the type of the dependence expressed by equation (7.3). This is probable, inasmuch as the helium content of the later, low-temperature beryls of the above deposit is 0.36×10^{-3} cm^3/gm. Some minerals of the pneumatolytic and even of the hydrothermal phase, i.e., the low-temperature minerals, can also contain excess helium, but in smaller quantities (10^{-5}–10^{-4} cm^3/gm). Traces of excess helium (2.6×10^{-5} cm^3/gm) were found by Gerling and Cherdyntsev [135] in magnetite from a modern volcanic bomb of the Kliuchevskii volcano on Kamchatka.

Aldrich and Nier [84], as already pointed out, have determined the relative He^3 content of helium isolated from beryl. They obtained a value of the same order of magnitude as that found for helium of the underground gas streams. This indicates a non-radiogenic origin of the excess helium. In addition, the authors have detected argon of non-radiogenic origin in beryls, as concluded from its isotopic composition. The content of excess argon reaches 1.0×10^{-3} cm^3/gm. The heats of diffusion of helium and argon in one of the beryls, according to our data, are equal, which points to similar conditions of the occurrence of excess argon and helium in the lattice of the mineral.

Cherdyntsev and Kozak [135] proposed the impregnation hypothesis of the origin of excess helium. The residual magmatic melt, giving rise to pegmatites, is enriched in the gas phase, including helium, which was released by the entire intrusion upon its remelting, so that the partial pressure of helium can be sufficiently high. During the formation of minerals, helium is incorporated into the crystalline lattices on a large scale, regardless of their types and composition and, later on, is retained by the close-packed minerals capable of its preservation. One should assume selective retentivity and not selective adsorption of helium. As the gas phase dissipates, the partial pressure of helium drops. Therefore, the low-temperature pegmatite minerals and the minerals of the later phases contain smaller amounts of excess helium. The increase in the average helium content of old beryls observed by Strutt [131] is perhaps explained by the fact that the erosion processes in old rock bodies can expose deep zones which contain high-temperature pegmatites. In young bodies, however, only the external zones of the batholith, containing low-temperature minerals, have been brought to the surface. Probably the age dependence is illusive.[79]

During the investigation of the helium content of the earth's crust it is necessary to take into account the possibility of helium losses by minerals, as well as the possibility of the enrichment of minerals in excess helium.

In a study of the extra-terrestrial objects, we have found 8.2×10^{-3} cm^3/gm excess helium in a single case of the Staroye Pes'yanoye achondrite. According to the data of Gerling and Levskii [201], the content of all isotopes of the rare gases (with the exception of Ar^{40} and He^3) is exceptionally high in this meteorite. At the same time, in the isotopic composition, neon and the light isotopes of argon are close to these isotopes in the earth's atmosphere, whereas the ratio Ar^{40}/Ar^{38} is ten times lower than on the earth (the lowest ever found under

[79] See paper by P. E. Damon and J. L. Kulp (*Amer. Mineralogist,* 43: 433–59, 1958).

natural conditions). The meteorite Staroye Pes'yanoye retained a large amount of rare gases, the composition of which has not been changed substantially either by the processes of splitting of atomic nuclei by cosmic rays or by the accumulation of radiogenic Ar^{40}. Evidently, these gases represent the remnants of a thick atmosphere of the primitive planet from which this meteorite originated.

8. ISOTOPIC COMPOSITION OF LEAD IN NATURAL MATERIALS

All isotopes of lead (with the exception of the lightest, Pb^{204}) are the end products of the decay of uranium and thorium isotopes. The half-lives of the radioactive elements are comparable to the time of the existence of the earth; therefore, the isotopic composition of lead is subject to considerable variations, the deciphering of which permits the solution of many geological and cosmogonical problems. The average content of Pb^{204} is 1.48 per cent, but this small value by no means points to the fact that an overwhelming proportion of lead has a radiogenic origin, inasmuch as for the heavy elements the content of the lightest isotope is always very low and never exceeds the indicated value [136].

Lead belongs to the elements of the sulfide field but possesses a complex geochemical characteristic, in that it has an affinity for the elements of the iron group as well as for those of the acidic magma. Its concentration in granites is of the order of 3×10^{-3} per cent and falls to $4\text{–}5 \times 10^{-4}$ per cent [137] in the deep-seated rocks of the earth's crust—basalts and gabbro. In stony meteorites, lead is low, ($4\text{–}9 \times 10^{-5}$ per cent,[80] and in iron meteorites it is even lower, 1×10^{-6} per cent; but troilites—the sulfide minerals of meteorites—are enriched in lead to the extent of 1.8×10^{-4} per cent [138].[81] However, lead enriches granitic magma to a considerably smaller degree than the radioactive elements, so that, for example, the ratio Pb/U increases from 3–4 in granites to 9 in the basic rocks and to 2,000 in troilite. For the earth's crust as a whole, the ratio $Pb/U \approx 6$ and $Pb/Th \approx 1.6$, that is, these ratios are apparently much lower than for primeval matter. Therefore, the accumulation of radiogenic lead under terrestrial conditions is manifested especially strongly.

Lead is the first element for which has been demonstrated the possibility of the variation of isotopic composition under natural con-

[80] According to recent determinations by R. R. Marshall and D. C. Hess (*Helvet. Phys. Acta,* **32:** 276–77, 1959) and by G. W. Reed, K. Kigoshi, and A. Turkevich (*Geochim. et Cosmochim. Acta,* **20:** 122–40, 1960), the lead in stony meteorites varies from as low as 0.06 to as high as 4 ppm.

[81] The correct content is 18 ppm. More recently, G. W. Reed, K. Kigoshi, and A. Turkevich (*Geochim. et Cosmochim. Acta,* **20:** 122–40, 1960) found that troilites of iron meteorites contain only 5–8 ppm lead.

ditions. As early as 1914, Soddy and Hyman and also Lembert showed that the atomic weight of lead from thorite is 208, whereas that of lead from a uranium mineral is 206. The accumulation of lead in radioactive minerals permitted the establishment of the "lead method" for the determination of the absolute age of geologic formations. Up to the present time, this method continues to be the most accurate and reliable. The age is found from the following relationships:

$$\left.\begin{aligned} Pb^{204} &= Pb_0^{204}, \\ Pb^{206} &= Pb_0^{206} + U(e^{\lambda_U t} - 1), \\ Pb^{207} &= Pb_0^{207} + AcU(e^{\lambda_{AcU} t} - 1), \\ Pb^{208} &= Pb_0^{208} + Th(e^{\lambda_{Th} t} - 1), \end{aligned}\right\} \qquad (8.1)$$

where the subscripts denote admixtures of non-radiogenic lead (the so-called "ore" lead) which can be accounted for from the content of the non-radiogenic Pb^{204}. Radioactive minerals of the pegmatite veins contain almost no ore lead, but thorium is high in uraninites (up to 10 per cent), and therefore thorium lead, Pb^{208}, is also high. In uranium oxides of the hydrothermal phase (for example, in pitchblende) thorium is very low, but these minerals are richer in the ore lead, which deposits its principal minerals precisely in this phase.

It is obvious from reactions (8.1) that there are three independent methods of age determination by means of lead isotopes. The age values are frequently discordant because of the possible migration of both the radioactive elements and lead. V. G. Khlopin and M. E. Vladimirova [139], using carefully selected samples of a high degree of preservation, for the first time obtained excellent agreement among the age values for a series of uraninites from the same geologic suite. For samples of a low degree of preservation it is sometimes possible to establish migrational escape of lead. The lead losses are also possible through the liberation from the mineral of intermediate decay products—radioactive emanations.

I. E. Starik [126] proposed age determination on the basis of the ratio of actinium (Pb^{207}) to uranium lead (Pb^{206}). In the absence of the ore lead, we have

$$\frac{Pb^{207}}{Pb^{206}} = \frac{1}{138} \times \frac{e^{\lambda_{AcU} t} - 1}{e^{\lambda_U t} - 1} \qquad (8.2)$$

(the normal ratio of uranium isotopes $AcU/U = 1/138$ is accepted). The ratio Pb^{207}/Pb^{206} is not altered if the ratio of the radioactive elements in the mineral was changed during their migration in the surface zone.

Some results of the age determination of radioactive minerals are given in Table 14, according to [68, 140, 141]. For samples of a high degree of preservation, the ages obtained by using different variants

TABLE 14

AGE OF RADIOACTIVE MINERALS ACCORDING TO DIFFERENT VARIANTS OF LEAD METHOD

MINERAL*	CONCENTRATION IN MINERAL (PER CENT)			ISOTOPIC COMPOSITION OF LEAD			AGE (MILLION YEARS) DETERMINED FROM RATIOS			
	Pb	U	Th	Pb^{204}	Pb^{207}	Pb^{208}	$\frac{Pb^{207}}{Pb^{206}}$	$\frac{Pb^{206}}{U}$	$\frac{Pb^{207}}{U}$	$\frac{Pb^{208}}{Th}$
Uraninites:										
Karelia, Kamennaya Taibola	16.58	55.9	1.28	<0.005	11.25	0.72	1,870	1,760	1,800	1,800
Trans-Baikal	16.1	64.2	0.91	.02	11.56	1.05	1,860	1,500	1,670	1,240
Canada, Manitoba	15.47	54.25	12.36	.022	16.17	6.51	2,475	1,564	1,985	1,273
Africa, Gordonia	10.21	55.0	11.75	<.001	7.35	5.42	1,037	1,148	1,106	914
India, Rajputana	7.95	72.9	1.4	<.001	6.39	0.81	740	733	733	935
Altai	6.81	69.55	0.44	.05	6.7	2.0	590	640	630	508
Pitchblendes:										
Canada, Great Bear Lake	8.88	52.32	...	.063	9.76	2.51	1,420	1,030	1,180	...
Canada, Beaverhill Lake	5.62	51.16	...	.056	6.31	3.09	410	720	646	...
Pitchblende [140]	14.65	58.8	...	.05	11.4	1.8	1,680	1,470	1,600	...
Monazites:										
Africa, Rhodesia	0.34	0.074	2.39	<.01	10.4	1.92	2,680	2,675	2,680	2,645
Karelia, Chkalov Mine	0.86	0.49	7.01	.14	23.13	4.24	1,710	1,900	1,800	1,930
Canada, Manitoba	1.52	0.28	15.64	.011	11.6	2.11	2,590	3,217	2,839	1,827
India, Rajputana	0.53	0.68	16.45	.008	13.58	1.03	865	660	700	713
Monazite [140]	0.81	0.13	8.64	0.036	6.44	1.12	1,640	2,130	1,880	1,830

* Thorium minerals (Pb^{208} = 100); uraium minerals (Pb^{206} = 100)

of the lead method agree within ±5 per cent. The data of the lead method were first used for the construction of an absolute geologic time scale.

We shall now consider the isotopic composition of the common ore lead. Over the span of the earth's history, radiogenic lead has accumulated in rocks and minerals. In the course of the magmatic processes it became mixed with ore lead, causing its isotopic composition to deviate more and more from the primeval composition and toward enrichment in radiogenic isotopes. The processes of remelting occurred irregularly, encompassing regions of different volumes and different abundances of radioactive elements. The change in the isotopic composition of the earth's lead had a common trend, but in different sectors of the earth's surface it proceeded according to a different pattern. In certain cases the local enrichment of radioactive elements gave rise to a radiogenic isotope excess (lead of anomalous composition). There was observed a variation in the isotopic composition within one ore deposit, which pointed to the addition of lead of a different origin. In a given case, the isotope ratio serves as a natural radioactive indicator of great importance in the solution of the practical questions of metallogenics.

The increase in the relative content of radiogenic isotopes for young ore leads was first detected by Nier and co-workers [142]. The large experimental material accumulated subsequently [143, 144, 145] permitted A. P. Vinogradov [137] to establish the average isotopic composition of lead from the most abundant mineral, galena (PbS), of the various age groups.

Table 15 shows the isotopic composition of lead of different origins. The data for galenas of different ages were obtained by processing nearly two hundred analyses from which the "anomalous" cases of radiogenic lead enrichment were excluded. For comparison, there are shown in the table examples of "anomalous" leads versus ancient leads

TABLE 15

AVERAGE ISOTOPIC COMPOSITION OF LEAD FROM GALENAS OF DIFFERENT AGES [137]

Sample Description			Content of Isotopes*		
Period of Folding	Age Interval (Million Years)	No. of Samples Studied	Pb^{206}	Pb^{207}	Pb^{208}
Alpine	25– 180	42	18.22	15.57	38.22
Variscan	200– 260	85	18.16	15.70	38.17
Caledonian	280– 400	7	17.32	15.23	37.27
Proterozoic	600–1,200	32	16.62	15.56	36.77
Upper pre-Cambrian	1,400–2,000	10	15.28	15.18	34.69
Lower pre-Cambrian	2,000–3,000	19	13.97	15.00	33.96

TABLE 15—*Continued*

ISOTOPIC COMPOSITION OF "ANOMALOUS" AND "ANCIENT" LEAD SAMPLES FROM GALENAS [137]

Samples	Content of Isotopes*		
	Pb^{206}	Pb^{207}	Pb^{208}
"Anomalous" leads:			
Canada, Wilburforce, zone of uranium deposits	146.63	24.12	56.30
Canada, Worthington Mine	26.00	16.94	52.11
Canada, Hardy Mine	23.23	16.77	52.64
Altai, Sokol'nyi Mine	23.00	17.32	41.90
U.S.A., Joplin	22.38	16.15	41.61
"Ancient" lead:			
Transvaal, Rosetta Mine	12.65	14.27	32.78
Ivigtut, Greenland, age about 600 million years	14.65	14.65	34.77

* The Pb^{204} content = 1.

ISOTOPIC COMPOSITION OF METEORITIC LEAD [146]

Samples	Content of Isotopes*		
	Pb^{206}	Pb^{207}	Pb^{208}
Stony meteorites:			
Forest City, Iowa, U.S.A.	19.27	15.95	39.05
Modoc, Kansas, U.S.A.	19.48	15.76	38.21
Nuevo Laredo, Mexico	50.28	34.86	67.97
Iron meteorites:			
Troilite from Canyon Diablo and Henbury (average)	9.50	10.36	29.16

* The Pb^{204} content = 1.

which, during the earth's history, experienced no significant dilution with radiogenic isotopes and are close to the primordial lead. In addition, there are given data on lead from the stony and iron meteorites [146].

The regularity in the change of isotopic lead in the earth's crust is described by relationships (8.1), where Pb_0 designates the initial lead content and U and Th are the average radioactive-element content corresponding to the given content of lead isotopes. The change in the isotopic composition of lead in the time interval from t_1 to t_2 is given by the expressions

$$\left.\begin{aligned} \Delta Pb_0^{206} &= U(e^{\lambda_U t_2} - e^{\lambda_U t_1}), \\ \Delta Pb_0^{207} &= AcU(e^{\lambda_{AcU} t_2} - e^{\lambda_{AcU} t_1}), \\ \Delta Pb_0^{208} &= Th(e^{\lambda_{Th} t_2} - e^{\lambda_{Th} t_1}). \end{aligned}\right\} \quad (8.3)$$

Having determined Δ and t_2 and t_1 from the experimental data (see Table 15), we find that the earth's content of the radioactive elements in units of the atomic content of $Pb^{204} = 1$ is as follows: U = 11.4, Th = 43.2, whence Pb/U = 6, Pb/Th = 1.6, and Th/U = 3.8, which is close to the value accepted on the basis of direct determinations of the composition of the earth's crust (Th/U = 3–4, see Table I of the Appendix, p. 265).

The probability of thorium decay is smaller than the decay constant of uranium by approximately the same factor, so that the activities of thorium and uranium in the earth's crust are about equal:

$$\mathrm{Th}\lambda_{\mathrm{Th}} \approx \mathrm{U}\lambda_{\mathrm{u}}. \tag{8.4}$$

Therefore, the additional amounts of thorium (Pb^{208}) and uranium lead (Pb^{206}) in a young ore lead are about the same.

The diagram of the change of the isotopic composition of lead with time, according to reactions (8.1) and the experimental data, is shown in Figure 8.

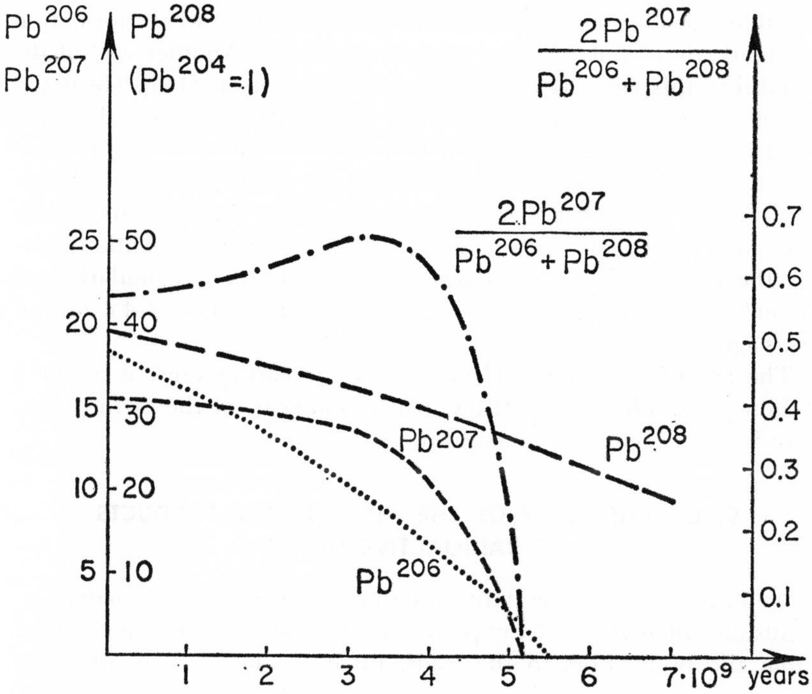

FIG. 8.—Change in the isotopic composition of ore lead during the existence of the earth's crust (in billions of years from our time).

By assigning certain values to the initial lead content of the earth's crust and knowing the regularity of the change in the isotopic composition of lead with time, it is possible to determine the age of the earth's crust. If we assume that $Pb_0 = 0$, that is, if we consider all terrestrial lead to be of radiogenic origin, we obtain the following increased age values: 5.8 billion years according to Pb^{206}; 5.2 billion years according to Pb^{207}; and 12.1 billion years according to Pb^{208}. The lowest of these values is still the maximum age of the earth's crust. From the fact that thorium lead yields the highest age value, it certainly follows that there was a preponderance of Pb^{208} in primordial lead.

In iron meteorites the amount of radioactive elements is very small, and the radiogenic lead admixtures can be neglected. Assuming that primordial lead of the earth's crust had the same isotopic composition as the lead of the iron meteorites,[82] we obtain, according to (8.3), these close values of the age: 3.8 billion years on the basis of Pb^{206}; 4.3 billion years on the basis of Pb^{207}; and 3.9 billion years on that of Pb^{208}. About 4 billion years ago the isotopic composition of the lead of the earth's crust coincided with the lead of the iron meteorites. Assuming a single origin of the matter of the solar system, it is quite possible that the value found is equal to the true age of the formation of the earth and of the solar system as a whole. Another way of determining this age has been proposed by Patterson [146]. He determined the isotopic composition of the stony meteorites and subtracted from it the non-radiogenic lead, taking for its isotopes the ratio observed in the iron meteorites (see Table 15). The age determined according to reactions (8.2) varies from 4.4 to 4.6 billion years, which is in good agreement with the maximum age value of 4.8 billion years for the stony meteorites, as determined from the accumulation of argon.[83] Evidently, the solar system was formed about 4–4.8 billion years ago.

The age of the most ancient lead of the earth's crust is about 3 billion years. The history of the first billion years of the earth's existence is as yet completely unknown.

9. GEOCHEMISTRY OF THE INTERMEDIATE PRODUCTS OF RADIOACTIVE DECAY

We have examined the status in nature of the heavy radioactive elements and their stable decay products—the lead and helium isotopes. From the progenitors to the leads, there are long chains of inter-

[82] F. G. Houtermans (*Nuovo Cimento,* **10:** Ser. 9, 1623–33, 1953) and C. Patterson, G. Tilton, and M. Inghram (*Science,* **121:** 69–75, 1955), who originally made this assumption, calculated the Pb^{207}/Pb^{206} age of the earth to be 4.5×10^9 years. The isotopic composition of the primordial lead, i.e., lead from iron meteorites, which was used in these calculations, had been determined earlier by C. Patterson, G. Tilton, M. Inghram, and H. Brown (*Phys. Rev.,* **92:** 1234, 1953).

[83] Presently accepted maximum K-Ar age value for the stony meteorites is 4.4×10^9 years (see J. Geiss and D. C. Hess, *Astrophys. Jour.,* **127:** 224–35, 1958).

mediate decay products with half-lives ranging from millionths of one second to hundreds of thousands of years. Their behavior under natural conditions is both complex and unique. For old minerals which did not undergo secondary processes of migration, there is established a radioactive equilibrium. In this condition, the activities of elements of the same series are equal:

$$n_1\lambda_1 = n_2\lambda_2 = n_3\lambda_3 = \cdots = \text{Const.}, \tag{9.1}$$

or, in other words, the absolute concentrations of atoms are directly proportional to their half-lives:

$$\frac{n_1}{T_1} = \frac{n_2}{T_2} = \frac{n_3}{T_3} = \cdots = \text{Const.} \tag{9.2}$$

Consequently, for example, the amount of radium ($T_{1/2} = 1{,}622$ years) in nature is approximately three million times less than that of uranium ($T_{1/2} = 4.4 \times 10^9$ years).[84] If radioactive elements of a mineral are in equilibrium, then it is sufficient to measure the content of one component (for example, radium), and the content of any other component (for example, uranium) is obtained by means of a simple calculation according to series (9.2). This method is commonly used in laboratory practice.

However, departures from equilibrium conditions of the elements are frequently observed in nature. The present section is devoted to the investigation of the displacement of the equilibrium of elements, particularly of isotopes, under the influence of migration processes.

Soon after the discovery of radioactivity, M. Curie [147] found that many secondary uranium minerals of the uranium mica type contain less radium than the amount in equilibrium with uranium. At the same time, it is possible for some minerals to be enriched in the secondary radium of migrational origin. Thus, according to the data of V. G. Khlopin and M. A. Pasvik [148], the radium content of barites approaches 1×10^{-5} per cent.

In studying the migration of radioactive elements, we shall distinguish the following limiting cases:

1. The secondary mineral at the instant of its formation contained only the isotopes of uranium. This case in its relatively pure form is observed in many minerals which were formed under the action of sulfate-bearing waters. Common in the surface zone, particularly in the oxidation zone of sulfide deposits, these waters easily transport uranium, whereas radium, being sparingly soluble, is not retained in the sulfate solution. As for thorium (and its isotope ionium), it yields almost no vadose compounds [3]. Subsequently, the mineral which is enriched in uranium accumulates quantities of ionium, radium, and

[84] The accepted half-life of uranium is 4.51×10^9 years.

actinium according to the laws of the accumulation of these isotopes:

$$\left.\begin{aligned} \mathrm{Io} &= \mathrm{U}(1 - e^{-\lambda_{\mathrm{Io}}t}), \\ \mathrm{Ra} &= \mathrm{U}\left(1 - \frac{\lambda_{\mathrm{Ra}}}{\lambda_{\mathrm{Ra}} - \lambda_{\mathrm{Io}}} e^{-\lambda_{\mathrm{Io}}t} + \frac{\lambda_{\mathrm{Io}}}{\lambda_{\mathrm{Ra}} - \lambda_{\mathrm{Io}}} e^{-\lambda_{\mathrm{Ra}}t}\right), \\ \mathrm{Ac} &= \mathrm{AcU}(1 - e^{-\lambda_{\mathrm{Pa}}t}), \end{aligned}\right\} \quad (9.3)$$

where U and AcU denote the amounts corresponding to the equilibrium with the given radioactive element. The growth of the short-lived actinium is practically determined by the accumulation rate of protactinium.

In these cases, the concentration of the radioactive daughter element depends only on the accumulation time, i.e., the ratio of the daughter to the parent can be utilized for the age determination. The equilibrium in the uranium and actinouranium series is reached within several hundred thousand years. In the thorium series, the half-lives of all decay products are very short (see Fig. 6) and do not exceed 6.7 years ($MsTh_1$). The equilibrium in this radioactive series is attained in a comparatively short time—of the order of tens of years. Because of this and also the insignificant geochemical activity of thorium, the shift in the radioactive equilibrium for thorium minerals is considerably smaller than for uranium minerals.

2. The minerals which are depleted in one or another radioactive element because of its migration. The extent and nature of the process depend on the physicochemical properties of the element and the surrounding medium.

3. The minerals precipitated from natural waters and containing predominantly the daughter products—the isotopes of radium, thorium, and other short-lived elements. To this type of formation belong mineral-well deposits (for example, radiobarite) and certain sea deposits. The decrease in the content of the radioactive element proceeds according to the simple law of radioactive decay:

$$\mathrm{Ra} = \mathrm{Ra}^0 e^{-\lambda_{\mathrm{Ra}}t}, \qquad \mathrm{Io} = \mathrm{Io}^0 e^{-\lambda_{\mathrm{Io}}t}, \quad (9.4)$$

etc., where the superscripts denote the initial content of the isotope.

4. The natural waters which are the principal agent of the migrational transport of radioactive elements. The departure from radioactive equilibrium is manifested here in a most intense manner.

Of course, under natural conditions, objects are usually found in which the described conditions occur in different degrees of combination. For the earth's crust as a whole and for the majority of primary minerals, an equilibrium relationship is observed among the radioactive elements.

The passage of uranium and radium into the liquid phase was first investigated by I. E. Starik [149], who showed that for the radioactive elements it is necessary to distinguish between the extreme cases of dissolution and of leaching.

In the course of dissolution, the passage of radioactive elements into the liquid phase takes place with an accompanying breakdown of the crystalline lattice of the mineral. The process, in principle, is not different from the solution of the stable elements. The solution is the only possible way whereby the parent substance can enter the aqueous phase, although the process may also take place for the decay products.

During the leaching of the radioactive elements, the passage of daughter products into the liquid phase occurs without the disturbance of the crystalline lattice of the mineral. At the instant of their formation, the recoil atoms of the decay products have an energy of $4/A \times E \approx 100$ kev (where E is the energy of the α-particle and A is the atomic weight). The path of the recoil atoms in the solid matter comprises fractions of 1 μ, i.e., the atoms travel through hundreds of the crystalline lattice sites. The real crystals of natural minerals possess a complex structure. They often consist of microblocks, contain microinclusions of minerals of different composition, and are usually intersected by an intricate network of microcracks caused by the tectonic, as well as the postmagmatic, processes. If a recoil atom becomes lodged in a microcapillary, it may, under favorable conditions, be released from the mineral. But even if such an atom stops in one of the intercorner lattice spaces, it remains there bound weakly by a foreign body.

I. E. Starik and N. M. Segel' [150] investigated the release of radium and uranium from the mineral khlopinite into solutions of varying acidity. Radium extraction is observed even in an alkaline medium, regardless of the low solubility of radium carbonate. With increasing acidity of the medium, the extraction is strongly enhanced. At a high acidity of the medium the solution process shields off the process of leaching. The solution of uranium is observed as a weak process only in the acid medium, and only at a high concentration of the acid (1 formal HCl) does the process become comparable with the dissolution of radium.

The experiments involving repeated leaching of radium show a decrease in the radium content of the successive extractions relative to the first extraction. However, following prolonged storage (for more than one year) of the sample, repeated extractions removed radium in almost the same amount as the first extraction. Hence it follows that the fundamental fact in the extraction of radium is the diffusion of atoms in the surface layers of the mineral.

In nature, the migration of radium is realized on a very large scale.

The effective age of minerals computed from the ratio Ra/U fluctuates from 8 to 286 thousand years for samples of the same deposit. This is probably caused by the migrational escape of radium [126].

Khlopin [151] pointed out that ionium as an isotope of thorium is subject to migration to a lesser extent than is radium. Indeed, a series of investigations confirmed that, in natural minerals with a small ratio Ra/U, the ratio Io/U is much closer to the equilibrium value. Inasmuch as the equilibrium between radium and ionium is established very rapidly, this clearly indicates escape of radium.

Within minerals we shall, by convention, distinguish the following zones (the existence of sharp boundaries between them is doubtful):

1. Undisturbed crystalline lattice. The radioactive elements in this lattice may be distributed inhomogeneously; this depends on the conditions of the formation of the mineral. The elements either enter micro-inclusions of the foreign minerals or form enrichment zones within the given mineral. If present in sufficient concentrations, the elements build a crystalline lattice of the corresponding micro-inclusion. The diffusion of the heavy atoms of radioactive elements through an undisturbed mineral at moderate temperatures is vanishingly small.

2. Disturbance zones made up of the destroyed mineral, probably in a colloidal state. These zones fill the microcapillaries which crisscross the mineral or form the surface layer of microfractures. The average chemical composition of the zones may be substantially different from the composition of the mineral. Thus the disturbance zones of sulfide minerals are enriched in the material which has been oxidized to sulfates. Diffusion of radioactive elements through these zones is possible, but release to the exterior in this way can occur only for atoms of the sufficiently long-lived isotopes. The adsorption processes here are very intense.

3. Microfractures filled with water and air. The recoil, atoms after finding themselves in an aqueous medium, diffuse out rapidly. Particularly rapid is the liberation of gaseous emanations in those cases where the microfractures are filled with air. The actual surface of the mineral is determined by the total surface of its microfractures and its geometric surface. In the purest form, the migration of radioactive elements is realized for the radioactive emanations because the behavior of these inert gases is not influenced by the adsorption processes. The exit of the emanation atoms from the mineral may take place through capillaries filled with water as well as air; it is not dependent on the chemical conditions of the environment.

Emanation of Minerals

The first study of the emanation, i.e., of the release of radioactive emanations by minerals, was made with artificial crystals of salts by L. S. Kolovrat-Chirvinskii [152], who performed his early work in the laboratory of Marie Curie. Kolovrat-Chirvinskii showed that each sample possessed a definite emanation coefficient—the ratio of the amount of the emanation released to that which was produced in a given preparation. With increasing temperature, the emanation coefficient increased and attained the value of 100 per cent (a complete release of the emanation) at the fusion temperature of the salt. The coefficient increased with increasing true surface of the crystals. Later on, Strassmann [153] studied radium-containing barium salts of fatty acids. He found that the release of emanation increased as the ionic bonds in crystals became weaker.

The emanation of natural minerals was first studied by V. I. Spitsyn [154]. He found that the pulverization of the sample enhanced the emanation, but to an extent which was considerably smaller than the corresponding increase in the total geometric surface of the sample, i.e., the release of radon took place through microfractures. I. E. Starik and O. S. Melikova [155] showed that the emanation of the secondary minerals was greater than the emanation of the primary minerals and increased with the degree of the breakdown of the mineral. These experiments included not only the emanation of radon but, that of thoron as well. For the primary minerals, the emanation coefficient, K is very small (for khlopinite, $K_{Rn} = 0.17$ per cent, $K_{Tn} = 0.13$ per cent; for allanite, $K_{Tn} = 0.25$ per cent; for lovchorrite, $K_{Tn} = 0.10$ per cent). It increases abruptly for the secondary minerals (tyuyamunite, $K_{Rn} =$ 32.0–45.9 per cent) and is especially large for the zones of the surface destruction of minerals ("crust" from allanite, $K_{Tn} = 87.5$ per cent; "crust" from lovchorrite, $K_{Tn} = 98.5$ per cent). According to the data of V. G. Khlopin and M. E. Vladimirova [139], the emanation coefficient of radon for well-preserved uraninites varies from 0.04 to 0.6 per cent.

N. D. Kosov and V. V. Cherdyntsev [156] investigated the release by minerals of all radioactive emanations: radon, actinon, and thoron. For the investigated primary minerals, the emnation coefficients of radon and actinon were practically equal. These data indicate that emanation at room temperature takes place by giving off the atoms of radioactive recoil. The time of diffusion through microcapillaries may be ignored, even for the short-lived actinon ($T_{1/2} = 3.92$ sec.). Since the progenitors of radon and actinon are isotopes and enter the crystalline lattice isotropically, their products in the mineral should distribute themselves almost uniformly. For the majority of natural minerals the emanation coefficients are sufficiently large (larger than 0.1 per cent). It is possible to show that in this case the interfracture distances are shorter, on the average, than the path of the recoil atoms. At the same time, the liberation of isotopes is nearly independent of the energy of these atoms. If there were diffusion of atoms in the disturbance zone, the emanation coefficient of actinon would be much smaller than the corresponding coefficient of radon ($T_{1/2} = 3.83$ days).

For the secondary minerals (fossilized bones) there was observed a relative increase in the emanation of radon, apparently at the expense of the diffusion of its atoms through the porous matter of these minerals.

According to the data of I. E. Starik and co-workers [157], for uraninite, the emanation of actinon is less than that of radon.

Generally speaking, the emanation coefficients of radon and thoron in the primary minerals differ considerably (see Table 16), the coefficient for thoron being usually larger than the coefficient for radon.

TABLE 16

AVERAGE VALUES OF EMANATION COEFFICIENTS OF RADON AND THORON FOR SOME MINERALS

MINERALS	NO. OF SAMPLES	AVERAGE $\frac{Th}{U}$	K_{Rn} (PER CENT)			K_{Tn} (PER CENT)			$\frac{K_{Tn}}{K_{Rn}}$		
			From	To	Average	From	To	Average	From	To	Average
Tantalite-columbite...	15	0.09	0.41	46	1.72	1.2	47	8.56	0.22	15	4.18
Sphenes.......	4	2.1	0.6	3.4	1.61	2.0	3.4	2.91	1.0	3.3	1.62
Monazites.....	8	23	0.13	2.0	0.35	0.1	3.9	0.37	0.98	1.95	1.38
Cassiterites....	4	1.6	2.6	8.0	4.37	2.6	12	5.83	0.93	2.2	1.32
Ilmenites......	7	3.5	2.3	12	4.11	1.3	15	4.12	0.3	3.8	1.00
Tungstates.....	4	2.0	10	37	20.6	0.5	8	2.55	0.026	0.7	0.13

Some minerals, in particular those with a low thorium-uranium ratio, preferentially emanate thoron (e.g., tantalites). For tungstates the opposite effect is observed. Since the actinon data reveal that diffusion along microfractures does not lead to a decrease in the emanation, it is necessary to conclude that thorium and uranium—the parent substances of thoron and radon—can enter the crystalline lattice of many minerals anisotropically relative to the system of microdislocations. Thus the investigation of the emanation can yield valuable information on the distribution of microcomponents in the mineral.

The experiments of V. V. Cherdyntsev, N. S. Strashnikov, and V. A. Rabinovich (quoted from [156]), as well as those of I. E. Starik and co-workers [157], have shown that, with increasing temperature, there is an increase in the emanation of the short-lived actinon and thoron, and also of radon (see Table 17), but the ratio K_{Tn}/K_{Rn} of the emana-

TABLE 17

EMANATION COEFFICIENTS OF THORON, RADON, AND ACTINON AS FUNCTION OF TEMPERATURE [156, 158]

T (° C.)	Monazite			Sphene			Tantalite		
	K_{Tn}	K_{Rn}	$\frac{K_{Tn}}{K_{Rn}}$	K_{Tn}	K_{Rn}	$\frac{K_{Tn}}{K_{Rn}}$	K_{Tn}	K_{Rn}	$\frac{K_{Tn}}{K_{Rn}}$
20.	0.035	0.042	0.83	0.21	0.02	10.5	8.04	0.128	62.8
200.	.037	. . .	. . .	0.27	0.051	5.04	12.38	0.206	60.1
400.	.041	0.37	.11	0.79	0.195	4.06	11.76	0.392	28.8
600.	.097	0.69	.14	1.22	0.312	3.91	25.37	0.932	27.2
800.	.320	2.16	.14	1.45	8.24	0.18	51.06	8.06	6.3
1,000.	0.736	5.66	0.13	6.79	73.98	0.09	. . .	. . .	. . .

URANINITE

T (° C.)	K_{Tn}	K_{Rn}	K_{An}	$\frac{K_{An}}{K_{Rn}}$	$\frac{K_{Tn}}{K_{Rn}}$
21.	1.44	2.1	0.3	0.14	0.54
230.	1.10	1.5	0.35	.23	.73
410.	0.97	1.5	0.47	.31	.65
560.	1.6	17.8	0.51	.03	.09
780.	5.3	42.5	0.62	.015	.12
900.	12.3	86.0	4.1	0.05	0.14

tion coefficients drops sharply, for example, by more than one hundred times for sphene during heating to 1,000° C. Abdulgafarov and Cherdyntsev [202] discovered that on the curve $K = f(T)$, which ascends with increasing temperature, minima can be observed. They are located within equal temperature intervals during the liberation of both radon and helium, and they evidently mark the temperature regions of the rebuilding of the crystalline lattice of the mineral.

It is interesting to note the irreversible decrease in the emanation of minerals after heating. Thus, for sphene, the emanation coefficient of radon decreases by a factor of 20. Probably this phenomenon is caused by the restoration and stabilization of the crystalline lattice of the mineral which was disarranged by tectonic processes in the course of its existence.

The liberation of helium and of radioactive emanations increases with increasing temperature. However, the regularities of the liberation are different for the short-lived emanations (Tn and An) and for radon or helium [202]. Ordinarily, the emanation of thoron and actinon increases only slightly up to 800°–900° C., i.e., as far as the region near the temperature of the breakdown of the crystalline lattice. Often there is observed a decrease in the emanation in the interval of 300°–500° C. We explain this by the stabilization of the lattice of a real crystal which has been disturbed by tectonic processes during its residence in the deeper regions of the earth. Evidently, up to a very high temperature, the liberation of Tn and An is determined by the recoil atoms. For radon and helium the liberation at higher temperatures depends on the diffusion of atoms through the crystalline lattice. The liberation coefficients, K, and the diffusion coefficients, D, of both gases vary uniformly, the K_{He} being always greater than K_{Rn} and D_{He} greater than D_{Rn}. This is probably explained by the smaller mass and size of the helium atoms. It should be noted that, in spite of a parallelism between the liberation of Rn and that of He during the heating of the primary minerals, their emanation and retentivity of He are, generally speaking, not related. Columbites and ilmenites, which retain their helium so well as to be suitable for age determinations by the helium method, show a higher degree of emanation than do monazites, for which helium losses can be quite large. These losses are explained by two processes: direct escape of α-particles into microcapillaries and prolonged diffusion through the crystalline lattice. Direct loss of helium, similar to the escape of emanations from the primary minerals, is not large. Its magnitude is comparable to the emanation coefficient. In principle, helium is lost from minerals by means of diffusion at moderate temperatures in the course of geologic time. In this temperature region, the liberation of the short-lived radon is possible only at the expense of the recoil atoms, and the behavior of radon resembles that of actinon.

The difference in the nuclear properties leads to the fact that the mechanism of the liberation of uranium, radium, emanations, etc., is unlike the mechanism of the liberation of stable helium. At the same time, an identical mechanism may be used by different isotopes, depending on thermodynamic conditions and the state of the given system.

Radon Content of Natural Waters

Emanation of minerals produces radon enrichment in natural waters. Increased radon content was recorded soon after the discovery of radioactivity. It is usually of the order of 10^{-10}–10^{-9} curie per liter (1 curie corresponds to the activity of 1 gm. of radium in the state of radioactive equilibrium), although in the individual cases it is as high as 10^{-6} curie per liter. Naturally, the radon concentration is highest in waters of radioactive deposits. However, some mineral waters often possess high activity (Mondovi, Italy, up to 1.0×10^{-6} curie per liter; Oberstein, Central Europe, 0.9×10^{-6} curie per liter).

The radium content of natural waters is considerably lower (in equilibrium units) and usually does not exceed 10^{-13}–10^{-11} gm. per liter. Meyer and Schweidler [158], while processing the data on radioactivity of natural waters, came to the conclusion that there is no proportionality whatever between the content of radium and that of radon but rather an inverse relationship.

Underground waters are enriched in radon because of the emanation of host rocks. One cm.[3] of rock liberates in 1 second the following amount of emanation:

$$q_{Rn} = q_{Ra}\lambda_{Ra}K_{Rn}\rho,$$

where q_{Ra} is the weight concentration of radium in the rock, λ_{Ra} is the decay constant of radium, K_{Rn} is the emanation coefficient of the rock, and ρ is the average density of the sample. If W is the moisture content of the rock, the amount of the emanation released every second into a unit volume of water is $\lambda_{Rn} \times n_0$, where

$$n_0 = \frac{q_{Ra}\lambda_{Ra}K_{Rn}\rho}{\lambda_{Rn}W} = Q_{Ra} \times K_{Rn} \times \frac{\rho}{W}, \tag{9.5}$$

where Q_{Ra} is the radium content of the rock in units of the equilibrium radon. The accumulation of radon in water is described by the expression

$$\frac{dn}{dt} = \lambda_{Rn}(n_0 - n),$$

where n is the concentration of radon. Assuming initial conditions $n = 0$ at $t = 0$, we find

$$n = \frac{Q_{Ra}K_{Rn}\rho}{W}(1 - e^{-\lambda_{Rn}t}) = n_0(1 - e^{-\lambda_{Rn}t}). \tag{9.5a}$$

This expression was first obtained by I. E. Starik [159] and applied to the experimental data on natural waters. Ordinarily, for the short-lived radon,

$$n = n_0, \tag{9.5b}$$

with the radon enrichment taking place during the last stage of the underground circulation of water. Among the parameters of the right side of equation (9.5*a*), the emanation coefficient is most capable of variations. The enrichment of waters in radon and the fluctuation of the activity of natural waters are essentially determined by the emanation of the host rocks (aside from waters of radioactive deposits). According to the data of Starik [159], there are found among rocks of one region varieties for which K_{Rn} varies from 0.002 to 45 per cent, i.e., by a factor of more than 20,000.

The emanation of rocks depends primarily on the degree of tectonic preservation. The largest emanation coefficient is possessed by rocks in the zones of tectonic disturbances. These disturbances evidently cause the development of a system of microfractures and an increase in the actual surface area of the crystalline bodies.

Frequently there is observed increased activity of the deep-flowing mineral waters. These waters are radioactive, not because they are underground waters, but because, during their flow to the surface, they usually become enriched in radon, since their discharge is possible only through the fracture zones and the rocks of these zones possess an increased degree of emanation.

In the course of prolonged underground circulation, the natural waters become enriched in radium isotopes. Radium is unstable in the ordinary alkaline medium of the deep-flowing waters because of the insolubility of its carbonate and sulfate. The element is retained in the water only because its concentration never reaches the solubility limit of the salt. However, if there is a precipitation of sediment or an exchange of water and the solid-phase ions, radium is easily adsorbed or co-precipitated. A drastic change in the state of the deep-flowing water when it reaches the surface (temperature drop, evolution of a gas phase) leads to the deposition of sediments which carry radium. In the adsorption zone, among the radium isotopes, Ra^{226} is unquestionably the most abundant. The cold surface waters which pass through this zone become enriched in radon.

Thus, within one occurrence of mineral waters, we usually find (1) underground waters with an increased content of radon and a high content of radium and (2) cooled surface waters which have lost their radium but are saturated with radon. This effect is explained in the work of Starik and co-workers [159].

On the average, the radon content is higher for the waters of igneous rocks than for those of the sedimentary stratum because of a relative enrichment of the former in radioactive elements. The dependence of the activity of waters on tectonic conditions is very clearly traced. Even for the waters of the sedimentary stratum of the Russian flatland, the activity is higher than for the regions of the intensified movements which are weak on that platform. Within the individual tectonic uplifts, zones are found where the radon content of waters is increased by a fatcor of 2–3. These zones are located in the wings of the brachyanticlines [160] and are probably associated with the "halo effect"—the intensification of tectonic manifestations in certain ring-shaped zones. Investigation of radon in waters and in the soil air may prove to be a method for exploring oil-bearing structures.

On a much larger scale is manifested the dependence on the tectonic conditions for waters of mountainous regions, where the radon content may vary by many hundreds of times, depending on the degree of tectonic preservation of the rocks. A dependence of radon content on the fundamental hydrogeological characteristics—the chemical composition of water, mineralization, temperature, or discharge—is ordinarily not observed.

Radium Isotopes in Natural Waters

We shall now turn to the behavior of radium in natural waters. The early investigations were of a sporadic nature. In 1921 in Heidelberg (Germany) a radioactive water was found with a radium content of 1.79×10^{-10} per cent. Salomon explained the activity of this water as an incidental combination produced by mixing of brines and radium-bearing waters of the underlying granites [161].

Beginning with the 1920's, an extensive investigation of radium-bearing waters was conducted in the Soviet Union under the direction of V. I. Vernadskii and V. G. Khlopin. It turned out that the increased radium content of waters is not at all unique. It is characteristic of waters under the petroleum layer, which belong to the class of the sulfate-free sodium chloride brines. B. A. Nikitin and L. V. Komlev [162] have shown that the increased radium content of these waters depends on two fundamental factors: (1) the stability of radium in the water of such composition and (2) the long time of the accumulation of radium.

Thus the connection between radium and petroleum waters is purely extraneous, just like the connection between helium and petroleum gases. The presence of organic substances of petroleum leads to the reduction of the sulfate to the sulfide ion. Specific sulfate-free brines are formed in which radium is stable.

The accumulation of radium by waters from rocks takes place according to the law of the type (9.5) [163]:

$$n_{\mathrm{Ra}} = \frac{Q_{\mathrm{Ra}} K_{\mathrm{Ra}} \rho}{W} (1 - e^{-\lambda_{\mathrm{Ra}} t}) = n^0_{\mathrm{Ra}} (1 - e^{-\lambda_{\mathrm{Ra}} t}), \qquad (9.6)$$

where K_{Ra} is the leaching coefficient of radium. After the process of the liberation of radium has been established, this coefficient is close to the emanation coefficient of radon, K_{Rn}. The application of equation (9.6) is possible only in the absence of adsorption losses of radium, which is apparently the case for the weakly mineralized surface waters and the waters with a favorable chemical composition.

For old waters—for example, those from under the petroleum layer—one may neglect the exponential term in equation (9.6). Under this condition the radium and radon contents (in equilibrium units) are equal, and this is confirmed by experimental data [163].

According to equations (9.5*a*) and (9.6), the radium-radon ratio in natural waters (provided that there is no adsorption of radium) assumes the following form:

$$\frac{n_{\mathrm{Ra}}}{n_{\mathrm{Rn}}} = \frac{K_{\mathrm{Ra}}}{K_{\mathrm{Rn}}} (1 - e^{-\lambda_{\mathrm{Ra}} t}) \approx 1 - e^{-\lambda_{\mathrm{Ra}} t}. \qquad (9.7)$$

Thus is it possible to estimate the time of the subsurface circulation of water:

$$t = \frac{1}{\lambda_{Ra}} \ln \frac{1}{1 - (n_{Ra}/n_{Rn})} \tag{9.8}$$

or, for small values of t,

$$t = \frac{1}{Ra} \frac{n_{Ra}}{n_{Rn}}. \tag{9.9}$$

The age determination of natural waters by this method is not accurate because of the possible losses of radioactive elements, the differences between the coefficients of their liberation from rocks, and, most of all, the possible difference in the behavior of the radioactive elements in the zone of radium accumulation, i.e., in the entire zone of underground circulation of water and in the region of radon accumulation during the final phase of the circulation of water. The method is suitable only for an approximate estimate of the age, which, after all, is of definite interest in the field of hydrology. Indeed, the experimental material shows that, on going from the surface to underground waters, the age according to equation (9.9) increases independently of the activity of water. Some examples of this are given in Table 18 [163, 164].[85]

TABLE 18

RADIUM AND RADON CONTENTS OF SOME NATURAL WATERS

NATURAL WATER	CONTENT OF		$\frac{n_{Ra}}{n_{Rn}}$	AGE ACCORDING TO EQUATION (9.8)
	Radon (10^{-9} Curie/Liter)	Radium (10^{-12}Gm/Liter)		
Surface waters:				
Caucasus	386	7.3	1.9×10^{-4}	170 days
Kirgiziya	45	0.5	1.1×10^{-4}	100 days
Kirgiziya	7.6	0.25	3.3×10^{-4}	280 days
Fresh waters under petroleum layer:				
Caucasus	3.5	0.79	2.2×10^{-3}	5 years
Subsurface thermal waters:				
North Caucasus	11.7	9.5	8.1×10^{-3}	19 years
Trans-Caucasus	0.46	7	0.15	380 years
Trans-Caucasus	1.46	89	0.61	2,200 years
Matsesta Station, Oil Well 2	5.84	89	0.15	380 years
Matsesta Station, Oil Well 7	9.9	21	0.21	550 years
Agura, Oil Well 9	1.27	34	0.27	740 years
Petroleum waters:				
Central Asia	3.0	300	1.0	∞

[85] According to the data on tritium (see Sec. 5, p. 45), the age of thermal waters in the United States is of the order of 50 years, which is in agreement with the data of Table 18. [Author's footnote.]

Fractionation of Isotopes of Radioactive Elements in Nature

The radioactive properties of the heavy elements determine special possibilities for change in their isotopic composition which do not exist for the stable elements. The decayed atoms, after recoil, pass into different sites of the crystalline lattice, where they reside in the form of foreign, generally weakly bound, inclusions. In this process the content of isotopes does not change, but their condition in the interior of the mineral is not the same. The migration of the elements of the earth's crust is realized essentially by natural waters. During the interaction of these waters with minerals, the radioactive-decay products pass into solution to a greater extent than do the isotopes, which did not undergo similar decay. A comparison of the behavior of the various decay products shows that their accumulation in the liquid phase is described by the law

$$n = n_0(1 - e^{-\lambda t}), \tag{9.10}$$

i.e., for the short leaching times, one should observe enrichment of young waters in the short-lived isotopes. In the course of underground circulation, water interacts with rocks containing radioactive elements with a normal isotopic composition, which practically corresponds to the condition of radioactive equilibrium. As a result of the interphase exchange, the isotopic composition of radioactive elements in water reverts to a normal composition. At the same time, the composition of these elements in the solid phase remains nearly unchanged, since their total concentration in waters is much lower than that in the host rocks. We shall follow up these general considerations by using the examples of the individual elements.

Uranium.—In nature there are three isotopes of uranium of which UII (U^{234}) is a decay product of the progenitor of the uranium series, UI (U^{238}). If a portion of a radioactive mineral is immersed in solution and if uranium is isolated chemically from another portion (i.e., the isolation involves a breakdown of the mineral lattice), then uranium which passed into solution can be strongly enriched in the light isotope, UII. During the filtration of natural waters, i.e., upon separation from the solution of colloidal particles, the isotopic composition of uranium in the fractions may be markedly different. If one considers the common difficulties of the fractionation of isotopes of the stable elements, then the ease of the fractionation of the heavy isotopes in these cases is very striking.

The change of the isotopic composition of uranium in an extract from a mineral was first observed by Cherdyntsev and Chalov [59].

Uranium in a zircon extract showed the ratio UII/UI = 1.8.[86] A similar process also occurs in nature. For uranium of the surface waters, the observed ratio UII/UI = 7–8. The secondary minerals enriched in uranium of natural waters are often relatively enriched in UII (in a complex uranium sulfate, schrockengerite, the ratio UII/UI = 3.7, and in petrified bones it is as high as 5.1). Starik and co-workers [204] have shown that uranium sublimated from pitchblende at $T =$ 800° C. is enriched in UII to the extent of UII/UI = 3.2. During prolonged action of natural waters, minerals can lose substantial amounts of UII, so that the ratio UII/UI becomes low [59, 205]. Uranium with a non-equilibrium ratio of the isotopes occurs widely in the zone of the surface migration of the elements of the earth.

Thorium.—The analogues of UI and UII in the thorium series are the progenitor Th^{232} and its decay product, RdTh (Th^{228}). Cherdyntsev and Khaidarov [59] have shown that RdTh is extracted from ferrithorite into an aqueous medium with considerably greater ease than thorium is. The migrational losses of radiothorium result in some samples of the mineral having the ratio of the decay products of Th and RdTh, $MsTh_1/ThX = 4$. The uranium series has two isotopes of thorium—the decay products, UX_I (Th^{234}) and Io (Th^{230}). According to our data, the relative content of the short-lived UX_I increases by 6–8 times in the process of the extraction from minerals. The extraction from a uranium mineral showed that the ratio of radiothorium (in thorium units) to ionium (in uranium units) approaches RdTh/Io ≈ 1, i.e., the extraction of radiothorium takes place preferentially. By contrast, ionium is released preferentially from thorium minerals. In this example we see that the radioactive element which is present in low concentration is evidently less firmly bound in its lattice than the principal element, and the products of its decay are leached with greater facility. The enrichment of natural waters with UX_I in the proximity of uranium deposits may be quite large (up to $UX_I/Io = 80$), but in the course of the interphase exchange it rapidly approaches the equilibrium ratio.

Radium.—As early as 1934, Popov and Cherdyntsev found a natural water with an increased content of Th*X* (Th*X*/Ra = 220, the ratio being given in thorium and uranium equilibrium units). We have shown that waters enriched in the short-lived Th*X* [163] and Ac*X* [160] are often found among surface waters, predominantly among those of high-altitude regions. A high relative content of the short-

[86] In this paragraph we shall use the equilibrium units of the content of the radioactive elements. In the equilibrium state, UII/UI = 1. In discussing the isotopes of the uranium and actinium series we assume that in the equilibrium condition the ratio of these isotopes is also equal to 1. [Author's footnote.]

lived radium isotopes (Th*X*/Ra = 600; Ac*X*/Ra = 40) indicates only the young age of the water and by no means local enrichment of thorium.

In the old petroleum waters [165, 166], the isotopes of radium are present in practically the same ratio as in rocks (Th*X*/Ra $\approx$ 3). However, a close ratio is also observed for the majority of young waters, although, according to equation (9.10), we are fully justified in expecting an enrichment in Th*X*. Even for the waters with a high ratio Th*X*/Ra, this value is always smaller than the ratio Rn/Ra (i.e., Th*X*/Rn <|), although the accumulation rate of radon and Th*X* in waters is the same (incidentally, the decay constants of these isotopes are almost equal). The decrease in the Th*X* and Ac*X* content of waters is established in the process of the interphase exchange, during which the concentration of atoms does not decrease, but the short-lived isotopes in water are replaced by the long-lived isotopes preponderant in the solid phase. This process is traced especially clearly in the course of the passage of waters through the surface zone of the adsorbed radium in which the short-lived isotopes of this element have almost completely decayed. Here the concentration of Th*X* in water can decrease to as low a value as Th*X*/Ra = 0.02 [163]. Thus the ratio Th*X*/Ra in natural waters can vary by factors of tens of thousands.

A considerable enrichment (by tens of times) of mineral extracts in the short-lived isotopes of radium was observed by Cherdyntsev [59] and Starik and co-workers [167].

Emanation.—The variation in the isotopic composition of emanations follows from the inequality of the emission coefficients of radon, thoron, and actinon for many minerals. Obviously, thoron and actinon decay rapidly after being liberated. Therefore, in atmospheric air, aside from the bottom layer, the only remaining emanation isotope is radon.

Lead.—Begemann and others [168] found that the modern lead mineral cotunnite ($PbCl_2$) from the crater of Vesuvius is enriched in the short-lived lead isotope RaD (Pb^{210}). Naidenov and Cherdyntsev [206] have established that ThB is released from minerals into solutions more readily than is RaD. The latter, in turn, is liberated with greater ease than are the stable lead isotopes—the decay products. The lead present in radioactive minerals as an admixture (the ore lead) is released even more readily than RaD and, in fact, more readily than radiogenic lead. This has been confirmed by mass spectrometric work [207, 208, 209].

There is observed a general regularity: a subordinate element (or the products of its decay) in a given mineral is usually liberated with greater ease than a dominant element. This can be explained by more stable bonds of that element which essentially determines the crystalline lattice of the given mineral.

Radioactive Elements in Secondary Minerals

The minerals enriched in radium contain practically only the long-lived isotope—the radium proper, the amount of which decreases with time according to the law

$$\mathrm{Ra} = \mathrm{Ra}^0 e^{-\lambda_{\mathrm{Ra}} t}, \tag{9.11}$$

which forms a basis for determining the age of an object. An attempt of this kind was made by L. M. Kurbatov [169] with the purpose of determining the age of spherosideritic sea deposits. However, the possibilities of this method are limited by the fact that the initial radium content, Ra^0, is not known, and the growth of the concretion is difficult to link with the geologic scale of the relative chronology.

A decay product of uranium—ionium—is unstable in sea water and escapes into sediments. Piggot and Urry [170] worked out an ionium method of age determination of sea oozes which is based on the measurement of radium, upon the assumption of its equilibrium with ionium. However, it has been shown [59, 171] that this ratio deviates from equilibrium because radium and even ionium are capable under these conditions of active migration. Picciotto and Wilgain [172] propose age determinations of sea oozes from the ionium-to-thorium ratio. These authors assume that thorium is deposited in oozes from the solution and does not get there together with the solid particles—the products of the destruction of rocks. If this is true, then

$$\left(\frac{\mathrm{Io}}{\mathrm{Th}}\right)_{\mathrm{ooze}} = \left(\frac{\mathrm{Io}}{\mathrm{Th}}\right)_{\mathrm{sea\ water}} \times e^{-\lambda_{\mathrm{Io}} t}. \tag{9.12}$$

We shall consider the secondary uranium minerals in which, by contrast, the accumulation of the decay products takes place. This can also be used for the determination of the absolute age of young formations. The secondary minerals of the ore zones of oxidation are practically unsuitable for this purpose, inasmuch as migration processes are actively at work here, transporting not only radium and uranium but the isotopes of thorium as well. More reliable material is petrified bones, particularly convenient because it is upon these objects and upon the bone-containing dwellings of primitive man that the chronologic scale of quaternary geology and archeology is constructed. V. V. Cherdyntsev and V. I. Meshkov [173] developed a method of age determination from the ratio AcX/Ra. However, the data are often misrepresented because of the migrational escape of radium. More suitable is the method based on the measurement of the ratio of the thorium isotopes UX_1, Io, and RdAc, as well as of the isotopes of uranium, even though this ratio for uranium of the surface zone may deviate from the equilibrium ratio, as shown by Cherdyntsev, Khitrik, and Mambetov [59, 210, 211]. If one assumes the time of mineralization of the bone to be short compared with the subsequent time, then the age of the bone can be found from the following ratios:

$$\left.\begin{aligned} \frac{\mathrm{Io}}{UX_1} &= \frac{\mathrm{UII}}{\mathrm{UI}}\left(1 - e^{-\lambda_{\mathrm{Io}}t}\right), \\ \frac{\mathrm{RdAc}}{UX_1} &= 1 - e^{-\lambda_{\mathrm{Pa}}t}. \end{aligned}\right\} \qquad (9.13)$$

If, however, mineralization proceeded at a constant rate during the entire existence of the object, then the age is at least twice as high, i.e., the value of t according to equations (9.13) is too low.

This method can encompass the time interval up to 200–300 thousand years. In a number of cases this limit can be pushed up if one uses the data on the isotopic composition of uranium. Thus the possibilities here are considerably greater than in the radiocarbon method, which evidently has only limited application for objects older than ten thousand years. The most reliable data obtained by the method of thorium isotopes are given in Table 19.

Apparently, the utilization of the absolute radioactive method of dating could throw light on many chronologic problems of quaternary geology and history of primitive society which at the present time are known perhaps more poorly than the chronology of cosmogonic processes. Different samples from the profile of the same occurrence show in a number of cases increasing age on going toward the deep strata. For example, the age of the Upper Paleolithic strata of the Molodova (the Dnieper region) living quarters is, according to our data, 22 thousand years; that of the intermediate strata, 110 thousand years; and that of the lower strata (the Middle Paleolithic), 235 thousand years. The estimates of the age of the Paleolithic made earlier by scientists on the basis of speculative considerations turned out to be too low. The species *Homo sapiens,* which evolved at the beginning of the Upper Paleolithic, has existed for not less than 100 thousand years, and we can pride ourselves on being members of such an ancient race.

The total concentration of the short-lived radioelements in the earth's crust remains constant, in equilibrium with the total amount of the parent substances. However, the ratio of the decay products and the isotopic composition of radioactive elements for the individual, naturally occurring objects undergo extreme variations as a result of migration processes which are governed by both the laws of nuclear decay and the physicochemical laws. The combination of these condi-

TABLE 19

AGE DETERMINATION ON PETRIFIED BONES USING RATIOS OF THORIUM ISOTOPES

Time	Description of Samples	Isotope Ratio in Equilibrium Units: $\frac{Io}{UX_1}$	Isotope Ratio in Equilibrium Units: $\frac{RdAc}{UX_1}$	Age in Thousands of Years Determined from Ratio: $\frac{Io}{U\,II}$	Age in Thousands of Years Determined from Ratio: $\frac{RdAc}{UX_1}$	Probable Average Age in Thousands of Years
Lower Quaternary	Serafimovka	~1	1.1	>250	>100	>250
	Berdiansk, southern elephant	1.8 (U II/U I ≈ 2)	~1	250–700	>100	250–700
Lower Paleolithic	Tunguz-Khriashchevka gigantic deer	0.84 ± 0.01	~1.5	210	>100	210
Intermediate Paleolithic	Teshik-Tash, goat	0.80 ± 0.03	0.9	180	~120	150
	Il'skaya (av. of 5 determinations)	0.70	~1	135 ± 25	>100	
	Kodak, goat	0.99 (U/U I ≈ 1.5)	~1	120	>100	
	Akhshtyr cave	0.50 ± 0.02	~1	80	>100	
Upper Paleolithic	Siberia, Mal'ta (av. of 4 samples)	0.54	~1	90 ± 10	>100	40–90
	Ulan-Ude	0.48	...	76	...	
	Kostenki (av. of 36 samples)	0.30	0.5	41 ± 5	~35	

tions imparts to the distribution of the short-lived radioelements specific features which distinguish the behavior of these species from that of other isotopes of the earth's crust. Some of the regularities of the distribution of these radioelements have been studied and are described in this chapter. Further investigations will undoubtedly bring to light many new and interesting characteristics.

II

The Elementary Theory of Stability of Atomic Nuclei

10. STATEMENT OF THE PROBLEM. GAS MODEL OF ATOMIC NUCLEI

In this chapter we shall consider the foundations of the theory of stability of atomic nuclei which are indispensable for the explanation of the regularities of atomic abundances to be stated in the next chapter, as well as for understanding the causes of the instability of radioactive elements which were discussed in the preceding chapter.

There are two reasons for the contemporary cosmic abundance of atomic nuclei: the conditions of their formation and the possibility of their transmutation. The formation of atomic nuclei depends on the properties of a given nucleus, as well as on the state of the system, and the preservation in nature indicates stability with respect to all possible modes of spontaneous radioactive decay and artificial transmutation. Radioactive decay is feasible if it takes place with the liberation of energy. However, this condition is not sufficient. A nuclear mechanism is needed to bring about a transition into a more stable state with the transition probability being sufficiently high. In this chapter we shall examine successively the problems of the binding energy of atomic nuclei and of their stability against the processes which change their charge or their mass number.

Basic Information on Nuclear Transmutations

The atomic nucleus consists of protons and neutrons, which may be considered as the two states of a heavy elementary particle—the nucleon. The total number of particles is equal to the atomic weight or, more rigorously, to the mass number A. The nuclear charge Z

(in units of the elementary charge) is determined by the number of protons, so that the number of neutrons is $A - Z$.

During the transmutation of atomic nuclei, there takes place emission from the nucleus of heavy particles, that is, the nuclear charge is changed. Externally this corresponds to the emission or capture of light particles (electrons, positrons, neutrinos) and internally to the transformation of a proton into a neutron, or vice versa.

The nuclear particles are held together by specific nuclear forces. These forces are capable of saturation, like, for example, those forces of electromagnetic origin that determine the covalent binding of the ions of a crystalline lattice. Like the forces of the gravitational field, the nuclear forces are independent of the charge of the interacting particles; but, unlike the gravitational and electromagnetic fields, the field of nuclear forces, extremely powerful in the interior of the atomic nucleus, diminishes very rapidly with distance and is practically zero outside the nucleus, i.e., at a distance greater than $n \times 10^{-13}$ cm.

The principal role in the energetics of the nucleus is played by the energy of the nuclear field. However, of great importance also is the electrostatic energy. In the nucleus there are charged particles of the same sign only—the positive protons. Therefore, here the effect of saturation of the electrostatic forces is absent. The electrostatic field, unlike the field of nuclear forces, manifests itself in the external interactions of the nucleus. The field holds a definite number of electrons—the electronic envelope—thus binding the nucleus and the electrons into a single system—the atom. All the atomic processes take place in the electrostatic field of the nucleus, just as the phenomena on the surface of the earth take place in the gravitational field of the earth. But, as the phenomena on the surface of the earth have only slight connection with the processes in its depths, so direct connection of the nuclear with the atomic phenomena is also very weak. One may point to the phenomenon of capture by the nucleus of an electron from the outer shell (usually the first atomic shell, the K-shell) and to the interaction of nuclear particles with electrons which gives rise to an anomalous isotopic shift in the spectral lines. However, generally, the nuclear processes and the processes of the atom that take place in the electrostatic field of the nucleus proceed in large measure independently of each other.

But the electrostatic field of the nucleus, while determining the structure of the atom, also "shields" the atomic nucleus from penetration into it of the positively charged particles of the exterior world (for example, by hindering nuclear reactions upon collision of two nuclei). The interaction between the nucleus with the charge Z and an α-particle with the charge $Z = 2$, which are separated by the distance r, leads to a Coulomb repulsion with the energy

$$U = \frac{2Ze^2}{r}. \tag{10.1}$$

The potential of this repulsion for atomic nuclei of intermediate atomic weight is 10–20 Mev. Over short distances the Coulomb repulsion is replaced by the attraction of the nuclear field, which can be considered constant in the interior of the nucleus. Thus the energy of the interaction forms a potential barrier which prevents the charged particles with the ordinary energies of our surroundings (see Fig. 9) from penetrating into the interior of the atomic nucleus.

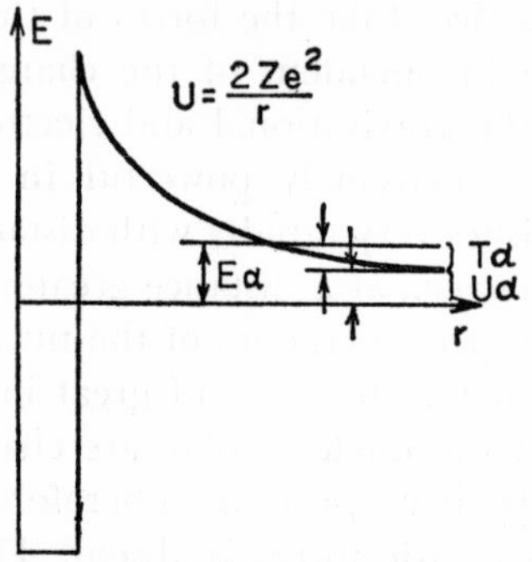

FIG. 9.—Schematic diagram of the potential barrier of atomic nucleus for α-particles. $T\alpha$, $U\alpha$, $E\alpha$ are the kinetic, potential, and total energies of α-particles which approach the atomic nucleus.

If four free protons (the hydrogen nuclei) combined to form an α-particle, the energy that would be liberated in the process would be very high—about 28 Mev. However, under the thermodynamic conditions of the earth, even a combination of two protons is improbable because of strong electrostatic repulsion of the nuclear particles.

Only in stellar interiors at a temperature of the order of 10^7 degrees and at high densities, is transmutation of protons into α-particles feasible, as pointed out in Section 5. But even there the process is realized by the indirect route of a catalytic reaction in which carbon and nitrogen take part. The probability of this reaction is so small that the time of hydrogen-burning in the sun is estimated at 10^{10}–10^{11} years, and the principal constituent in the chemical composition of the cosmos is a non-equilibrium hydrogen. Still smaller are the transmutation possibilities for the heavy atomic nuclei.

Many nuclei of the primordial system in which they were formed turned out to be unstable and decayed rapidly. Preserved among them were only those nuclei for which the probability of radioactive decay or artificial transmutation was small during the entire time of their subsequent existence. A considerable proportion of the survived nuclei is capable of spontaneous decay, but their number could not have diminished noticeably, so that the present abundance of these nuclei reflects the conditions of the original system. This leads to the fundamental implication that the abundance of these stable nuclei of the cosmos which were preserved until today is, in most cases, determined neither by their energetics nor by their decay probability. The concepts of abundance and stability are in many cases independent, at least for the nuclei with an average lifetime greater than the several billion years during which the earth has existed.

The principal distinction between the nuclear and atomic systems is that the former are not in a state of thermodynamic equilibrium. For atomic systems including the macroscopic objects, the transition into this state occurs quite rapidly. This permits broad utilization of the simple and powerful tools of statistical physics for the description of these systems. For nuclear systems, only the decay of the excited nuclei takes place rapidly. Inasmuch as we cannot even speak of thermodynamic equilibrium of contemporary atomic nuclei, the very concept of stability, so simple and unconditional in application to atomic systems, is limited and vague in nuclear physics. It is permissible to speak of stability only with respect to a definite type of nuclear transmutations.

For example, lithium in the ground state is absolutely stable against spontaneous α-decay but is easily split by protons of even low energies (of the order of 0.1 Mev). The α-unstable uranium can be successfully split only by protons of high energies (of the order of 10 Mev). On the other hand, uranium is more abundant in the earth's crust than are approximately twenty other elements (for example, arsenic, selenium, silver), all of which are stable against spontaneous decay. Often a radioactive isotope of the given element is present in greater amounts than its stable companion (isotopes of indium, rhenium). This requires complete and precise formulations to be made in the determination of the stability of atomic nuclei. This, however, is not always observed in physical literature and is, unfortunately, almost completely neglected in geochemical literature.

The slowness of the transition of nuclear systems into the equilibrium condition is a fact of decisive importance in the energetics of the cosmos. The slow, but powerful, nuclear processes determine the liberation of atomic energy in both the stellar interiors (as a result of thermonuclear reactions with participation of the light elements) and the earth's crust (spontaneous decay of natural radioactive elements). This energy ultimately controls the course of an overwhelming majority of processes of the surrounding universe and causes departures of atomic systems from the state of thermodynamic equilibrium into which they would rapidly have passed if there were no contribution from the energy of nuclear origin.

From the standpoint of rates, nuclear reactions may be divided into the following categories:

1. Decay reactions of the excited nucleus (for example, of the nucleus that captured a particle). The decay takes place with the emission of heavy particles or the γ-quanta. The decay time depends on the excitation energy and the nature of the system but ranges ordinarily from 10^{-17} to 10^{-12} second.

2. Reactions of β-unstable nuclei. The atomic nuclei whose charge for a given atomic weight does not correspond to the lowest possible energy, we shall call "β-unstable." Usually the decay of these nuclei consists of change in their charge and not in their mass, i.e., by the emission of electrons (β-decay in a narrow sense) and positrons (β^+-decay) or by capture of external electrons (K-capture) to which there corresponds a transmutation of a heavy nuclear particle. The velocity of this process is small, and therefore the lifetime of β-unstable nuclei is fairly long. Usually it is 10^2–10^5 seconds and decreases with increasing energy of transition.

3. Reactions with penetration of the potential barrier. There are atomic nuclei that are unstable for any value of the charge. For these nuclei, decay is possible with the emission of the heavy charged particles (α-decay, fission) which pass through the potential barrier of the nuclear field. The probability of such reaction is essentially determined by the energy of the flying particles, and for the majority of α-emitters it is small. Several of them have such a long lifetime that they have been preserved in nature as independent isotopes.

Gas Model of Atomic Nuclei

For the description of the stability of atomic nuclei we need to choose a model which permits a study of the entire aggregate of atomic nuclei.

The method of models is common in atomic physics because the properties of the microcosm are often much different from the properties of the macrocosm, which is easily perceived by human sense organs. A simple and graphic model of the atom was, for example, the Rutherford-Bohr planetary model, which played an important role in the development of atomic physics and did not lose its significance as a simple means of describing the atom.

One of the difficulties in describing the nucleus is that, to this day, our knowledge of nuclear forces is imperfect. There is also another difficulty. The atomic nucleus represents a system of a large number of equivalent bodies, so that it is impossible to apply to it the model of a particle situated in the field of some force center—the model widely used in atomic physics and in celestial mechanics. On the other hand, the number of particles in the nucleus is relatively small, and the method of studying the systems with a large number of particles—the method of statistical physics—also cannot be accurate.

For an approximate description of the system of bound particles the model of a quantum gas residing in a "potential well" formed by the field of force is convenient. The free particles occupy definite energy levels, and in each of these levels there can be, according to Pauli's principle, only two identical particles with opposite orientation of

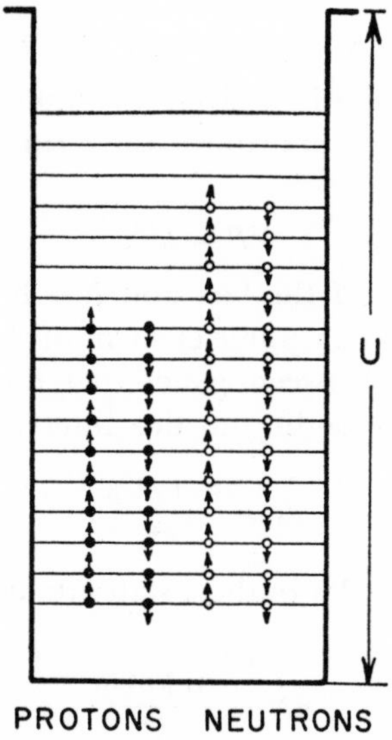

FIG. 10.—Schematic diagram of the distribution of energy levels of protons and neutrons according to the gas model of atomic nuclei.

their mechanical moments—the spins (see Fig. 10). Consequently, in the nucleus on the first filled level there are two protons and two neutrons. This corresponds to the first atomic nucleus with saturated nuclear bonds—the configuration of α-particles.

In the model of the potential well, we conventionally divide the binding energy into the potential energy, equal to the depth of the well, and the kinetic energy, which determines the position of the given level.

The model of a quantum gas is applicable to the atomic nucleus only in the solution of a statistical problem of the ground state of the nucleus when all the allowed states of nuclear particles are occupied and no change takes place in the states of the particles during their collision. Under these conditions, the gas is in the state of extreme degeneracy, i.e., in that of the complete absence of excitation energy.

Highly Degenerate Gas

We shall consider the properties of a highly degenerate gas in the limiting cases: (1) non-relativistic energy of particles, $W \ll mc^2$, where m is the rest mass of the particle; (2) highly relativistic energy, $W > mc^2$.

Let the gas be inclosed in a rectangular box whose sides are l_1, l_2, l_3. According to Bohr's postulate, the quantum conditions of the gas particles are

$$p_1 l_1 = n_1 h, \quad p_2 l_2 = n_2 h, \quad p_3 l_3 = n_3 h, \tag{10.2}$$

where p is the momentum in a given direction and n designates some integral numbers. Having multiplied these three expressions (10.2) by each other, we obtain

$$VP = nh^3,$$

where V is the volume of the box and $P = p_1 p_2 p_3$ is the volume of the momentum space. The volume element of this space with the value of the moments lying between p and $p + dp$ is $dp = 4\pi p^2 dp$. The number of states corresponding to this interval is

$$ds = \frac{4\pi V p^2 dp}{h^3}, \tag{10.3}$$

and the number of particles in these states (taking into account Pauli's principle) is

$$dN = \frac{8\pi V p^2 dp}{h^3}. \tag{10.4}$$

By integration, we find

$$N = \frac{8\pi V p^3{}_{\max}}{3h^3},$$

where $p_{\max}$ is the maximum momentum of the system. In a non-relativistic case, the maximum energy of the system is

$$W_{\max} = \frac{p^2{}_{\max}}{2m} = \frac{h^2}{2m}\left(\frac{3N}{8\pi V}\right)^{2/3} = \frac{h^2}{2m}\left(\frac{3}{8\pi}\frac{\rho}{m}\right)^{2/3}, \tag{10.5}$$

where ρ is the density of the gas.

By definition, the average value of the energy is

$$\overline{W} = \frac{\int W dN}{\int dN} = \frac{1}{2m}\frac{\int_0^{p_{\max}} p^4 dp}{\int_0^{p_{\max}} p^2 dp} = \frac{3}{5} W_{\max}, \tag{10.6}$$

i.e.,

$$\overline{W} = \frac{3}{10}\frac{h^2}{m}\left(\frac{3N}{8\pi V}\right)^{2/3}. \tag{10.7}$$

In the relativistic case the relationship between the energy and the momentum is

$$W^2 = c^2p^2 + m^2c^4. \tag{10.8}$$

In the limiting, highly relativistic case, $W > mc^2$, and

$$W_{\max} = cp_{\max} = ch\left(\frac{3\rho}{8\pi m}\right)^{1/3}. \tag{10.9}$$

The average value of the energy in this case is

$$\overline{W} = \frac{\int WdN}{\int dN} = c\,\frac{\int_0^{p_{\max}} p^3dp}{\int_0^{p_{\max}} p^2dp} = \frac{3}{4}\,W_{\max} \tag{10.10}$$

or

$$\overline{W} = \frac{3}{4}\,ch\left(\frac{3}{8\pi}\,\frac{\rho}{m}\right)^{1/3}. \tag{10.11}$$

Expressions (10.6) and (10.10) for the average energy in the limiting non-relativistic and highly relativistic cases, respectively, differ only by an insignificant change in the coefficients.

In describing the atomic nucleus as a highly degenerate quantum gas it is permissible to use the non-relativistic case, since the energy of the particles (of the order of 10 Mev) is much smaller than their rest energy (equal to almost 1,000 Mev).

Atomic Nuclei with Closed Shells

The distribution of nuclear particles among the individual energy levels determines the periodic properties of atomic nuclei, just as the electronic shells of the atom explain the periodic table of the elements. Numerous attempts (for example, Meitner [215], Sonder [216], Niggli [217], and, in the Soviet Union, S. A. Shchukarev [218], I. P. Selinov [219], and others) were devoted to the explanation of the periodic properties of the nucleus. The first steps in this direction were based on the material dealing with the abundance of isotopes, inasmuch as, among the characteristics of the atomic nuclei, their abundance, historically, had been studied first; or rather this property of the elements was recognized as a nuclear property. This permitted the addition of considerable material assembled by the science independently of the development of nuclear physics to the study of the nucleus.

I. P. Selinov [219] in 1934 found that the isotopes with the number of neutrons equal to 50 and 82 are the most abundant in the series of the neighboring elements. Later on, Mayer [220],[1] using the vast material of modern nuclear physics, showed that atomic nuclei tend to have a definite number of protons and neutrons. In these states, the atomic nuclei differ sharply from other nuclei in abundance, binding energy, stability against various nuclear reactions, and other parameters. These so-called "magic" (or "special") numbers are

$$2, \quad 8, \quad 20, \quad 28, \quad 50, \quad 82, \quad 126. \tag{10.12}$$

The simplest statistical model that we have analyzed is not sufficient for the explanation of this regularity. For this purpose it is necessary to use a more rigorous quantum-mechanical solution. The nuclear particles are examined in their own "self-consistent" field, whose potential can be approximately represented as a square well inside which there are distributed particles with different quantum numbers among distinct levels. A more precise solution can be found by assuming a well-shaped barrier with rounded-off edges:

$$U = -V + ar^2, \tag{10.13}$$

which is a better approximation of reality. Utilizing this model, we obtain the same alternation of levels as in the case of the square well; but some levels draw closer together, forming layers similar to separate layers of the electronic envelope of the atom. The states are characterized by the quantum number l, in some measure analogous to the azimuthal quantum number of atomic physics that determines

TABLE 20

Layer	State	No. of Particles in Given Level	Total No. of Particles
1.....	1s	2	2
2.....	1p	6	8
3.....	1d 2s	10 2	20
4.....	1f 2p	14 6	40
5.....	1g 2d 3s	18 10 2	70
6.....	1h 2f 3p	22 14 6	112
7.....	1i 2g 3d 4s	26 18 20 2	168

[1] See also M. G. Mayer and J. H. D. Jensen, *Elementary Theory of Nuclear Shell Structure* (New York: John Wiley & Sons, Inc.; London: Chapman & Hall, Ltd., 1955).

the mechanical momentum. Using the common spectroscopic terminology, we denote the states with $l = 0, 1, 2, 3, 4, 5, 6$, by the letters *s, p, d, f, g, h, i,* in that order.

Each completed layer includes $2(2l + 1)$ particles in different quantum states. The theory gives (see Table 20) the alternation of the layers which does not coincide with the indicated series of the "magic numbers" (10, 12). Mayer [220] and Keilson [221] postulated a hypothesis that in the field of the nucleus a splitting of the levels takes place, with the values of the total momentum $j = l + 1/2(2l + 2$ particles) and $j = l - 1/2$ ($2l$ particles). In this case the number of particles in the individual closed layers is in agreement with experimental data (see Table 21).

The term "magic numbers" has an advertising tinge and unambiguous idealistic roots. Therefore, we shall call these numbers simply the numbers of particles in the closed shells.

The most important experimental characteristics of the nuclei with closed shells is their high abundance and stability against various nuclear transmutations.

Helium is the next to the cosmically most abundant isotope ($Z = 2$, $A - Z = 2$). On the earth the most abundant isotopes are oxygen ($Z = A - Z = 8$) and silicon ($Z = A - Z = 14$). On the abundance curve the segments of isotopes with $A - Z = 50$ and $A - Z = 82$ stand out sharply. A more detailed consideration of this problem will be given in the next chapter.

TABLE 21

Layer	State	No. of Particles in Given Level	Total No. of Particles
1.......	$1s_{1/2}$	2	2
2.......	$1p_{1/2}$, $p_{3/2}$	6	8
2a......	$1d_{5/2}$	6	14
3.......	$1d_{3/2}$ $2s_{1/2}$	4 2 } 6	20
3a......	$1f_{7/2}$	8	28
4.......	$1f_{5/2}$ $2p_{3/2}$, $p_{1/2}$ $1g_{9/2}$	6 6 } 22 10	50
5.......	$1g_{7/2}$ $2d_{5/2}$, $d_{3/2}$ $3s_{1/2}$ $1h_{11/2}$	8 10 } 32 2 12	82
6.......	$1h_{9/2}$ $2f_{7/2}$, $f_{5/2}$ $3p_{3/2}$, $p_{1/2}$ $1i_{13/2}$	10 14 } 44 6 14	126
6a......	$1i_{11/2}$ $2g_{9/2}$ $3d_{5/2}$	12 10 } 28 6	154

From hydrogen ($A = 1$) to lead ($A = 208$) there are 275 different atomic nuclei, including isobars. The number of protons, Z, changes from 1 to 82, and that of neutrons, $A - Z$, from 0 to 126. Thus, on the average, for each Z there are 3.2 atomic nuclei, and for each $A - Z$ only 2.2 nuclei. For the numbers corresponding to the closed shells, the number of states strongly increases, with the manifestation of the closed shells being stronger for the neutrons (see Table 22).

TABLE 22

No. of Particles in Closed Shell	No. of Atomic Nuclei with Given Number of	
	Neutrons	Protons
20.	5	6
28.	5	5
50.	6	10
82.	7	4

Inasmuch as the neutron shells are identified by certain values of the quantum numbers, the model of the closed shells should be helpful in the systematics of the mechanical moments of atomic nuclei. Indeed, utilizing this model, it was possible to explain a number of regularities in the mechanical moments, as well as to examine a range of the related questions (magnetic moments, quadrupole moments, isotopic shift of spectral lines, etc.). In addition, it was possible to project the regularities in the processes essentially dependent on the nuclear momentum—for example, in the process of β-decay. We shall not be concerned with these important questions because they are only indirectly connected with the principal direction of our presentation.

The stability of atomic nuclei with closed shells against spontaneous decay is very clearly manifested for α-emitters, as will be shown in Section 13. Here we shall consider the special stability of these nuclei in the process of fast-neutron capture. The probability of splitting the atomic nucleus with slow neutrons depends on the incidental fact of the presence in the nucleus of the energy level in the region of the given energy, i.e., the probability has a sharply pronounced resonance character. During the interaction of fast neutrons with nuclei, the energy range of these nuclei is greater than the separation between the nuclear levels, and the capture of neutrons is determined by the properties of the nucleus as a whole. As seen from Figure 11 (according to [222]), the cross-section for the fast-neutron capture by isotopes with the number of neutrons equal to 50, 82, and 126 is tens and hundreds of times smaller than the cross-sections of their neighbors.

It is characteristic of nuclear systems that the isotopes for which the number of neutrons is near that in the closed shell often possess properties similar to the specific isotopes with closed shells (high binding energy, great abundance or stability against α-decay, small neutron-capture probability, etc.). In the vicinity of closed shells there is observed a general change in some nuclear properties, with the greatest manifestation for the isotopes with closed nucleonic shells. In this,

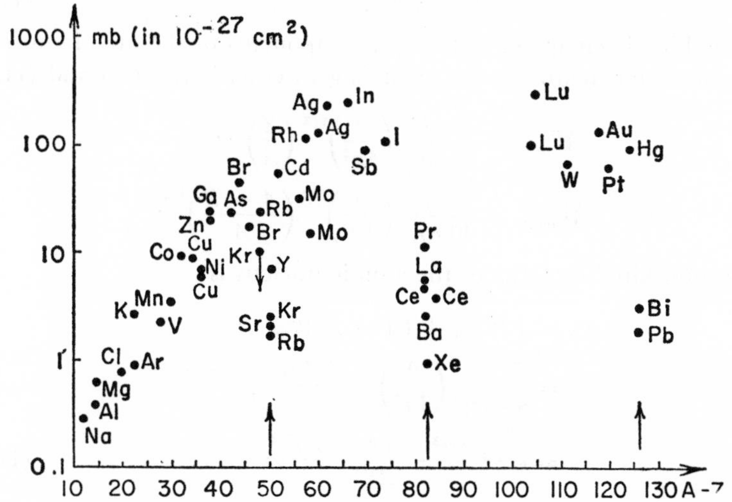

FIG. 11.—Cross-section for fast-neutron capture as a function of the number of neutrons in atomic nuclei. The arrows indicate the regions of the closed shells.

the atomic nuclei differ substantially from the atomic shells, where, on the contrary, the difference in the chemical properties of the elements is greatest in the region of the filling of the electronic shells (difference between the alkali metals, inert gases, and halogens). In conclusion, it should be noted that the periodic properties of atomic nuclei are, in general, manifested in an incomparably smaller measure than the periodic properties of the electronic shells.

11. ENERGY AND CHARGE OF ATOMIC NUCLEI

Using the gas model even in its simplest form, it is possible to describe correctly the basic features of the heavy nuclei with saturated nuclear bonds and also the relationship between the number of protons, Z, and the number of neutrons, $A - Z$.

We shall consider the atomic nucleus as a spherical drop of "nuclear gas" in a state of extreme degeneracy (the absence of excitation energy). The density of the medium can, to a first approximation, be considered constant:

$$\rho = \frac{A}{V} = \frac{A}{\frac{4}{3}\pi R^3} = \text{Const.},$$

where R is the radius of the nucleus. If one introduces the average distance between the nuclear particles $r_0 \approx 1.4 \times 10^{-13}$ cm, then

$$V = \tfrac{4}{3}\pi R^3 = \tfrac{4}{3}\pi A r_0^3, \tag{11.1}$$

whence

$$R = r_0 A^{1/3}. \tag{11.2}$$

The kinetic energy of individual components of the atomic nucleus —protons and neutrons—is, according to equations (10.7) and (11.1),

$$\overline{W}_{\text{prot}} = \frac{3}{40}\frac{h^2}{mr_0^2}\left(\frac{9}{4\pi^2}\right)^{2/3}\left(\frac{Z}{A}\right)^{2/3},$$

$$\overline{W}_{\text{neutr}} = \frac{3}{40}\frac{h^2}{mr_0^2}\left(\frac{9}{4\pi^2}\right)^{2/3}\left(\frac{A-Z}{A}\right)^{2/3}.$$

The total kinetic energy of the atomic nucleus is

$$\begin{aligned} E_k &= Z\overline{W}_{\text{prot}} + (A - Z)\overline{W}_{\text{neutr}} \\ &= \frac{3}{40}\frac{h^2}{mr_0^2}\left(\frac{9}{4\pi^2}\right)^{2/3}\frac{Z^{5/3} + (A - Z)^{5/3}}{A^{2/3}} \\ &= \epsilon 2^{2/3}\frac{Z^{5/3} + (A - Z)^{5/3}}{A^{2/3}}, \end{aligned} \tag{11.3}$$

where

$$\epsilon = \frac{3}{160}\frac{h^2}{mr_0^2}\left(\frac{9}{\pi^2}\right)^{2/3} \approx 12 \text{ Mev}.$$

We shall introduce the following identities:

$$\left.\begin{aligned} Z &= \frac{A}{2} - \frac{A - 2Z}{2} = \frac{A}{2}(1 - K), \\ A - Z &= \frac{A}{2} + \frac{A - 2Z}{2} = \frac{A}{2}(1 + K), \end{aligned}\right\} \tag{11.4}$$

where $K = (A - 2Z/A$ is the ratio of the excess of neutrons over protons to the total number of particles. We rewrite equation (11.3) in the form

$$E_k = \frac{\epsilon A}{2}[(1 + K)^{5/3} + (1 - K)^{5/3}]. \tag{11.5}$$

Expanding equation (11.5) into a series with decreasing K, we find

$$E_k = \epsilon A\left(1 + \frac{5}{9}K^2 + \frac{5}{243}K^4 + \ldots\right). \tag{11.6}$$

The experiment shows that, for the light atomic nuclei, $K = 0$ and for the heavy ones it increases to 0.2. The additional terms in equation (11.6), even for the heavy nuclei, do not exceed 2 per cent of the principal term, i.e., $E_k \approx \epsilon A$, and the kinetic energy per nuclear particle does not, to a first approximation, depend on the atomic weight.

According to the accepted model, the potential energy of atomic nuclei is

$$E_p = -Au,$$

where u is the depth of the potential well. The quantum-mechanical theory of the deuteron shows that this depth is of the order of 25 Mev.

The total energy of particles in the nuclear field (the "volume" energy) is

$$E_p + E_k \approx -A(u - \epsilon) = -Av. \tag{11.7}$$

From the experimental data, $v = 12$ Mev, i.e.,

$$E_k \approx -\frac{E_p}{2}.$$

In conformance with the virial theorem, this relationship is approximately applicable to a broad range of mechanical systems.

We have assumed that the nuclear bonds that hold nuclear particles together are saturated. This is true only of the inner nucleons, which are surrounded on all sides by other nuclear particles. For the surface particles, some bonds remain unsaturated. This results in the presence in the atomic nucleus of a surface energy similar to the surface-tension energy of the liquid macroscopic bodies. In the interior of the nucleus, in the state of the densest packing, each particle is surounded by twelve neighbors, resembling the densest packing of spheres of the same radius—for example, in the atomic lattices of metals. On the surface, an average of three out of twelve bonds turns out to be unsaturated, so that the surface energy per particle is $v/4$. If the surface of the nucleus is $4\pi R^2 = 4\pi r_0^2 A^{2/3}$ and the classical cross-section of one particle is πr_0^2, then the surface of the nucleus can accommodate $4A^{2/3}$ particles.

The total surface energy of the nucleus is

$$E_{\text{surf}} = \frac{v}{4} \times 4A^{2/3} = sA^{2/3}, \tag{11.8}$$

where $s \approx v = 12$ Mev.

The essential component of the nuclear energy is the Coulomb energy, which we define as the electrostatic energy of the uniformly charged sphere. According to the theory of electricity,

$$E_{\text{Coul}} = \frac{3}{5}\frac{Z^2e^2}{R} = c\,\frac{Z^2}{A^{1/3}}, \tag{11.9}$$

where Ze is the charge on the atomic nucleus and $c = 3e^2/5r_0 \approx 0.6$ Mev.

For the heaviest nuclei the additional terms in the nuclear energy expression are extremely large: $E_{surf} \approx 400$ Mev and $E_{Coul} \approx 800$ Mev. The factor by which they are too large is approximately 2. This, however, as we shall see later on, is not accidental but has a special character. The total energy of the system is

$$E = E_k + E_p + E_{surf} + E_{Coul}$$
$$= -Au + sA^{2/3} + \frac{cZ^2}{A^{1/3}} + \epsilon 2^{2/3} \frac{Z^{5/3} + (A - Z)^{5/3}}{A^{2/3}}. \quad (11.10)$$

Because of the approximate nature of the underlying reasoning, this expression is inaccurate and incomplete. Nevertheless, by using it, it is possible to establish the basic regularities of the energetics of the heavy atomic nuclei.

Dependence of Atomic Weight on Charge

It is obvious that the kinetic energy has a minimum when the number of protons is equal to the number of neutrons: $Z = A - Z$, $K = 0$. However, the large number of protons causes an increase in the Coulomb energy that is quadratic with respect to Z. Therefore, in the case of the heavy nuclei, there is observed a relative decrease in the number of protons as compared with the number of neutrons, namely, such that the energy of the system (11.10) has the lowest value.

This value we find from the condition of the minimum energy for some optimum magnitude of $Z = Z_0$:

$$\left.\frac{dE}{dZ}\right|_{Z-Z_0} = 0, \quad (11.11)$$

or, since only the kinetic and the Coulomb components of nuclear energy depend on the charge,

$$\left.\frac{dE_k + dE_{Coul}}{dZ}\right|_{Z=Z_0} = 0.$$

From equations (11.10) and (11.11) we find

$$\frac{5}{3}\epsilon 2^{2/3} \frac{(A - Z)^{2/3} - Z^{2/3}}{A^{2/3}} = 2c \frac{Z}{A^{1/3}}.$$

Applying equation (11.4), we obtain

$$(1 + K)^{2/3} - (1 - K)^{2/3} = \frac{6}{5}\frac{c}{\epsilon}\frac{Z}{A^{1/3}}. \quad (11.12)$$

Expanding the left side of equation (11.12) into a series of decreasing K, we find

$$K + \frac{2}{27}K^3 + \frac{7}{243}K^5 + \ldots = \frac{9}{10}\frac{cZ}{\epsilon A^{1/3}}.$$

Limiting ourselves to the first term of the series $K = (A - 2Z)/A$, we obtain

$$A - 2Z = \frac{9}{10}\frac{c}{\epsilon} ZA^{2/3};$$

setting $Z = A/2$ to a first approximation, we finally have

$$A - 2Z = \eta A^{5/3}, \qquad Z = \frac{A}{2}(1 - \eta A^{2/3}), \tag{11.13}$$

where $\eta = 9c/20\epsilon = 0.02$.

The relationship of the type (11.13) was first pointed out by Heisenberg [223]. Its quantitative derivation on the basis of the gas model was given by Ya. I. Frenkel' and V. V. Cherdyntsev [224]. A comparison with experiment shows that the increase in the number of neu-

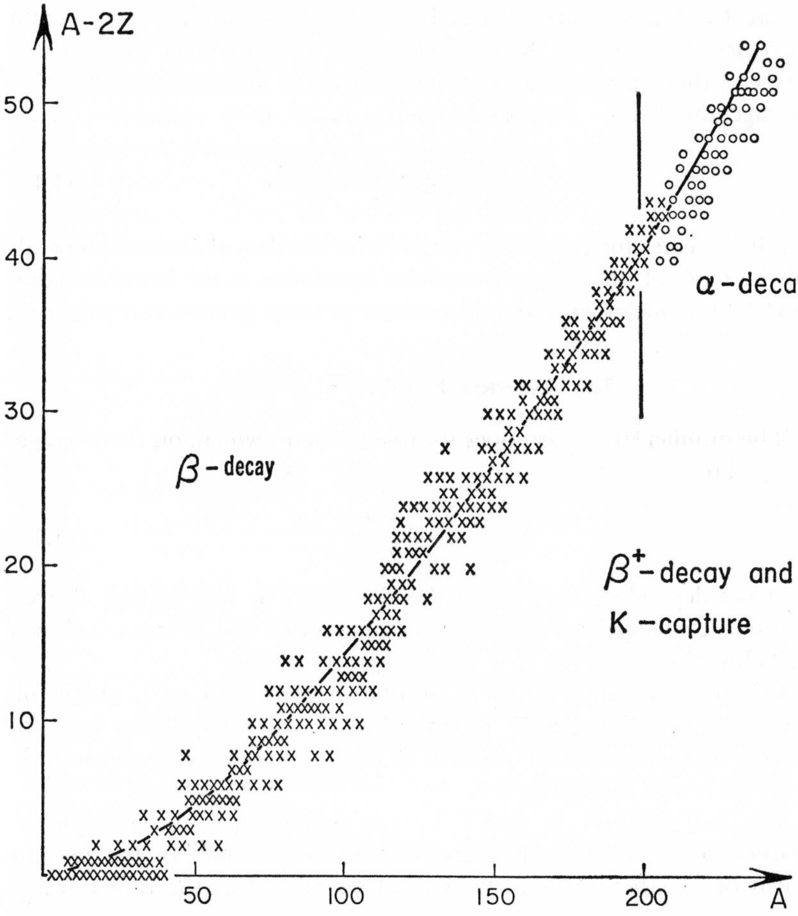

FIG. 12.—Dependence of the excess of neutrons over protons $(A - 2Z)$ on atomic weight (Z) for stable nuclei.

trons $A - Z$ over the number of protons Z—i.e., the neutron excess $A - 2Z$—indeed becomes larger with increasing atomic weight, in agreement with the law (11.13). The numerical coefficient turns out, in reality, to be somewhat smaller: $\eta = 0.006$.

The atomic nuclei for which the charge is optimum, i.e., corresponds to a minimum energy, are the β-stable nuclei. They are distributed over a certain region of the diagram $A - 2Z = f(A)$ (see Fig. 12). The states situated above this region are characterized by a decreased number of protons, that is, have a tendency toward β-decay (the β-decay region). The states below the β-stable region contain, correspondingly, an excess of protons and pass into a stable condition by emitting positrons or capturing electrons, from the K-shell of the atom first (K-capture).

The stable isotopes existing in nature occupy the atomic-weight interval $A = 1–208$ and the charge interval $Z = 1–82$. The atomic weight increases more rapidly than the charge of atomic nuclei, and for one element there are several isotopes—nuclei of different weight. The average number of isotopes is readily found from equation (11.13):

$$I = \frac{dA}{dZ} = 2 + \frac{5}{3}\frac{A - 2Z}{Z}, \tag{11.14}$$

i.e., it increases for the heavy nuclei. The number of isotopes depends on the type[2] of nuclei, in view of the instability of the heavy odd-odd nuclei—the nuclei with an odd number of both protons and neutrons.

The Average Number of Isotopes

The number of odd isotopes for one element, which, on the average, is equal to

$$I_{\text{odd}} = 1 + \frac{5}{6}\frac{A - 2Z}{Z}, \tag{11.15}$$

does not depend on the type of the element. The distribution of even and odd elements having a different number of odd isotopes is shown in Table 23.

In most cases the number of isotopes is equal to 1 or 2, which follows from equation (11.15). In several cases (two for the even and two for the odd elements) the number of odd isotopes is zero, and in only one case (tin, $Z = 50$) $I_{\text{odd}} = 3$.

We shall examine in detail the case when $I_{\text{odd}} = 0$, that is, when neither of the states with a given charge is β-stable. In the present status of the theory these states must be viewed as the rare cases of

[2] Here and further on, speaking of the type of nuclei, we shall understand even and odd values of atomic weight. [Author's footnote.]

TABLE 23

NUMBER OF ODD ISOTOPES, I_{odd}, IN ELEMENTS

I_{odd}	With Odd Nuclear Charge		With Even Nuclear Charge	
	No. of Elements	Total No. of Isotopes	No. of Elements	Total No. of Isotopes
0......	2	0	2	0
1......	31	31	25	25
2......	9	18	13	26
3......	0	0	1	3
Total.....	42	49	41	53

departure of the number of isotopes from the average value $I_{odd} = 1–2$. Among even elements, odd isotopes are absent from argon and cerium. The odd neighbors of argon, chlorine, and potassium each have two

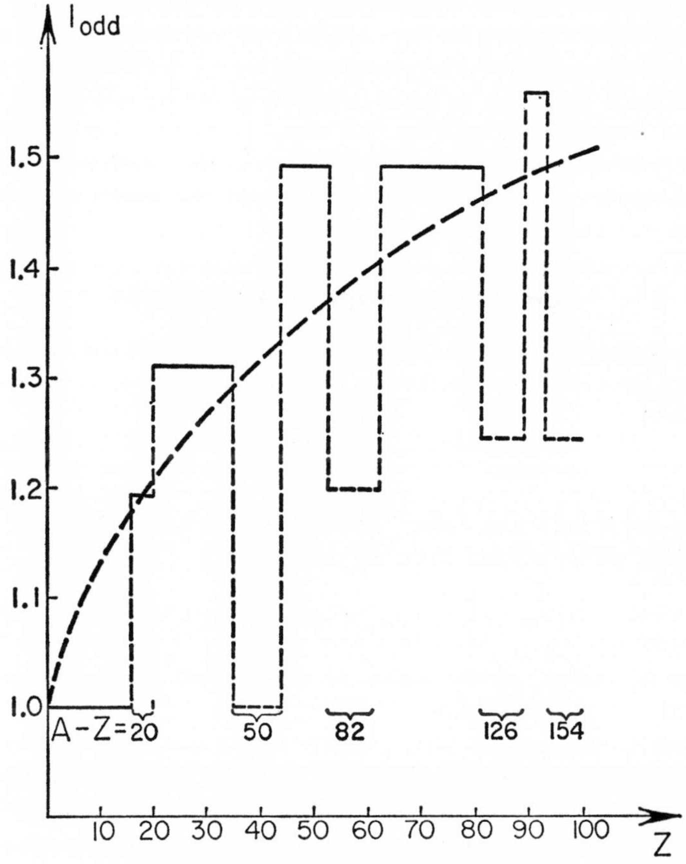

FIG. 13.—The average number of odd isotopes.

odd isotopes (the first elements of the periodic table for which $I_{odd} = 2$), but in the intermediate element, argon, there is not a single odd state present.

For odd elements, only odd isotopes are stable, and if such isotopes are absent, the elements in general have no stable isotopes, that is, are not found in nature. Such elements are technetium ($Z = 43$) and promethium ($Z = 61$). The β-stable isotopes of these elements have been obtained artificially and are now very well studied. As in the case of argon, the even neighbors of these elements in both cases contain two odd isotopes each, but the intermediate odd elements do not have a single stable state.

The search for the elements $Z = 43$ and $Z = 61$ in nature has been conducted for a long time. Now we know that the search was destined to fail, and the absence of stable isotopes in these elements, although an interesting circumstance, is not more surprising than the absence of odd isotopes in argon and cerium.

The number of odd isotopes increases, on the average, for heavy elements, but the increase does not proceed uniformly (see Table 33, p. 174). Figure 13 shows the average number I_{odd} for individual groups of elements and also indicates the course of the theoretical curve (11.15). The departures from this curve point out the approximate nature of the results obtained on the basis of the simplest macroscopic model. Some refinements are introduced by the model of nucleonic shells.

The Binding Energy of Atomic Nuclei

The negative energy of nuclear particles residing in the intranuclear field of force leads to a decrease in their mass, according to the Einstein relation;

$$\Delta m = \frac{U}{c^2}, \tag{11.16}$$

where Δm is the "mass defect" and U is the binding energy of nuclear particles, which we find from the expression

$$U = -\frac{E}{A} = [Zm_p + (A - Z)m_n - M]c^2, \tag{11.17}$$

where m_n and m_p are the masses of neutron and proton, respectively, and M and E are the mass and energy of the nucleus.

Modern mass spectrometry permits very accurate determination of the binding energy of atomic nuclei from the magnitude of the mass defect. As a nuclear unit mass M_0, it is convenient to adopt the mass of particles of some nucleus with saturated nuclear bonds, because in such a case the masses of the majority of atomic nuclei turn out to be approximately whole numbers. An accepted standard is the mass of the oxygen atom O^{16}: $M = 16.000\ M_0$. It went over into nuclear physics from chemistry, where it is convenient to adopt the element oxygen as a standard, inasmuch as it forms compounds with many elements which are widely used in laboratory practice. In chemistry the accepted unit mass is one-sixteenth of the average value of the mass of one oxygen atom of a natural mixture of oxygen with a normal isotopic composition. Since oxygen consists essentially of the isotope O^{16}, with the content of two other isotopes being low (0.24 per cent), the chemical and physical units of mass are almost equal (the conversion factor being 1.000275). The nuclear mass unit M_0 is equivalent to 931 Mev.

According to equations (11.10) and (11.17), the binding energy of nuclear particles is

$$U = v - sA^{-1/3} - \frac{cZ^2}{A^{4/3}}. \qquad (11.18a)$$

At the same time, we consider that the volume energy of the nuclear field, i.e., the sum of the kinetic and potential energy calculated for one particle, is a constant quantity. Using equation (11.13), it is possible to represent the binding energy as a function of atomic weight only:

$$U = v - sA^{-1/3} - \frac{c}{4} A^{2/3}(1 - \eta A^{2/3})^2. \qquad (11.18b)$$

A semiempirical expression for the binding energy was first given by Weizsäcker [225]. He used early concepts regarding the difference in the forces of interaction between the oppositely and identically charged particles. As a result, Weizsäcker complicated the binding-energy equation with additional terms. Expression (11.18*b*) was proposed by us in 1938 [226].

With increasing atomic weight, the binding energy shows an initial increase. This is caused by a decrease in the surface energy per particle. Further on, some decrease in the binding energy takes place at the expense of the increasing Coulomb energy. The maximum in the energy of particles can be obtained from the expression

$$\left.\frac{dU}{dA}\right|_{A = A_{max}} = 0.$$

Neglecting the squared term in parentheses of equation (11.18*b*), we have

$$A_{max} = 2\frac{s}{c}\frac{1}{1 - 4\eta A^{2/3}_{max}}, \qquad (11.19)$$

whence, considering that $s/c \approx 20$, we find $A_{max} \approx 64$. This value agrees with experiment (see Fig. 14). The largest binding energy is observed in Ni^{64}, Ni^{60}, Co^{59}, Cu^{65}, Cr^{54}, and other neighboring isotopes. The data on the binding energy of atomic nuclei are listed in Table III of the Appendix (p. 272), according to Dzhelepov and others [227], with supplements by Halsted and others [228, 245–48].

The maximum on the binding-energy curve for atomic nuclei makes possible the following exothermic reactions: the destruction of the heavy nuclei, with the formation of nuclei of the central part of the periodic table, and the synthesis of nuclei with saturated bonds—first of all, helium, from the light nuclei with small binding energy. The

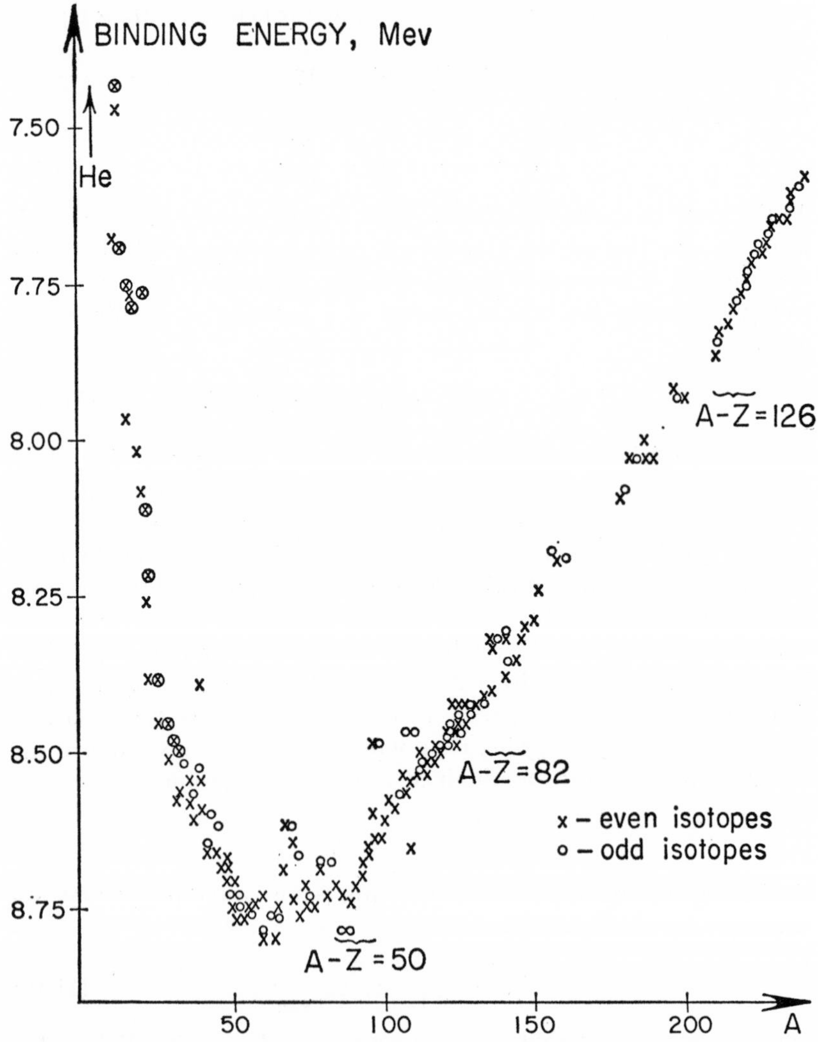

FIG. 14.—The binding energy of atomic nuclei as a function of atomic weight. In the figure are shown regions of isotopes with closed neutron shells.

former process is realized during natural radioactive decay, and the latter in thermonuclear reactions.

For the very heavy nuclei, the relative number of protons Z/A decreases in accordance with equation (11.13). This brings about a decrease in the Coulomb energy per particle and an increase in the binding energy. Formally, the effect is stipulated by the negative term $\eta A^{2/3}$ in equation (11.18*b*). The minimum caused by this in the binding energy is located, as can be shown, at $A \approx 400$, i.e., outside the region of the known stable isotopes.

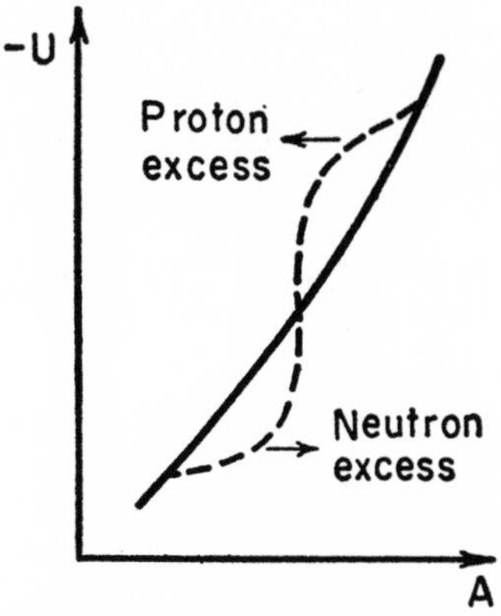

FIG. 15.—A schematic diagram of the departure of binding energy in the region of the closed neutron shells (*dashed curve*) from the theoretical curve of the statistical model for atomic nuclei (*solid curve*).

For the light nuclei, the binding-energy curve does not have a smooth course but shows a maximum at He^4, Be^8, C^{12}, O^{16}, and other isotopes of the type $A = 2Z = 4n$, where n is an integer. Such "helium-like" nuclei appear to be made up of an integral number of α-particles, with n varying from 3 in C^{12} to 10 in Ca^{40}. Some of these nuclei are distinguished by a high abundance (O^{16}, Mg^{24}, Si^{28}, Ca^{40}).

The nuclei with the atomic weight $A = 5$ and $A = 8$ are generally unstable, which means that the α-particle is unable to bind stably another α-particle or a nucleon. These are the only states that are missing from the table of the stable isotopes in the range from $A = 1$ to the upper limit of $A = 208$ at the onset of the region of natural α-emitters (in addition, the nucleus $A = 147$, an isotope of samarium, although occurring in nature, decays by α-emission).

Atomic nuclei tend to achieve states with closed neutron shells. In this region the first nuclei, the lightest for a given value of $A - Z$, have a proton excess relative to that excess expected in accordance with the simple statistical model, whereas the heaviest nuclei are proton-deficient.

Because of both the proton deficiency and a decrease in the electrostatic energy, the binding energy for the lightest isotopes is greater than the expected energy; but for the heavy nuclei of this type it is, on the contrary, smaller than the expected energy. This causes departures of the binding energy in the region of the closed shells from the smooth curve of the statistical model (see Fig. 14 and the schematic Fig. 15).

As a result of the high binding energy of some nuclei with closed neutron shells, the excited nuclei, for which the number of neutrons is too large by 1, can go over into the ground state by emitting not only γ-quanta but also neutrons, even in those cases where the excitation energy is relatively small. The nuclei of this kind can be formed during the preceding β-decay. Their decay takes place according to the following equations:

$$\left.\begin{array}{llll} N^{17} \rightarrow O^{17*} & \xrightarrow{n} O^{16} & (A - Z = 8); \\ & \xrightarrow{\gamma} O^{17} & \\ Br^{87} \xrightarrow{\beta} Kr^{87*} & \xrightarrow{n} Kr^{86} & (A - Z = 50); \\ & \xrightarrow{\gamma} Kr^{87} & \\ I^{137} \xrightarrow{\beta} Xe^{137*} & \xrightarrow{n} Xe^{136} & (A - Z = 82) \\ & \xrightarrow{\gamma} Xe^{137} & \end{array}\right\} \qquad (11.20)$$

(the asterisks denote the excited states). The emission of neutrons from these nuclei takes place practically instantaneously, but the isotopes themselves are formed according to the law of radioactive decay of the parent substances. Such neutrons are called "delayed neutrons."

Dependence of the Binding Energy on the Odd-Even Effect

The abundance of even isotopes is considerably greater than that of odd isotopes. We shall examine the extent to which this is connected with the energetics of atomic nuclei. The odd states in the region of low atomic weights possess a lower binding energy. But for isotopes in the oxygen-calcium region the difference is not too large and is reduced to zero for heavy atomic nuclei. Let us introduce the parameter ΔE, which represents the difference between the energy of even and odd atomic nuclei. This difference can be determined from the relationships

$$\left.\begin{array}{l} \Delta E = E_{2n} - \dfrac{E_{2n+1} + E_{2n-1}}{2}, \\ \Delta E = \dfrac{E_{2n} + E_{2n+2}}{2} - E_{2n+1}, \end{array}\right\} \qquad (11.21)$$

where $2n$ and $2n + 2$ are the atomic weights of even, and $2n \pm 1$ of odd, neighboring isotopes. The average values of ΔE and of the ratio $\Delta E/E$ ($E = -AU$, the energy of the nucleus) are shown in Table 24 for different intervals of atomic weight.

TABLE 24

Atomic Weight Interval	No. of Cases	Average Value of ΔE in Mev	Theoretical Value of ΔE in Mev According to Equation (11.23)	$\frac{\Delta E}{E}$
6– 12.......	4	5.6	3.8	0.07
12– 40.......	14	1.5	2.2	.01
40–120.......	17	1.3	1.1	.002
120–200.......	10	0.5	0.45	.0005
>200.......	36	−0.1	0.2	−0.00005

The calculation is only of an illustrative nature. But it demonstrates definitely that, for sufficiently heavy atomic nuclei, the binding energy is practically independent of the type of atomic weight.

The odd isotopes differ from the even ones, in that their nuclei deviate from spherical symmetry. The data on the magnitude of the magnetic and quadrupole moments of atomic nuclei permit of the idea that, to a first approximation, the deviation from spherical symmetry is caused by an odd particle situated on the surface of the nucleus. With such a crude macroscopic model we shall examine the theoretical magnitude of the departure of the energy for odd states. Obviously, the odd particle changes only the Coulomb and the surface components of the nuclear energy:

$$\Delta E = \int_{V=\text{const}} d(E_{\text{Coul}} + E_{\text{surf}}) = \int_{V=\text{const}} \frac{\partial(E_{\text{Coul}} + E_{\text{surf}})\, dR}{\partial R}. \quad (11.22)$$

where $R = R(\phi, \theta)$ and the volume V is constant. Considering the departure from spherical symmetry to be small and using the theorem of averages, we rewrite equation (11.22) to read

$$\Delta E = \frac{\partial(E_{\text{Coul}} + E_{\text{surf}})}{\partial R} \Delta R.$$

Since $E_{\text{surf}} \sim R^2$ and $E_{\text{Coul}} \sim R^{-1}$,

$$\Delta E = (2E_{\text{surf}} - E_{\text{Coul}}) \frac{\Delta R}{R},$$

or, according to equation (11.2),

$$\Delta E = \frac{2E_{\text{surf}} - E_{\text{Coul}}}{3A} \Delta A, \quad (11.23)$$

where ΔA is the quantity describing, in terms of units of A, the departure of the nucleus from spherical symmetry. As an approximation, $\Delta A = 1$.

The quotient $\Delta E/\Delta A$ decreases with increasing A (see Table 24). This is caused by the fact that the Coulomb energy for the heavy nuclei increases more rapidly than the surface energy. When

$$2E_{\text{surf}} - E_{\text{Coul}} = 0, \tag{11.24}$$

or, taking into account (11.8) and (11.9),

$$\frac{Z^2}{A} = \frac{2s}{c} \approx 40, \tag{11.25}$$

the energies of the even and odd (asymmetrical) states are equal, i.e., the atomic nucleus becomes indifferent toward the change of its shape. This corresponds to the classical criterion of the stability of atomic nuclei against spontaneous fission. This criterion was first obtained by Ya. I. Frenkel' [229].

Considering the approximate nature of the calculation, the theoretical values of ΔE are very close to the experimental values. For the purpose of agreement with experiment, it is necessary to accept $\Delta A =$ 1–2. Thus only the light even nuclei possess greater binding energy than do odd nuclei. The energy of atomic nuclei in the central part of Mendeleyev's table is practically independent of their type, and for the heavy nuclei the difference between the energies of odd and even states generally tends to zero.

12. DEPENDENCE OF THE ENERGY OF ATOMIC NUCLEI ON CHARGE

The dependence of the energy of atomic nuclei on the type of atomic weight is significant only for the lightest nuclei. By contrast, the dependence of the energy of the nuclei on the type of charge determines essentially the stability of heavy isotopes and gives rise to the unique effect of the existence of even isobars. The change in the energy of the atomic nucleus, when its charge Z deviates from an optimum value Z_0, is given in a general form by the expression

$$E(Z) - E(Z_0) = \alpha\delta^2 - \beta\delta^3, \tag{12.1}$$

where $\delta = Z - Z_0$. The coefficients α and β may be obtained from the expression for the energy of the nucleus with $Z = Z_0$ (11.10).

The Odd-Odd Nuclei

Let us examine the isotopes with even A and odd Z, i.e., the isotopes which contain an odd number of protons as well as an odd number of neutrons (the odd-odd atomic nuclei). Experience shows that the heavy odd-odd isotopes are unstable. They are stable only among the lightest nuclei for which the electrostatic energy is small, the number of neutrons is equal to the number of protons, and—following the accepted model—both the odd proton and the odd neutron in the state of the highest energy occupy the same energy level. In all, only four such isotopes are known. The data on them are given in Table 25.

TABLE 25

THE STABLE ODD-ODD ISOTOPES

	Element			
	Hydrogen	Lithium	Boron	Nitrogen
Isotope	$_1D^2$	$_3Li^6$	$_5B^{10}$	$_7N^{14}$
Abundance in per cent	0.015	7.52	18.7	99.64
Nuclear spin momentum (in $\hbar$-units)	1	1	3	1

A remarkable property of the odd-odd stable isotopes is their integral, different from zero, spin momentum. The heavier nuclei of this type are unstable. For example, the nucleus $_9F^{18}$ emits a positron and transforms into oxygen $_8O^{18}$.

As we have seen in the preceding section, odd isotopes are equally probable for both even and odd elements. For the heavy even isotopes the situation is quite different. The states of odd charge, for which the upper neutron and proton levels each contain one particle, turn out to be unstable.

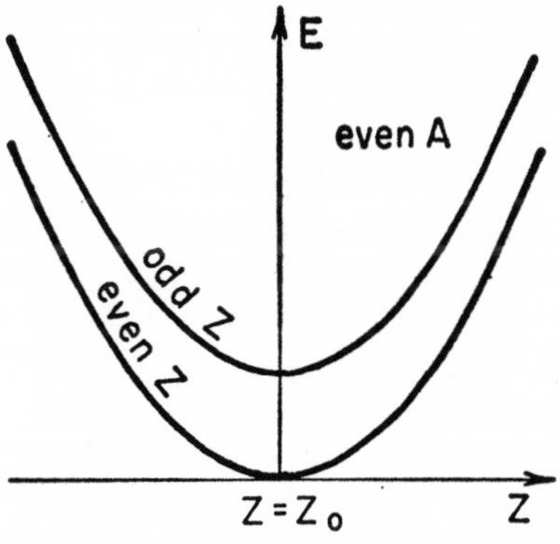

FIG. 16.—Diagram of the dependence of energy of even nuclei on charge.

Even the simplest gas model qualitatively shows that odd-odd states possess additional energy. Let us consider atomic nuclei of the same A and different Z. According to equation (12.1), these nuclei are located on the parabola whose vertex corresponds to the optimum value Z_0 of the charge. For odd states the parabola has the same shape but is displaced toward the region of higher energies by a certain, approximately constant, amount (see Fig. 16). The transition of these unstable odd-odd nuclei into the stable state is, generally speaking, possible with increase (β-decay) as well as with decrease (K-capture) of the charge. As a result of the decay, stable even isotopes are formed which possess the same atomic weight and even charge that differs by two units (even isobars).

The overwhelming majority of odd-odd isotopes did not survive under natural conditions and decayed with the formation of even isobars. However, several unstable odd-odd nuclei are known in nature for which the probability of decay is so small that they have been preserved until the present time. According to the experimental β-decay theory, the probability is connected with the decay energy E by means of the law

$$\lambda = \sum_{n=0}^{5} a_n E^n, \tag{12.2}$$

where a_n represents certain parameters. If during the decay there is a change Δj in the mechanical momentum of the nucleus, then the transition becomes forbidden—its probability decreases, roughly speaking, as the ratio

$$\frac{\lambda_{\Delta j}}{\lambda_0} = \left(\frac{R}{\Lambda}\right)^{2\Delta j}, \tag{12.3}$$

in which R is the radius of the nucleus and Λ is the de Broglie electron wave length ($\Lambda \approx 100R$).

The odd-odd nuclei which have been preserved in nature (see Table 26) are referred to these forbidden transitions. The abundance of these

TABLE 26

NATURALLY OCCURRING HEAVY ODD-ODD ISOTOPES

	Potassium	Vanadium	Lanthanum	Lutecium	Tantalum
Isotope	$_{19}K^{40}$	$_{23}V^{50}$	$_{57}La^{138}$	$_{71}Lu^{176}$	$_{73}Ta^{180}$
Radiation	β, K	K, β(?)	K, β	β	?
Decay products	$_{18}Ar^{40}$, $_{20}Ca^{40}$	$_{22}Ti^{50}$, $_{24}Cr^{50}$	$_{56}Ba^{138}$, $_{58}Ce^{138}$	$_{72}Hf^{176}$	?
K/β	1/8	?	16	0	?
Half-life (billion years)	1.2	4.8×10^5	70–200	75	?
Energy of β-radiation (Mev)	1.33	1.28	1.0	0.4	?
Energy of K-capture (Mev)	1.63	2.39	...	...	?
Nuclear spin momentum in $\hbar$-units	4	6	?	7	?
Concentration in elements (per cent)	0.0119	0.24	0.089	2.60	0.0123

isotopes is small (0.01–2.6 per cent in the isotopic composition of the given element), which cannot be explained by their slight stability. Only K^{40} has decayed substantially during the time of the existence of atomic nuclei, but its initial relative content was nonetheless small (about 0.1 per cent). As for other isotopes, their content within that time could not have decreased by more than several per cent.

Even Isobars

In our consideration of even isobars we shall distinguish two cases (see Fig. 17).

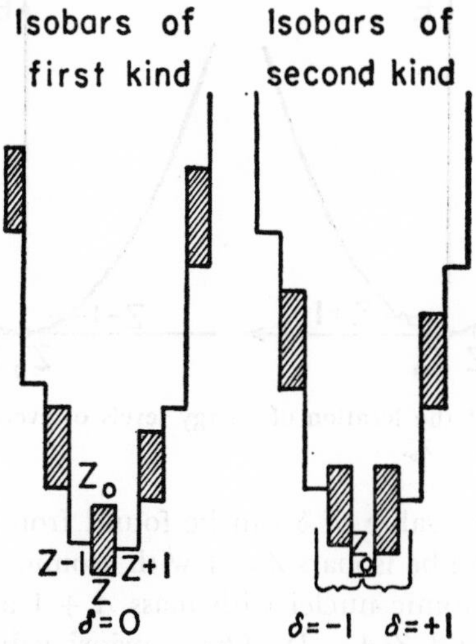

FIG. 17.—Energy-level diagram for even isobars of the first and second kind. The shaded areas symbolize additional energy of odd states.

Isobars of the first kind.—The optimum charge Z_0 is odd. The formation of even isobars with approximately the same energy of the ground state is compulsory. Inasmuch as odd isotopes possess even as well as odd charges with equal probability, for even isotopes we should also expect that half the cases correspond to odd values of the optimum charge, that is, to unstable odd-odd nuclei from which isobars of the first kind are formed.

Isobars of the second kind.—The optimum charge Z_0 is even, and its state is stable. However, the additional energy of the neighboring odd states with the charge $Z_0 \pm 1$ can be so large that their ground energy states lie higher than those for the nuclei with $Z_0 \pm 2$, and consequently the latter are in a quasi-stable state. They are separated from the ground level by a unique potential barrier, to overcome which it is necessary to emit or capture two electrons simultaneously.

The cases are possible when in a quasi-stable state there is only one of the neighboring even isobars. In this manner, for isobars of the second kind the existence of isobar pairs or isobar triplets is permissible, in which case one of the states (in the case of isobar triplets, the intermediate state) possesses the lowest energy.

If one denotes the charges of isobars by $Z + 1$ and $Z - 1$ (Z is odd), then, according to the accepted symbolism (12.1), $\delta = 0$ for the isobars of the first kind and for those of the second kind $\delta = \pm 0$. Obviously, if $\delta < 0$, the energy level of the isobar $Z - 1$ lies higher than the level of the isobar $Z + 1$, and vice versa (see Fig. 18).

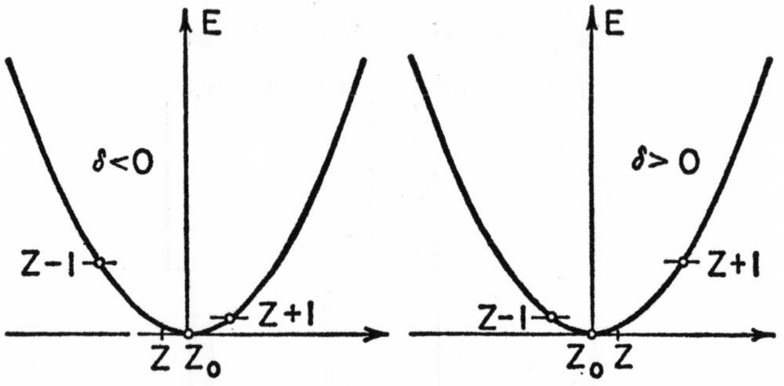

FIG. 18.—Diagram of the location of energy levels of even isobars in the case of different values of $\delta = Z - Z_0$.

The approximate value of δ can be found from the following consideration. Let there be isobars $Z \pm 1$ with atomic weight A, while the neighboring odd atomic nuclei with mass $A + 1$ and $A - 1$ have the charges $Z(A + 1)$ and $Z(A - 1)$. The a priori value of the optimum charge Z_0 should be

$$\left.\begin{aligned} Z_0 &= \frac{Z(A+1) + Z(A-1)}{2}, \\ \delta &= Z(A) - \frac{Z(A+1) + (A-1)}{2} \end{aligned}\right\} \qquad (12.4)$$

For some isobars the masses are known with an accuracy sufficient for the determination of the difference $E(Z - 1) - E(Z + 1)$ between the energy levels. In Table 27 are listed some of these isobars, together with the differences between the energy levels and with the δ-values obtained from equations (12.4).

The average value of the energy difference decreases with increasing δ. The proposed method of the determination of δ is evidently suitable for the estimation of the energy states of isobars for which accurate mass values are as yet unknown. The difference in the energies of isobars of the second kind ($|\delta| = 1$) is, on the average, about 3 Mev.

TABLE 27

DIFFERENCE IN ENERGY LEVELS OF EVEN ISOBARS

A	Elements to Which Belong Isobars with Charges:		$E(Z-1) - E(Z+1)$ (Mev)	δ According to Equation (12.4)	Average Value of $E(Z-1) - E(Z+1)$ for Given δ (Mev)
	$Z-1$	$Z+1$			
48...	Ca	Ti	3.6	−1	3.1
130...	Te	Xe	3.5	−1	
96...	Zr	Mo	3.4	−1	
116...	Cd	Sn	2.6	−1	
100...	Mo	Ru	2.3	−1	
128...	Te	Xe	2.4	−0.5	1.5
110...	Pd	Cd	1.8	−0.5	
124...	Sn	Te	1.8	−0.5	
86...	Kr	Rb	1.2	−0.5	
94...	Zr	Mo	1.1	−0.5	
114...	Cd	Sn	0.6	−0.5	
122...	Sn	Te	0.6	0	−0.35
40...	Ar	Ca	−0.25	0	
36...	S	Ar	−0.4	0	
108...	Pd	Cd	−0.6	0	
64...	Ni	Zn	−1.1	0	
54...	Cr	Fe	−0.3	0.5	−1.6
50...	Ti	Cr	−1.2	0.5	
74...	Ge	Se	−1.2	0.5	
92...	Zr	Mo	−1.25	0.5	
112...	Cd	Sn	−1.8	0.5	
126...	Te	Xe	−2.0	0.5	
120...	Sn	Te	−2.4	0.5	
106...	Pd	Cd	−0.8	0.5	
96...	Mo	Ru	−2.8	1	−2.8

It is interesting to note that β-decay of Ca^{48}, which leads to the formation of the odd-odd Sc^{48}, has been energetically solved, i.e., the ground state of Ca^{48} lies higher than the ground state of Sc^{48}. Nonetheless, careful investigation could not detect the β-transition $Ca^{48} \rightarrow Sc^{48}$, which apparently is forbidden. Perhaps there takes place a double β-decay, with direct formation of Ti^{48} [230].

Let us examine the behavior of isobars in the regions of different atomic weights.

For the lightest atomic nuclei ($Z = 1$–7), odd-odd isotopes are stable. Consequently, even isobar pairs are not formed. For the heavier nuclei, these states are unstable. But their additional energy is small compared with the difference between the energies of the neighboring states of the nuclei. Because of a large change in the binding energy of the light nuclei during their transition into the neighboring states, the probability of the existence of even isobars in this region ($Z = 8$–15) is small.

The first pair of even isobars in the table of isotopes is S^{36} and Ar^{36}. Including the last stable even element, lead, 62 cases of isobars are known in the interval $A = 36$–204: 58 pairs and 4 triplets (see Table V of the Appendix, p. 282). In the region of α-decay, a large number of even isotopes were produced artificially, many of which are even isobars of the earlier-known α-emitters. The last stable nucleus in the table of isotopes, Pb^{208}, also forms an isobar pair with the artificially obtained Po^{208}.

In the interval S^{36}–Pb^{206} there are 86 even atomic nuclei. A priori it may be assumed that half of them (i.e., 43 isotopes) possess odd Z_0 and separate into pairs of even isobars of the first kind. Consequently, the isobars of the second kind comprise approximately $62 - 43 = 19$ cases of isobars.

The number of isobars of the second kind can also be estimated from the following consideration. In Table 28 are given the numbers

TABLE 28

DISTRIBUTION OF EVEN ELEMENTS WITH DIFFERENT NUMBERS OF ISOTOPES WHICH DO NOT FORM ISOBARS IN REGION OF EXISTENCE OF STABLE ISOBARS $_{16}S$–$_{82}Pb$

No. of Isotopes I	No. of Even Elements Which Contain a Given Number of Isotopes I		$n_1 - n_2$	Deficiency of Isotopes in Even Elements $(n_1 - n_2)I$
	Odd n_1	Even n_2		
0......	2	13	−11	0
1......	18	16	2	2
2......	13	5	8	16
3......	1	0	1	3
Total....	...	...	...	21

of even elements containing a different number of even and odd isotopes in the region $Z = 16$–82. The isotopes which are members of even isobars are excluded, i.e., only the own isotopes of a given element for which the charge is optimum are entered. Together with isobars of the first kind, we also left out isobars of the second kind and among them isotopes with an optimum value of the charge. On the average, the number of elements with a given number of isotopes should be the same for even as well as odd isotopes. However, in Table 28 a deficiency of elements with a large number of even isotopes is observed. This is due apparently to the fact that we have excluded from the table isobars of the second kind, not knowing how to separate them from isobars of the first kind. The total deficiency of even isotopes is 21, which means that among isobars there should be approximately 21 isobars of the second kind.

The two summations given show that about 20 cases of isobars are isobars of the second kind. They positively include four cases of isobars which form triplets. Sometimes, out of the two possible side states of an isobar of the second kind, only one is a quasi-stable state, i.e., an isobar pair is formed.

The energy levels of isobars are described approximately by expression (12.1). Because of the presence of a cubic term, the curve $E = f(Z)$ is asymmetric, and the average value of the difference $E_{Z-1} - E_{Z+1}$ between the energy levels of isobars should be greater than zero. Unfortunately, the experimental material available is not yet sufficient for the verification of this assumption. The result of the asymmetry of the energy curve is that, out of the two side states of isobars of the second kind, the formation of a quasi-stable state of a higher charge ($\delta > 0$) is more probable, i.e., of the isobar which is situated on the gently sloping branch of the curve (12.1).

The distribution of isobars according to the values of $\delta = Z - Z_0$ is as follows:

	−3/2	−1	−1/2	0	+1/2	+1
Number of isobars.....	1	3	16	12	22	4

There is observed a marked preponderance of isobars with $\delta > 0$ over the states for which $\delta < 0$. Perhaps this is not accidental but is connected with the energetics of isobars of the second kind.

The existence of isobars increases considerably the number of isotopes for the even elements. The average number of isotopes per element is

$$I = 2 + \frac{5}{3}\frac{A - 2Z}{Z},$$

but, with odd elements, half the isotopes (even states) are unstable and form isobar pairs which are members of isotopes of the neighboring even elements. Therefore, on the average, the number of isotopes of even elements is doubled and turns out to be

$$I_{\text{even}} = 4 + \frac{10}{3}\frac{A - 2Z}{Z}, \qquad (12.5)$$

with isobars of the second kind not being taken into account by this expression. The average number of isotopes for even elements is about six per element, and for the elements beginning with Ca this numbr is never less than four. Particularly large is the number of isotopes for the elements of the intermediate part of Mendeleyev's table (tin, ten isotopes; xenon, nine; cadmium and tellurium, eight each).

The common structure of isotopes of the heavy elements is shown in Figure 19. The central isotopes of the element are represented by

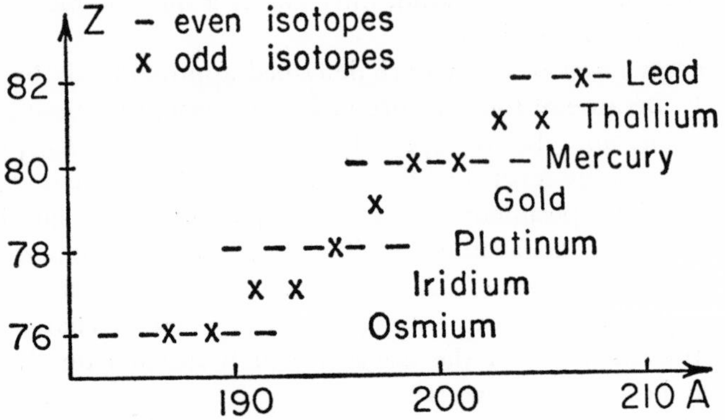

FIG. 19.—Schematic diagram of the structure of isotopes of the elements in the osmium-lead region.

a continuous sequence of odd and even states, these being the own isotopes of a given element which do not form isobars of the first kind. On both sides there lie isotopes—the components of isobars of the first kind, which, in the form of "small islands," fill the individual even states.

The number of the own even isotopes which do not enter into isobars is not large in the even elements. In the region of a particular development of isobars, among the rare-earth elements from neodymium ($Z = 60$) to ytterbium ($Z = 70$), all even isotopes enter into isobar pairs. Almost all elements with two own even isotopes are present at the beginning of the isobar region (these are sulfur, calcium, nickel, and zinc). For the heavier elements, there is known only one such element, namely, mercury (Hg^{200} and Hg^{202}). For the elements of the isobar region, the extreme (the lightest and the heaviest) isotopes certainly enter into isobars. The only exception is the adjacent extreme isotopes of the two neighboring elements Sr^{88} and Zr^{90} with a filled 50-neutron shell.

The sequence of even isotopes is not violated. Thus, for example, the isotopes of tin fill all even values from $A = 112$ to $A = 124$. A single exception is the absence of the isotope 146 in the samarium sequence ($A = 144$–54), which is connected with the instability of this isotope against α-decay.

Out of 275 varieties of stable atomic nuclei which differ in atomic weight and charge, 128—that is, somewhat less than half—enter into even isobars.

Inasmuch as isobars predominate among the heavy even nuclei, we have given this phenomenon sufficient attention, although isobars exist as separate entities in the history of atoms. Indeed, isobars differ with respect to charge; and the charge of the nucleus is precisely the fundamental characteristic that determines the geochemical distinction between the elements. Isobars enter the composition of elements which often differ greatly from each other in chemical properties. Thus, in the isobar triplet with the atomic weight of 124, one component has the charge of tin—a lithophile element—another—a principal component—is present in the composition of a rare chalcophile element tellurium, and the last is an isotope of the inert gas xenon. Only in isolated cases has the formation of isobars not yet been completed, and this links the geochemical destinies of such nuclei as Ar^{40} and Ca^{40}.

Isobars are studied only in nuclear physics. They have no practical importance either for the chemist in his laboratory or for the mineralogist. However, the isobar phenomenon is widespread, and, without it, it is impossible to understand the special feature of the isotopic composition of elements.

Double β-Decay

Rigorously, only isobars of the first kind are stable, whereas isobars of the second kind—about twenty of them—are in a "quasi-stable" condition. A transition into the ground state is possible for these isobars by the simultaneous emission of two β-particles (double β-decay) or by simultaneous capture of both electrons from the K-shell.

In recent years many experimental studies have been devoted to double β-decay. They often showed a great deal of ingenuity in the preparation and great care in the execution of the experiment [230–35, 249]. This was connected with the importance of the problem in the theory of β-decay. There were two different variants of the theory which assumed that the double β-decay proceeds according to the following equations:

$$_ZR \rightarrow {}_{Z+2}R + 2e^- \qquad \text{(decay time, } 10^{16} \text{ years)},$$

$$_ZR \rightarrow {}_{Z+2}R + 2e^- + \nu + \nu^- \qquad \text{(decay time, } 10^{22} \text{ years)},$$

where ν^- is the antineutrino. The latter variant assumed a real difference between the neutrino and its antiparticle. This problem could be resolved only experimentally. The experiment showed that in all cases the double β-decay period is longer than 10^{17} years [249]. Not a single laboratory investigation has proved, to any degree of confidence, the existence of this process, so that its probability is evidently very small. Perhaps the greatest event in the physics of the elementary processes in recent years was the discovery by T. D. Lee and C. N. Yang of the "non-conservation of parity." One of the consequences of this theory is the existence of the antineutrino. One can say that the neutrino and antineutrino differ from each other in that the direction of the spin relative to the direction of the motion forms a left-hand screw in the case of the former and a right-hand screw in the case of the latter. If the given spin direction is necessarily intrinsic in the particle, it means that it is independent of the velocity of motion of the observer. Hence it follows that the neutrino and antineutrino move with the velocity of light. Obviously, their rest mass is zero. Thus, of the two variants of the double β-decay theory, that one proves to be correct which has a "small probability" and assumes the existence of the antineutrino.

An interesting application of geochemical material during the search for the double β-decay of tellurium was made by Inghram and Reynolds [88]. The isotope Xe^{130}, which should be produced as a result of the decay of Te^{130}, was determined in old tellurium minerals. As already pointed out (see Sec. 5, p. 45), xenon was extracted which, indeed, was enriched in Xe^{130} and, to a still greater degree, in Xe^{129} and Xe^{131}. The authors consider that the latter isotopes were accumulated at the expense of the artificial transmutations of atomic nuclei, whereas Xe^{130} can be formed only in the process of double β-decay of Te^{130}. The half-life of this isotope is 1.4×10^{21} years. In the course of 1 year, approximately one tellurium atom per gram decays to Xe^{130}. Such low activity, at the present stage of laboratory techniques, can be determined only by indirect methods utilizing the accumulation in old minerals of the given element of certain reaction products.

The search for double β-decay led to the conclusion that, even if this process takes place, its probability is very small and corresponds to a lifetime of not less than 10^{21} years. During the existence of the earth, such weak processes have led to the decay of not more than 1 atom for every 10^{11} atoms of unstable isotopes.

Odd Isobars

The even isobars constitute a widespread phenomenon caused by the instability of the heavy odd-odd nuclei. For these isobars a charge difference of two units is necessary. At the same time, the existence of nuclei of the same weight is possible in which the neighboring states with charges Z and $Z + 1$ possess such closely spaced energy levels that a transition between them is unlikely and they can exist together in nature. Obviously, the atomic weight of such nuclei can only be odd, since, in the case of an even A, one of the states must have an odd charge, i.e., must be an unstable odd-odd nucleus. The stability conditions of such odd isobars are reduced to the impossibility of β-decay of the nucleus Z and of electron capture in the nucleus $Z + 1$. The transition $Z + 1 \rightarrow Z$ can also be brought about by way of positron decay, but the energtic conditions of this process are less rigid. Here the nucleus gives off energy corresponding to the electron rest mass m, and during electron capture it acquires this energy. Let us examine a limiting case when the energy of the emitted particles is zero and the absorbed electron is free, that is, its rest energy is not reduced by the amount of the binding energy in the atomic shell. The impossibility of β-decay and of electron capture can be recorded in the form of inequalities [212]:

$$\left.\begin{aligned} E(Z) &< E(Z+1) + mc^2, \\ E(Z+1) + mc^2 &< E(Z), \end{aligned}\right\} \tag{12.6}$$

where $E(Z)$ and $E(Z + 1)$ are the energies of the nuclei Z and $Z + 1$. The rest mass of the neutrino is set equal to zero. Combining these inequalities,

$$E(Z) < E(Z+1) + mc^2 < E(Z),$$

we find that

$$0 \leqslant E(Z+1) - E(Z) + mc^2 \leqslant 0,$$

i.e.,

$$E(Z) - E(Z+1) \equiv mc^2. \tag{12.7}$$

Such identity of the energy levels is improbable, and consequently the existence of the absolutely stable odd isobars is impossible. But, if the energy of transition is small and the change (Δj) in the mechanical momentum is large (the forbidden transitions), the half-life of the unstable component can be so long that odd isobars are preserved in nature as independent isotopes. Five such odd isobars are known (see Table 29), for two of which radioactive decay has not been observed and the difference in the energy states is, within measurement error [228], close to zero. For the remaining pairs, β-decay of the component with a lower charge is observed in which Δj is large and the decay energy is small. Thus, for Re^{187}, the energy is not greater than 8 kev, i.e., lies not within the realm of nuclear, but of atomic, transformations. The abundance of these unstable isobars could not have decreased substantially during the existence of the earth. Even the least stable Rb^{87} decayed in the course of this time to the extent of not more than several per cent.

Among α-emitters, pairs of odd isobars are also known the decay of which was not observed: At^{215}–Rn^{215}, Am^{243}–Cm^{243}, Cm^{247}–Bk^{247}. The

TABLE 29

DATA ON ODD ISOBARS

A	Z	ELEMENT	ABUNDANCE n_z IN ELEMENT (PER CENT)	$\frac{n_z}{n_z+1}$	DECAY MODE	HALF-LIFE (YEARS)	NUCLEAR SPIN MOMENTUM		ENERGY DIFFERENCE BETWEEN ATOMS $E(Z) - E(Z+1)$ (ENERGY OF DECAY) (MEV)
							i	Δi	
87..........	37 38	Rb Sr	27.85 7.02	3.97	Rb $\xrightarrow{\beta}$ Sr	6.3×10^{10} . . .	3/2 9/2	−3	0.130
113..........	48 49	Cd In	12.26 4.23	2.86	Decay unknown		1/2 9/2	−4	0.2 ± 0.2
115..........	49 50	In Sn	95.77 0.34	2.80	In $\xrightarrow{\beta}$ Sn	6×10^{14}	9/2 1/2	4	0.630
123..........	51 52	Sb Te	42.75 0.87	49.0	Decay unknown		7/2 1/2	3	−0.7 ± 0.7
187..........	75 76	Re Os	62.93 1.64	38.8	Re $\xrightarrow{\beta}$ Os	8×10^{10} *	5/2 . . .	. . .	<0.008

* For a new half-life value of Re^{187} see n. 70, p. 76.

existence of even isobars and of the rare phenomenon of odd isobars is therefore determined by different physical causes.

13. STABILITY OF ATOMIC NUCLEI AGAINST α-DECAY

It was not fortuitous that the radioactive properties were first discovered in α-emitters. These elements and their decay products play a fundamental role in the energetics of the earth and now in the atomic energetics of human society as well. In Mendeleyev's table, following the region of the stable elements, where only isolated nuclei are capable of radioactive decay, there begins a large region of α-emitters. The stable atomic nuclei lie in the vicinity of the curve.

$$A - 2Z = \eta A^{5/3}, \tag{13.1}$$

whose lower and upper portions are limited by the regions of β-unstable isotopes. If in the atomic nucleus the charge does not correspond to the atomic weight, that is, if the energy for the given charge is not minimum, then usually the charge and not the atomic weight is changed. Such isotopes turn out to be β-unstable and go over into a new state with the emission or absorption of the light elementary particles. However, in the isotopes of high atomic weight, electrostatic repulsion is so great that the nuclei are unstable for any value of the charge and disintegrate with the expulsion of the heavy particles.

Spontaneous nuclear transmutations with the change in atomic weight are possible if (1) the process takes place with the liberation of energy and (2) a nuclear mechanism exists which favors the given transition. Under such conditions it is necessary to distinguish between two limiting cases: the nucleus breaks up into two fragments of comparable weights (fission), or else it splits, releasing a heavy particle (for example, an α-particle) whose atomic weight (a) and charge (z) are much smaller than those of the nucleus itself.

Energetic Feasibility of α-Decay

Let the energy of the nucleus with the atomic weight A be E_A (we omit the charge subscript because we assume the nucleus to be in the ground state with an optimum value of the charge). The energy balance of the splitting reaction is

$$E_A = E_{A-a} + E_a + K_a, \tag{13.2}$$

where K_a is the decay energy. If $a \ll A$, the radioactive recoil energy is small, and K_a is approximately equal to the kinetic energy of the outflying particle:

$$K_a = E_A - E_{A-a} - E_a = \Delta E_A - E_a.$$

We express the difference in a differential form, since a is small:

$$\Delta E = \frac{dE}{dA}\Delta A = \frac{dE}{dA}a.$$

Setting $E_A = -AU_A$ and $E_a = -aU_a$, where U_A and U_a denotes, respectively, the binding energy of nucleons in the disintegrating nucleus and the emitted particle, we find

$$\Delta E = -\frac{d(U_A A)}{dA}a = -\left(U_A + A\frac{dU_A}{dA}\right)a$$

and

$$K_a = a\left[(U_a - U_A) - A\frac{dU_A}{dA}\right]. \qquad (13.3)$$

For a system consisting of a large number of particles—for example, a macroscopic solid body—it is legitimate to disregard the last term—the change in the average binding energy upon removal of one particle. Thus

$$K_a = a(U_a - U_A). \qquad (13.4)$$

During the evaporation of molecules from a crystal, one should understand under U_A the binding energy of ions in the crystalline lattice and under U_a the binding energy of ions in the molecule. In the ground state $U_A > U_a$, which means that the release of particles is not possible. If, as a result of the heating of the crystal, the binding energy of the individual excited particles decreases to the value $U_A = U_a$, the process of evaporation begins. We recall that the binding energy, according to our definition, is always positive.

In the atomic nuclei the number of particles is not large, and therefore the last term in equation (13.3), which determines the difference in the binding energy between the initial and final nucleus, cannot be ignored.

Let us consider the decay of the atomic nucleus with the emission of an α-particle ($a = 4$). The α-particles are not contained in the nucleus as its constant components but can be formed at the moment of liberation. By analogy, the molecules of NaCl do not exist in the crystal of the rock salt; they are released from it in a combined form because the removal of the ions Na^+ and Cl^-—that is, of the free particles, for which $U_a = 0$—requires a considerably higher excitation energy.

Out of nuclear systems, obviously, particles will also be released for which the energy level in the extra-nuclear state is as low as possible in comparison with the energy level of the intranuclear state, i.e., for which the binding energy U_a of the particles is large. The simplest particles with saturated nuclear bonds are precisely the α-particles.

The binding energy U_A of nuclear particles decreases for the heavy nuclei at the expense of the increasing Coulomb energy, but even for the heaviest nuclei this energy is greater than the binding energy of the components of α-particle. In other words, the value of $U_\alpha - U_A$ remains negative for all atomic nuclei. The emission of α-particles from the heavy nuclei is feasible because in this case the energy of the whole residual nucleus changes and the system goes over into the state with large binding energy (see Fig. 14). The liberated energy faciltates the α-transition. Mathematically, this means that the last term in equation (13.3), $A(dU_A/dA)$, for the heaviest nuclei, turns out to be negative, which is connected with a rapid increase in the Coulomb energy in that region.

In the simplest form, the binding energy as a function of atomic weight only, is given by the expression (11.18*b*)

$$U_A = v - sA^{-1/3} - \frac{c}{4}A^{2/3}(1 - \eta A^{2/3})^2.$$

From this we find

$$\frac{dU_A}{dA} = \frac{1}{3}sA^{-4/3} - \frac{c}{6}A^{-1/3} + \frac{2}{3}c\eta A^{1/3} - \frac{c}{2}\eta^2 A, \qquad (13.5)$$

$$K_\alpha = 4\left(U_\alpha - U_A - \frac{AdU_A}{dA}\right)$$
$$= 4(U_\alpha - v) + \frac{8s}{3}A^{-1/3} + \frac{5}{3}cA^{2/3} - \frac{14}{3}c\eta A^{4/3} + 3c\eta^2 A^2. \qquad (13.6)$$

The dependence of α-decay energy on atomic weight is of the same type as the dependence of the binding energy (with opposite sign). With increasing A, there is first observed a decrease in the energy K_α, together with a decrease in the surface energy of the nucleus by one particle; then K_α increases at the expense of the increasing Coulomb

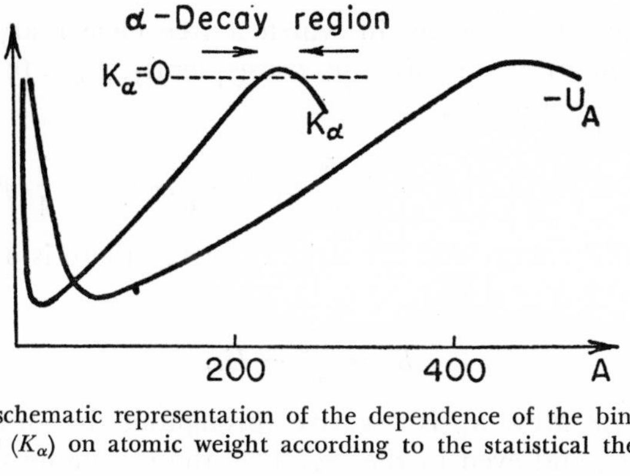

FIG. 20.—A schematic representation of the dependence of the binding (U_A) and α-decay energy (K_α) on atomic weight according to the statistical theory of atomic nuclei.

energy. For the very heavy nuclei, the relative number of protons in the nucleus decreases to such an extent that an increase in the term proportional to $A^{4/3}$ causes a decrease in K_α. Thus, in this region, the α-decay energy achieves a maximum. The course of the functions $U_A = f_1(A)$ and $K_\alpha = f_2(A)$ is similar, but the extreme points of the α-decay energy curve are shifted into the lower atomic-weight region (see Fig. 20). Thus, for example, a minimum is reached at $A = 10$–15. This point is of no practical interest; besides, it is located in the region of small A, where the application of the macroscopic model is already impossible. The maximum α-decay energy is at $A = 220$, if for η the experimental value of 0.006 is accepted.

The somewhat high value of A at which the binding energy attains a maximum can be readily estimated by neglecting the change in the surface energy term in the region of the heavy nuclei. Then, from the condition

$$\left.\frac{dK_\alpha}{dA}\right|_{A=A_{\max}} = 0,$$

we obtain

$$A_{\max} = \left(\frac{1}{\eta}\frac{14-\sqrt{61}}{27}\right)^{3/2} \approx 230. \tag{13.7}$$

The region of the maximum corresponds to the real region of α-emitters with the largest decay energy. Thus even the simplest macroscopic model already permits us to state the fundamental features of the stability of atomic nuclei, namely, the dependence of the binding and α-decay energy on atomic weight and on the position of the extreme points of these functions [226].

Assuming in equation (13.6) that $U_\alpha = 7.8$ Mev and substituting the above accepted values for the nuclear characteristics ($v \approx s \approx 20c = 12$ Mev), we find that, in the region of the maximum, the α-decay energy actually takes on a positive value, which means that α-decay is feasible.

The energy of the decay in which a free elementary particle—a proton or a neutron (in this case, consequently, $U_a = 0$)—is emitted, is given by the expression

$$K_n = -v + \frac{2}{3}sA^{-1/3} + \frac{5}{12}cA^{2/3} - \frac{7}{6}c\eta A^{4/3} + \frac{3}{4}c\eta^2A^2.$$

Between this energy and the α-decay energy there is a simple relationship:

$$K_n = \frac{K_\alpha}{4} - U_\alpha. \tag{13.8}$$

Since $U_\alpha = 7.8$ Mev, K_n is negative throughout the entire region of atomic nuclei, and even in the region of the maximum of K_α it does not exceed $K_n = -6$ Mev. Therefore, spontaneous decay with the expulsion of nucleons is not possible for the existing atomic nuclei.[3]

The Probability of α-Decay

We have examined the energetic feasibility of α-decay, i.e., the condition under which an α-particle formed in the nucleus has a positive energy. However, to leave the nucleus, the particle must penetrate the potential barrier of the Coulomb energy which surrounds the nucleus (see Fig. 9, p. 116). From the viewpoint of classical mechanics, this is impossible, since the particle must have a negative kinetic energy inside the barrier (the barrier height, which is equal to the potential energy U, is greater than the total energy E of the particle). According to quantum mechanics (for example, [212–14]), the particle has wave properties which permit it to "leak" through the potential barrier. The transparency coefficient for the square-shaped barrier is given by the expression

$$D = e^{-\frac{2\sqrt{2m}}{\hbar}\sqrt{U - E}x}, \tag{13.9}$$

where x is the barrier width. For the barrier of any shape,

$$D = e^{-\frac{2\sqrt{2m}}{\hbar}\int_{x_1}^{x_2}\sqrt{U - E}dx}, \tag{13.10}$$

with the integral being taken over the barrier width, that is, over the region in which $U - E > 0$.

In the case of α-decay, $U = 2Ze^2/r$, and

$$D = e^{-\frac{2\sqrt{2m_\alpha}}{\hbar}\int_R^{R_0}\sqrt{\frac{2Ze^2}{r} - E}dr}, \tag{13.11}$$

where R is the radius of the nucleus and $R = 2Ze^2/E$ corresponds to the point at which the α-particle leaves the barrier region. The probability of α-decay is

$$\lambda = CD, \tag{13.12}$$

C being the probability of the formation of an α-particle and of its collision with the inside wall of the barrier in a unit of time, and D is the transparency of the barrier (13.11). Solving the integral, we obtain with a sufficient accuracy,

$$\lambda = Ce^{-\gamma},$$

where

$$\gamma = \frac{2\pi Ze^2}{\hbar v} - 8e\frac{\sqrt{m_\alpha ZR}}{\hbar}, \tag{13.13}$$

[3] Kogan (*DAN SSSR*, **108:** 817, 1956) observed the emission of neutrons during the decay of RaC″. The neutrons are emitted by the excited nucleus RaD in accordance with the scheme of the "delayed" neutrons described on p. 136. [Author's footnote.]

and v is the velocity of the particle; for α-decay or in a general case of emission of a particle with the charge z from the atomic nucleus,

$$\gamma = \frac{2\pi z Z e^2}{\hbar v} - 4e\frac{\sqrt{2mzZR}}{\hbar}. \tag{13.14}$$

The available information on intranuclear life is extremely limited, and a theoretical determination of C cannot be accurate. Fortunately for the theory, the α-decay probability is determined in principle by the transparency coefficient of the barrier, so that the error in the estimate of C does not appreciably alter the determination of the decay constant. We may accept that

$$C = \frac{v}{R} \approx 10^{21}\ \text{sec}^{-1},$$

which is the upper limit of C.

It is obvious that, with increasing Z, the decay probability decreases (at the expense of the increasing barrier height), whereas, with increasing R, it increases (at the expense of the decreasing barrier width); however, the dependence of the probability upon the velocity (or the energy) of α-particles is manifested most strongly. With decreasing velocity, the decay probability decreases sharply, since in this case both the width and the height of the barrier increase. For the heavy α-emitters, a 1 per cent increase in v leads to a three- to fourfold decrease in the decay probability.

The α-decay energy in the region of the natural α-emitters varies by about a factor of 2. At the same time, the decay probability changes by 23 orders of magnitude:

For ThC′:	$E = 8.776$ Mev,	$\lambda = 2.3 \times 10^{7}$ seconds
For Th:	$E = 3.98$ Mev,	$\lambda = 1.6 \times 10^{-16}$ second.

The decay constant λ is connected directly with the width of the energy level $\Gamma = \hbar\lambda$. But the Γ-value is so small that, up to now, it lies outside the measurement limits for even the short-lived elements (thus, for ThC′, the width of the level is only 10^{-8} ev.). On the other hand, the decay constant λ is a decay probability of the atomic nucleus during a unit of time and has a simple statistical interpretation. If the number of nuclei is large, it is possible to use the macroscopic concept:

$$dn = -\lambda n\, dt, \tag{13.15}$$

where dn is the number of atoms which have decayed in time dt.

The decay of the heavy atomic nuclei, in which not α-particles but more complex nuclei with saturated nuclear bonds are emitted (for example, C^{12}, O^{16}, etc.), is energetically feasible, as can be readily shown from equation (13.3). However, the decay probability is exceedingly small because the potential barrier height during the interaction of the daughter nucleus with a heavy particle increases greatly.

The law of radioactive decay describes with remarkable accuracy the processes which take place at wholly different rates, from the excited nuclei with $T \approx 10^{-15}$ second to the long-lived radioactive elements. It is difficult to find an example of another regularity which would preserve its form over such a broad time interval. This, of course, is connected with the fact that, under terrestrial conditions, radioactive decay is practically unaffected by the external environment.

But even though the form (13.15) remains constant, the very probability of decay depends on many intranuclear factors; in the case of α-decay, first of all, on the decay energy. An α-particle leaving the nucleus has a tendency to utilize all the energy of transition from the initial to the final state. For β-decay, the energy conditions are not so rigid, and the daughter nucleus often turns out to be excited. The transition into the ground state usually takes place by way of the emission of a γ-quantum. But if the daughter nucleus is a short-lived α-emitter, then there is an increase in the probability of the emission of an α-particle directly from the excited level. In this state, the energy of α-particle becomes greater, and the decay probability strongly increases and becomes comparable to the γ-emission probability. Such particles are called "long-range α-particles."

Short-Range α-Particles

Of particular interest are the short-range α-particles. There are cases when the nucleus in an unexcited state emits, in addition to α-particles from the ground level, particles of a smaller energy, the so-called short-range α-particles. At the same time, the system remains excited and emits γ-quanta. In such a case, the excitation of the daughter nucleus is due to the fact that the α-particle has not fully utilized the transition energy (self-excitation). That the γ-radiation belongs to the daughter nucleus can be judged from the secondary X-ray emission. Apart from γ-decay, internal conversion can take place; the excited nucleus transmits the energy directly to a K-shell electron. The fast electron flies out, and its place is taken by an electron from the outer shells. This process is accompanied by the emission of X-ray quanta with a frequency proportional to Z^2.

Often there are observed several groups of short-range particles. The difference in their energies is small (the fine structure of α-rays), and the decay probabilities are comparable. With decreasing energy, the intensity of a given group of α-particles decreases somewhat in most cases, but to a much smaller degree than could be expected from the change in the decay energy. In some cases the emission of particles of smaller energy is even more probable.

The formation of α-particles in the nucleus is equally probable for all decay modes, in other words, the coefficient C in equation (13.12) does not vary. Since λ also hardly varies, it should be concluded that the parameter γ is almost the same for short-range α-particles of diverse energy. Inasmuch as in the expression for γ the only variables are v and R, it is obvious that a decrease in the decay probability brought about by a decrease in the velocity v—that is, by an increase in the potential barrier height—should be compensated for by an increase in the probability associated with an increase in the nuclear radius R, i.e., with a decrease in the barrier width. The relative change in the radius is easily obtained from equation (13.13):

$$\frac{\Delta R}{R} = \frac{(2\pi/\hbar)(Ze^2/v)(\Delta E/E) + \ln (n_1/n_0)}{(4e/\hbar)\sqrt{m_\alpha ZR}}, \tag{13.16}$$

where n_0 and n_1 are, respectively, the percentages of α-particles in the ground state and in the state of lower energy and ΔE is the energy difference between these states. In the majority of cases there is observed a several per cent increase in the radius of the excited nuclei which have emitted a short-range α-particle. Evidently, the excitation energy causes a departure of the system from spherical symmetry or an increase in the average distances between the nuclear particles, in analogy to the thermal expansion of macroscopic bodies.

The short-range particles are found predominantly in odd isotopes. For some of these isotopes the number of groups of such particles is as large as ten. In the odd actinouranium decay series, only one α-emitter does not show fine structure, and in the even thorium and uranium series this phenomenon occurs in less than half the cases. The impression is that the self-excitation energy of the daughter nucleus is directed toward a unique polarization of an odd nuclear particle which deflects the nuclear surface from the spherical symmetry, causes a local increase in the radius, and facilitates α-particle emission. The self-excitation phenomenon is by no means a decisive factor in the α-decay of nuclei which show a fine structure. Self-excitation facilitates the emission of α-particles with an energy smaller than that for the main transition but does not make the process more probable in comparison with that transition.

As we shall see in the next section, self-excitation is a necessary condition for nuclear fission.

Dependence of α-Decay Probability on Z and A

We shall rewrite the expression for the probability and the half-life of α-decay following expressions (13.12)–(13.14):

$$\ln \lambda = c_1 - \frac{c_2 Z}{\sqrt{E(Z,A)}}, \tag{13.17}$$

$$\ln T = c_3 + \frac{c_4 Z}{\sqrt{E(Z,A)}}, \tag{13.18}$$

where c_1, c_2, c_3, and c_4 represent some constants. The energy E of α-particle is close to the total energy of the α-transition:

$$K_\alpha = E\left(1 + \frac{4}{A}\right).$$

The dependence of the half-life T and of the decay energy K_α on

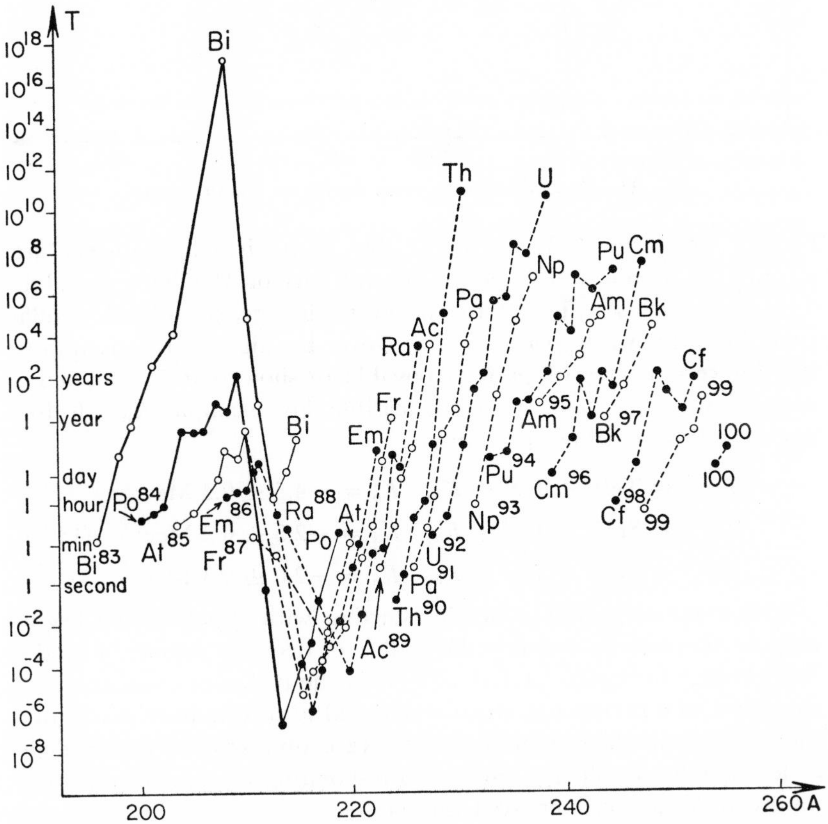

FIG. 21.—Dependence of the α-decay half-life on atomic weight.

the atomic weight for the heavy α-emitters is shown in Figures 21 and 22.

It is possible that at the beginning of the α-decay region there are isotopes for which the energy (and probability) of α-decay are so small that decay is practically unobserved. However, it is hardly certain that

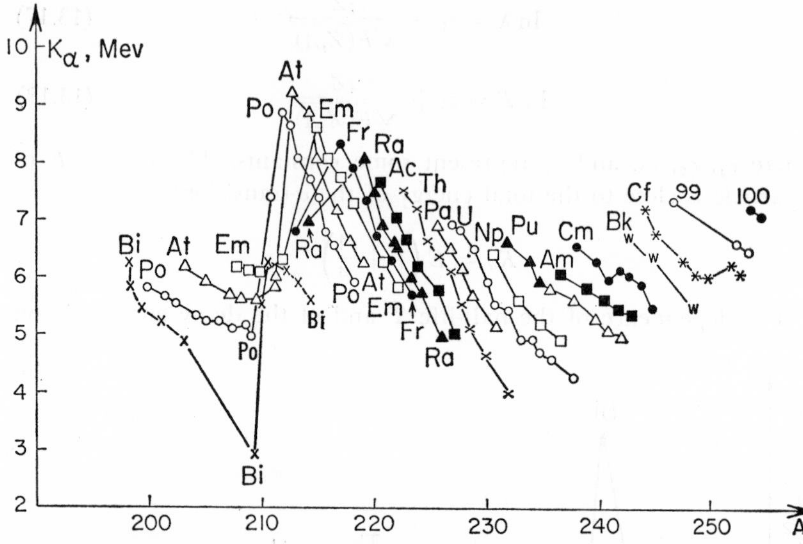

FIG. 22.—Dependence of α-decay energy on atomic weight.

Fermi's viewpoint [214] is correct that such virtual α-emitters are already the atomic nuclei of the central part of Mendeleyev's table. The precise mass values of the heavy nuclei are, until now, insufficiently well known to permit a consecutive tracing of this assumption. But for certain transitions it is possible to show that K_α assumes a negative value, i.e., α-decay is not feasible. For example, $K_\alpha < 0$ during the following transmutations:

$$\left.\begin{aligned} Xe^{132} &= Te^{128} + He^4 + K_\alpha, & K_\alpha &= -4.5 \pm 0.2 \text{ Mev;} \\ Te^{128} &= Sn^{124} + He^4 + K_\alpha, & K_\alpha &= -2.3 \pm 0.2 \text{ Mev;} \\ Cd^{110} &= Pd^{106} + He^4 + K_\alpha, & K_\alpha &= -2.0 \pm 0.3 \text{ Mev.} \end{aligned}\right\} \quad (13.19)$$

With increasing atomic weight, starting with $A = 208$ (the beginning of the α-decay region), the half-lives decrease rapidly, i.e., the decay energy increases. At $A = 215$–17, in the region of the short-lived α-emitters, the energy has already achieved a maximum. Upon a further increase in the atomic weight, there is observed, on the average, a decrease in the energy and a correspondingly gradual transition toward more stable, long-lived isotopes.

The existence of the long-lived isotopes which occupy the ascending segment of the curve (13.18) is a fact of exceptional significance. It is here that the natural radioelements are situated—the isotopes of uranium (UI and AcU) and thorium. A large family of the short-lived α-emitters is produced during the decay of only these three isotopes, and it does not have an independent existence. A relatively accidental fact of the presence in this region of α-emitters, the half-life of which is comparable with the duration of the earth's history, has vastly important consequences. All the energetics of the subcrustal processes—the formation of the earth's crust, of mountains, of mineral deposits, and of the topography of the earth's surface—are all connected with the liberation of the energy of these isotopes. In human society, the discovery and study of the atomic nucleus were also made by using the natural radioactivity of the heavy elements.

In the study of the stability of any system we usually find that, as we cross the stability limits and move away from them, the instability of the system increases. A different situation is found in the α-decay region. The boundary of the stable nuclei is almost directly adjoined by the maximum instability region (see Fig. 21). The main regularities of the α-decay region are satisfactorily explained even by the elementary theory stated by us.[4]

During natural transmutations the atomic weight does not change (β-decay) or else changes by four units. Therefore, if the atomic weight of the parent is a multiple of 4, for example, then the atomic weights of all products are also described by the expression $A = 4n$, where n is an integer. Obviously, four separate radioactive series are possible. The atomic weight of their members has the following forms:

$$\left.\begin{aligned} A &= 4n, && \text{the thorium series;} \\ A &= 4n+1, && \text{the neptunium series;} \\ A &= 4n+2, && \text{the uranium series;} \\ A &= 4n+3, && \text{the actinium series.} \end{aligned}\right\} \qquad (13.20)$$

Among the odd series, only the actinium series $(4n + 3)$, derived from the light uranium isotope actinouranium, exists in nature. The neptunium series is missing because the half-life of its products is much too short. The diagrams of the existing radioactive series were shown in Figures 4–6 (p. 77–78).

At the present time there is a large amount of data on α-emitters produced by artificial means. Among these emitters the following have been studied: (1) isotopes of transuranium elements, (2) members of

[4] It should be noted that in foreign literature, particularly in the books by Bethe and Bacher or in the later books by Bethe and Fermi, where the properties of atomic nuclei are discussed in detail, no attempt is made to explain the important effect of the existence of the region of the maximum α-decay energy. [Author's footnote.]

the neptunium decay series, (3) light isotopes of the elements—the components of even isobars of high charge. This permits complete investigation of the region of α-emitters up to the element with the charge $Z = 100$. The first isotopes of the elements with $Z = 101$ (named "mendeleevite" in honor of the author of the periodic table of elements) and $Z = 102$ have already been obtained.

The data on α-emitters in the α-decay region are given in Table VI of the Appendix (p. 286), according to a summary in [50] and [236]. Excluded from the table are the β-unstable isotopes for which α-decay has not been discovered. Included, however, are the isotopes which, together with α-decay, are capable of K-capture (the light isotopes) or β-decay (the heavy isotopes of a given element). For these isotopes the half-life is an effective quantity equal, in a general form, to

$$T_{\alpha} = T\left(\frac{K + \beta}{\alpha} + 1\right), \tag{13.21}$$

where K/α and β/α are the ratios of the K-capture and β-decay probability to the α-decay probability and T_{α} is the α-decay half-life which would be possessed by an isotope if the K- and β-processes were absent. The isotopes for which β-decay or electron capture are not observed, but are assumed from energy considerations, are denoted by the symbols β (?) or K (?) in column 4, Table VI (p. 286).

α-Decay of Isotopes with Closed Neutron Shells

In equation (13.6) we represented the α-decay energy as a function of atomic weight only. Regarding the dependence of this quantity on charge, it is possible to make certain qualitative remarks. The increase in the α-decay energy up to the maximum is connected with an increase in the nuclear charge, whereas the bend in the curve is caused by a decrease in the relative magnitude of the charge, that is, by an increase in the number of neutrons. Thus, for the isotopes of one element, the α-decay energy should decrease with increasing atomic weight, and, on going to the next element, it should increase with increasing charge. In reality, the curve $K_{\alpha} = f(A, Z)$ and the curve $T = f(A, Z)$ have exactly such a "sawlike" appearance.

In Figures 21 and 22 is shown the experimental material which includes the data on the natural α-emitters as well as on the artificially obtained isotopes of the α-decay region. An abrupt disturbance of the comparatively smooth course of the curves for the individual elements is shown only by the isotopes of the 126-neutron shell region. As we have pointed out, the heaviest isotopes in the region of the closed neutron shells possess an excess of protons, large Coulomb energy, and a substantially smaller binding energy than the lightest, proton-deficient isotopes. This stimulates the probability of α-decay of the heavy isotopes in the closed shell region.

In the 50-neutron shell region, α-emitters do not arise, inasmuch as this region is too close to the binding-energy maximum. However, in the region of the 82-neutron shell there are several α-emitting isotopes.

Among the even isotopes of samarium, which occupy the atomic-weight interval $A = 144$–54, there is a dip, the absence of an isotope with $A = 146$ [237]. Such a discontinuity in the even isotopes series is found in the table of elements at this point only. Dunlavey and Seaborg [238] obtained this isotope artificially. It proved to be an α-emitter with the energy of particles equal to 2.55 Mev, which corresponds to a half-life of only 1.5×10^7 years.[5]

The isotope Sm^{147} is also capable of α-emission, but its half-life is exceedingly long, $T = 1.4 \times 10^{11}$ years. Since the α-decay capacity increases with decreasing atomic weight, it should be expected that the lightest isotope of samarium, Sm^{144}, would also be radioactive. However, this is prevented because the nucleus produced during the decay of this isotope is unstable. The decay of Nd^{140} proceeds according to the scheme

$$Nd^{140} \xrightarrow[\text{3.3 days}]{K} Pr^{140} \xrightarrow[\text{3.3 minutes}]{K,\beta^+} Ce^{140}.$$

The β^+-decay energy of praseodymium is relatively high (2.23 Mev) —in fact, even higher than the α-decay energy of Sm^{147} (2.18 Mev). Thus the energy of transition of Sm^{144} into the stable condition of Ce^{140} is distributed among the three transitions. And if this isotope is α-active, then the energy and probability of its decay should be small.

Sm^{144} and Mo^{92} are the only isotopes among the heavy elements for which the resulting nucleus turns out to be K- and β^+-unstable in the case of an α-particle extraction. This is connected with the decreased number of neutrons $A - Z$ for a given Z for these isotopes, the heaviest among the atomic nuclei with closed 50- and 82-neutron shells.

The decay product of Sm^{146}—the neodymium isotope Nd^{142}—also has a closed neutron shell. The isotope Nd^{142} is the lightest and, at the same time, the most abundant of the neodymium isotopes. A combination of these properties among the elements heavier than zinc is found, in addition, only in the isotope Zr^{90}, also with a closed neutron shell. It is difficult to judge to what extent the anomalously high abundance of Nd^{142} is caused by enrichment at the expense of the extinct Sm^{146} and to what extent by the unusual stability of this isotope. In any event, there are no obvious indications that Sm^{146} once existed in the earth's crust.

Among the neodymium isotopes there also is an α-emitter, Nd^{144},

[5] The half-life actually reported by these authors is approximately 5×10^7 years.

which decays into Ce^{140}, the isotope in the center of the region of atomic nuclei with a closed 82-neutron shell.

For the rare-earth elements heavier than samarium, a number of isotopes with a decreased number of neutrons have been prepared artificially. Such isotopes acquire the capacity for both α-decay and K-capture. In Table 30 are shown the data on these isotopes.

TABLE 30

RADIOACTIVE ISOTOPES OF RARE-EARTH ELEMENTS AND OF METALS AT END OF PERIODIC TABLE

Z	Isotopes	K/α	Energy of Particles (Mev)	T_α	Intervals of Stable Isotopes
60....	Nd^{144}	0	1.9	$\sim 5 \times 10^{15}$ years	142–43, 145, 150
62....	Sm^{146}	0	2.55	5×10^{7} years	144, 148–54
62....	Sm^{147}	0	2.18	1.35×10^{11} years	...
63....	Eu^{147}	10^5	2.88	6×10^{3} years	151, 153
64....	Gd^{148}	0	3.16	140 years	152–60
64....	Gd^{149}	10^5	3.0	4×10^{3} years	...
64....	Gd^{150}	0	2.7	(Large)	...
65....	Tb^{149}	0	3.95	4.1 hours	159
65....	Tb^{151}	0	3.44	19 hours	...
66....	$Dy^{<153}$	0	4.21; 4.06	7 minutes, 19 minutes	156–64
66....	Dy^{152}	0	3.61	2.3 hours	...
66....	Dy^{153}	0	3.48	5 hours	...
66....	Dy^{154}	0	3.55	13 hours	...
67....	Ho	0	4.2	4 minutes	165
79....	Au^{183-87}	10^4	5.07	1 month	197
80....	$Hg^{<195}$	0	5.60	0.7 minutes	196–204

The effective α-decay half-life for the isotopes which are also capable of K-capture is expressed by the relationship

$$T_\alpha = T\left(\frac{K}{\alpha} + 1\right), \tag{13.22}$$

where K/α is the ratio between the K-capture and α-decay probabilities.

A comparison of the isobars Sm^{147}–Eu^{147} and Gd^{149}–Tb^{149} shows that the half-life decreases by millions of times with increasing charge.

The α-decay of elements heavier than holmium is unknown down to gold and mercury, which lie near the region of the heavy α-emitters. Among the artificially obtained light isotopes of these elements, α-emitters have also been found (see Table 30). Obvious regularity is observed. The lightest isotopes of the element are α-active or capable of K-capture; the heavier ones are stable; and the heaviest are β-active.

The usual increase in the α-decay half-life with increasing atomic weight of isotopes—that is, with a decreasing relative number of protons—is abruptly violated in the region of the 126-neutron shell. The course of the curve $T = f(A)$ or $E = f(A)$ suffers a break in this region for a large number of elements: bismuth, polonium, astatine, emanation, francium, and radium ($Z = 83$–88).

The behavior of bismuth is particularly characteristic. For the heaviest β-unstable isotopes of this element there is observed a decrease in the effective half-lives T_α, from 34 days in Bi^{214} (RaC) to 16 minutes in Bi^{211} (AcC). However, the next isotope, Bi^{210} (RaE), already has an effective α-decay half-life of about 3×10^4 years, and Bi^{209} a half-life as long as 2×10^{11} years.[6] This great stability is also favored by the fact that α-transition of Bi^{209} to Tl^{205} is connected with a four-unit change in the mechanical momentum and is therefore forbidden. From $A = 203$ to $A = 198$ there are located K-unstable isotopes of bismuth whose α-decay half-lives again decrease with decreasing atomic weight, as, generally speaking, the case should be.

The isotopes of the 126-neutron shell region with an anomalously low α-decay energy are also observed for polonium, astatine, emanation, francium, and radium.[7] These are K-unstable isotopes, that is, light, neutron-deficient isotopes. For the heavier elements (francium and radium), these isotopes are separated from the main group of isotopes by a large gap. The stability of the closed shell is not limited to one isotope of the element but is also observed for the neighboring isotopes. Thus for polonium a reverse trend—an increase in the decay energy with increasing atomic weight of the isotope—is traced in the interval $A = 207$–12 and $A - Z = 123$–28.

It is interesting to note that for all elements (except bismuth) the most α-stable isotope of the closed shell region turns out to be the isotope with the neutron number $A - Z = 125$ (in polonium $A - Z = 123$) and not the isotope with $A - Z = 126$). The causes of this phenomenon, which is observed for a number of elements, are unknown.

For lead, the element with $Z = 82$, i.e., with a closed proton shell, α-emitters are not known. Lead is the last element of Mendeleyev's table whose isotopes are stable against α-decay. The exceptional stability of lead isotopes causes a rapid transition into the region of the short-lived isotopes. Perhaps nowhere is the effect of the closed shells manifested with such clarity as in the α-emitters at the end of the periodic table of elements.

β-Instability of Isotopes in the α-Decay Region

The isotopes of the α-decay region are divided into β-stable and β-unstable. The former are subject to a series of general regularities of the β-stable isotopes.

[6] Bi^{209} has been reported by H. Faraggi and A. Berthelot (*Compt. rend.*, **232**: 2093–95, 1951) and by W. Riezler and W. Porschen (*Zeitschr. f. Naturforsch.*, **7a**: 634–35, 1952) to have a half-life of 2–3×10^{17} years.

[7] For a discussion of the unstable elements astatine and francium see a review article by E. K. Hyde (*Jour. Phys. Chem.*, **58**: 21–26, 1954).

The structure of isotopes of the even α-emitters can be represented in the following form. Just as for the stable elements, there is a basic central group which includes both even and odd isotopes. The extreme even isotopes, which form pairs of isobars of the first kind, are separated from this group. The intermediate odd states are capable of β-decay (the heavier isotopes with a neutron excess) or K-capture (the

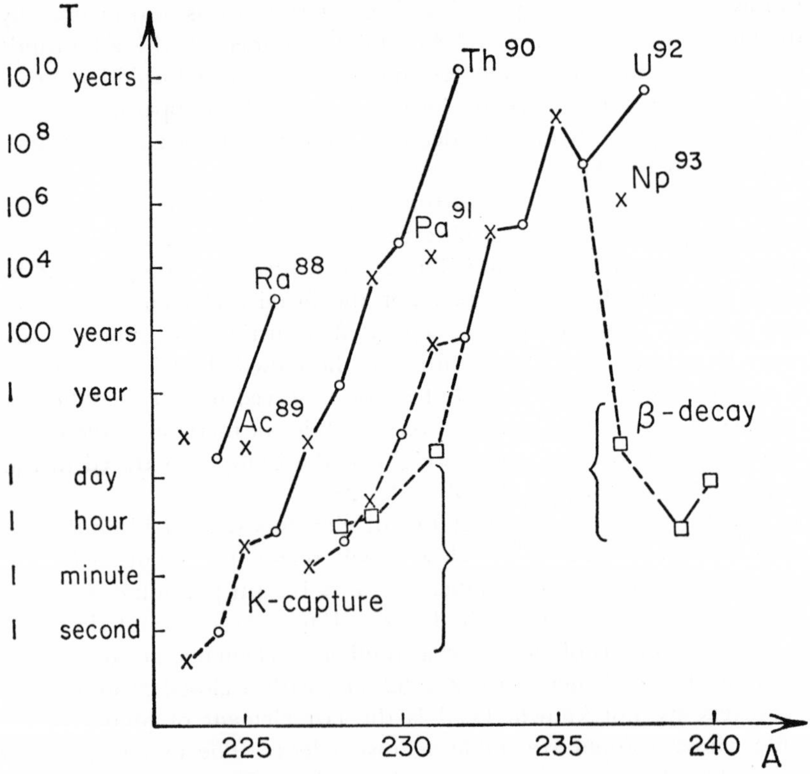

Fig. 23.—Dependence of half-life on atomic weight for elements in the radium-uranium region. o = even α-emitters; x = odd α-emitters; □ = isotopes capable of K-capture or β-decay. The solid lines connect β-stable isotopes, and the dashed lines β-unstable isotopes. The figure shows (1) increase in half-life with increasing atomic weight; (2) decrease in half-life with increasing charge; (3) greater stability of odd isotopes against α-decay; (4) short half-life of β-unstable isotopes.

lighter, neutron-deficient isotopes). The half-life of α-emitters of one element increases with increasing number of neutrons, i.e., with increasing atomic weight of the isotope. Farther beyond the extreme isotopes lie the isotopes that are β-unstable, regardless of the type of their atomic weight (see Fig. 23).

In the α-decay region there are pure α-emitters (similar to β-stable nuclei of smaller weight), but no pure β-emitters. However, if the atomic nucleus is unstable with respect to both β- and α-decay, then usually the former takes place.

The half-lives of β-emitters do not depend on the decay energy as much as do the half-lives of α-emitters, and, with the exception of the strongly forbidden transitions, they are seldom as long as the half-lives of the heavy α-emitters. But, in this case, if the β-decay half-life is long or, conversely, the α-decay half-life is short, "forks" are found—decay branchings of atomic nuclei with the emission of α-rays and β-particles (see Fig. 23).

Especially often is the branching observed (K-capture and α-decay) among the isotopes of low atomic weight for which the α-decay half-life is very short. The experimental detection of α-rays does not present difficulties, and the available radiation from the isotopes which decay by K-capture is limited to X-ray emission. Therefore, it is comparatively easy to study even weak α-radiation from atomic nuclei capable of electron capture.

The isotopes which disintegrate simultaneously by β-transmutation and electron capture are very seldom found in the α-decay region. Such an isotope, for example, is Pa^{230} ($T_{1/2} = 17$ days), which during electron capture yields a thorium isotope, Io (Th^{230}) (92 per cent of all disintegrations) and during β-decay a uranium isotope, U^{230} (8 per cent of all disintegrations). An estimate on the basis of equation (12.4) gives for this pair of even isobars $\delta = \frac{1}{2}$, which means that the more stable component is ionium. This is confirmed by the decay energy scheme. The β-decay energy is 0.57 Mev, and the electron-capture energy is 1.28 Mev. The α-decay probability for Pa^{230} is small (3×10^{-3} per cent) and corresponds to an effective life, T_α, of 1,600 years.

For many isotopes of low atomic weight, capture of electrons and even β-radiation are generally undetectable, so that these isotopes are entered in Table VI of the Appendix (p. 286) as pure α-emitters. However, an investigation of the decay energy shows that it is possible in a number of cases to establish that β-decay or K-capture is energtically feasible—for example, β-decay of AcA and RaA (decay energy, 0.8 and 0.33 Mev) and also of An (decay energy, 0.26 Mev). For β-emitters with such an energy it is possible to expect a half-life of the order of days. This is 10^3–10^6 times longer than the α-decay half-lives of these emitters, so that β-decay escapes observation.

For the short-lived elements, often the longest-lived isotope is the β-unstable isotope for which the state of the given charge (the charge belonging to the given element) turns out to be energtically unfavorable. Thus the only own isotope of actinium, Ac^{225}, has a half-life of 10.0 days, but for the β-unstable Ac^{227} the half-life increases to 21 years (at the same time, $T_\alpha = 1{,}800$ years). It is interesting to note that the β-stable isotope with the atomic weight of 227 is the isotope of high charge, RdTh (Th^{227}), whose half-life is only 18.6 days. The β-stability of a given isotope by no means indicates its greater stability in general.

With increasing charge, on passing to the next element, the half-life drops abruptly and rises again with increasing atomic weight of isotopes (see Figs. 21 and 23). On going from an even to an odd element, the following is observed. For isotopes of an even element, the atomic weight of the heaviest and consequently of the most stable even isotope (the components of the pair of isobars of the first kind) is greater than the atomic weight of the odd isotope of the next element. Therefore, the atomic weight of the even elements in the α-decay region, which practically agrees with the atomic weight of the heaviest and the most stable isotope, turns out to be greater than the atomic weight of the next odd element. Among the stable elements of Mendeleyev's table, there are found only several cases where the order of the increase of atomic weights with increasing atomic number is violated. In the region of the α-unstable nuclei such departure becomes regular.

As a result of α-decay, the daughter nuclei acquire a relative excess of neutrons and a tendency toward β-decay (see Fig. 24). In reality,

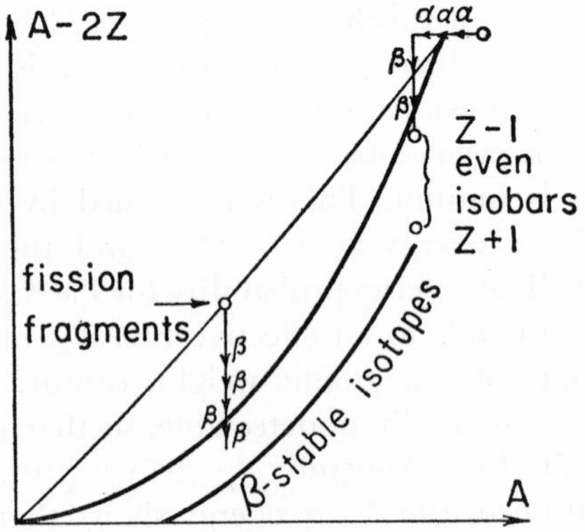

FIG. 24.—Instability of α-decay products and fission fragments against β-decay.

during α-decay the quantity $A - 2Z$ (the excess of neutrons over protons) does not change, since for α-particle $A - 2Z = 0$, but the atomic weight decreases by four units. Inasmuch as $A - 2Z$ should also decrease with decreasing atomic weight for the stable isotopes, the products of α-decay fall into the β-instability region. Out of the two possible states of even isobars, the α-decay series always passes through the isobar of lower charge—that is, through the state with a neutron excess—and completely by-passes the isobars of higher charge. The components of isobars of lower charge possess a smaller α-decay probability, so that the decay series deviates in the direction of the most stable states.

Dependence of α-Decay Probability on Type of Atomic Nuclei

The α-decay energy of isotopes of heavy elements decreases steadily with increasing atomic weight without showing noticeable dependence on the type of isotopes. However, with decay energy of the same order, the probability of α-particle emission from even nuclei is markedly greater than for odd nuclei. In other words, odd nuclei are more α-stable than are even nuclei.

Especially clearly is this observed in AcX (Ra^{223}), AcU (U^{235}), Pu^{241}, and Cm^{243}. In these cases, as expected, the energy of the odd α-emitter occupies an intermediate position between the energies of the neighboring even isotopes, but the half-life of the odd isotope is longer than that of both its neighbors. For AcU^{235} and Cm^{243} the half-life is tens of times longer than even for a heavier even isotope.

The α-decay probability is given by the expression

$$\ln \lambda = \ln C - \frac{4\pi Z e^2}{\hbar v} + \frac{8e\sqrt{m_\alpha R Z}}{\hbar}, \tag{13.23}$$

in which Z and v or the α-decay energy are determined directly. Among the other parameters, the probability C of α-particle emission and of its collision with the barrier remains unknown. Also somewhat undefined is the meaning of R. Sometimes the expression of type (13.23) is used, assuming a constant C. In that case, the only quantity not measured experimentally is R, so that the possible variations in C for different α-emitters lead to a variable value of R. It is more rational to express the nuclear radius in the form of (11.2), which has been confirmed by experiment,

$$R = r_0 A^{1/3},$$

and, with such an assumption, to investigate the variations in C. A survey of the data shows that for even nuclei this quantity, on the average, is ten times larger than for odd nuclei, which means that the probability of emission of α-particles from a decaying odd nucleus is smaller than the corresponding probability for an even nucleus [226].

Often in physical and geochemical literature there is found a general indication of greater stability of even than of odd isotopes. This is based on the fact that the longest-lived α-emitters are the even isotopes. We shall disregard the theory that the term "stability in general" is not applicable to atomic nuclei. But even in the consideration of the stability of α-emitters this conclusion is based on misunderstanding. All other conditions being equal, odd nuclei are more stable against α-decay than are even nuclei.

However, the conditions of the distribution of even and odd isotopes are not the same. The number of isotopes in even elements, on the average, is about four times greater than the number of isotopes in odd elements; they occupy a large atomic-weight interval up to the highest values of A, where lie the most stable isotopes, which form pairs of isobars of the first kind. To the special stability of the latter isotopes there corresponds an extremely small stability of the second component of the pair, the isobar of a higher charge; but these isobars in the chains of natural decay are generally not formed. The odd isotopes of an even element possess a smaller weight than the heavy even isotopes of the same element; and the odd isotopes of the next element have, in addition, a higher charge. Therefore, their half-lives turn out to be shorter than those of some even isotopes.

TABLE 31

EVEN ISOBARS IN REGION OF α-EMITTERS

A	$Z-1$	Element	T_{Z-1}	$Z+1$	Element	T_{Z+1}	T_{Z-1}/T_{Z+1}
208....	82	Pb	∞	84	Po	2.93 years	∞
216....	84	Po(RaA)	0.158 second	86	Em	10^{-4} second	1.6×10^3
220....	86	Em(Tn)	54.5 seconds	88	Ra	3×10^{-2} second	1.8×10^3
222....	86	Em(Rn)	3.825 days	88	Ra	38 seconds	8.7×10^3
226....	88	Ra	1,622 years	90	Th	30.9 minutes	2.8×10^7
230....	90	Th(Io)	8.0×10^4 years	92	U	20.8 days	1.4×10^6
232....	90	Th	1.39×10^{10} years	92	U	70 years	2.0×10^8
236....	92	U	2.39×10^7 years	94	Pu	2.7 years	8.9×10^6
238....	92	U(UI)	4.49×10^9 years	94	Pu	89.6 years	5.0×10^7
240....	94	Pu	6.58×10^3 years	96	Cm	26.8 days	9.0×10^4
242....	94	Pu	5×10^5 years	96	Cm	162.5 days	1.1×10^6
244....	96	Cm	19 years	98	Cf	45 minutes	2.2×10^5
246....	96	Cm	6,600 years	98	Cf	35.7 hours	1.6×10^6
248....	96	Cm	4.7×10^5 years	98	Cf	350 days	4.9×10^5
252....	98	Cf	2.2 years	100	Fm	22.7 hours	850
254....	100	Fm	3.24 hours	102		3 seconds	3.6×10^3

In Table 31 are given the half-lives of even isobars in the region of α-emitters. The β-unstable isobars are not included. The half-life of the component of lower charge is usually 10^5–10^7 times longer than the half-life of the component of the same pair with higher charge. In the region of α-emitters, several odd isotopes are known which form odd isobar pairs. For some of these isotopes, the decay schemes permit the establishment of the energetic possibilities of K-capture or β-decay. If these processes are not observed, then it is apparently because of the probability of large α-decay in the short-lived isotopes. Transitions have not been found between the following pairs of odd isotopes: At^{215}–Em^{215} and Am^{243}–Cm^{243}. The list of odd isotopes in the α-decay region is given in Table 32.

It seems natural that the isobar with a shorter half-life, as "less stable," should possess lower binding energy; but this is not necessary. For example, the energy of U^{238} is greater than that of Pu^{238}, which makes energetically possible the double β-decay of uranium with a transition energy of about 1.2 Mev. However, the half-life of Pu^{238} is

TABLE 32

ODD β-STABLE ISOTOPES IN α-DECAY REGION

A	Z	Element, Isotope Symbol	α-Decay Energy (Mev)	α-Half-Life
211	84	Po(AcC′)	7.58	0.52 second
213	84	Po	8.496	4.2×10^{-6} second
215	85	At	8.15	$\sim 10^{-4}$ second
	86	Em	8.8	$\sim 10^{-6}$ second
217	86	Em	7.89	$\sim 10^{-3}$ second
219	87	Fr	7.44	0.02 second
221	88	Ra	6.83	30 seconds
223	88	Ra(AcX)	5.855	11.2 days
225	89	Ac	5.90	10.0 days
227	90	Th(RdAc)	6.138	18.6 days
229	90	Th	5.11	7,340 years
231	91	Pa	5.131	3.43×10^{4} years
233	92	U	4.91	1.62×10^{5} years
235	92	U(AcU)	4.66	7.13×10^{8} years
237	93	Np	4.97	2.20×10^{6} years
239	94	Pu	5.238	24,360 years
241	95	Am	5.639	470 years
243	95	Am	5.430	7,600 years
	96	Cm	6.15	35 years
245	96	Cm	5.7	2×10^{4} years
247	96	Cm	(5.3)	$>4 \times 10^{7}$ years
	97	Bk	(5.67)	10^{4} years
249	98	Cf	6.19	360 years
251	98	Cf	(6.17)	800 years
253	99	E	6.63	20 days
255	100	Fm	7.03	21.5 hours

almost ten million times shorter than that of U^{238}. This is caused by the fact that the transition into the next stable state (UII) for Pu^{238} is brought about through one α-decay act with the energy of 5.586 Mev, whereas for U^{238} the transition takes place according to the scheme,

$$U^{238} \xrightarrow[4.25\text{ Mev}]{\alpha} UX_1 \xrightarrow[0.2\text{ Mev}]{\beta} UX_2 \xrightarrow[2.32\text{ Mev}]{\beta} \text{UII},$$

i.e., the transition energy distributes itself among three particles, with the energy share of one α-particle being smaller than the decay energy of Pu^{238}.

The isotopes U^{238} and Th^{232} are the only even α-emitters of the ascending branch of the curve for which α-decay is followed by β-decay or, more precisely, by two successive β-decays (this is necessary for the even isotopes, since, as a result of the first β-transmutation, an unstable odd-odd isotope is formed). The partition of the transition energy among several decay events contributes to the stability of these isotopes. For odd heavy isotopes, the β-unstable products of α-decay occur for AcU^{235} and Np^{237}. Actually, these are the most stable isotopes of the given region (half-lives of 7.13×10^8 and 2.2×10^6 years, respectively). But, just the same, the existence of successive β-transmutations should not be considered a principal factor in determining the α-stability of the isotope. The great stability of actinouranium is, first of all, explained by the fact that this isotope is the heavier one of the two odd isotopes of the element.

The elementary α-decay theory leads to a conclusion concerning the existence of the region of the short-lived α-emitters. With increasing atomic weight, the α-decay energy should decrease, and the half-life should increase. However, following the longest-lived α-emitters—the isotopes of thorium and uranium—there actually lie radioelements with shorter half-lives. To some extent, this is an apparent effect. If during the process of α-decay neutron-enriched products arise, i.e., the longest-lived isotopes of the given element, then in artificial transmutations of atomic nuclei there are formed, as a rule, products poor in neutrons, the short-lived isotopes of the given element. In reality, the preparation of new α-emitters is realized by way of α-particle capture with the emission of neutrons, for example,

$$Pu^{239} + \alpha = Cm^{238} + 5n,$$

$$Pu^{239} + \alpha = Cm^{240} + 3n,$$

$$Pu^{239} + \alpha = Cm^{241} + 2n,$$

$$Pu^{239} + \alpha = Cm^{242} + n.$$

Of the even atomic nuclei of this region, there were artificially produced first the light, less stable isotopes of transuranium elements, particularly the components of the isobar pairs of high charge (Pu^{236}, Pu^{238}, Cm^{240}, and others). The heaviest even isobars of transuranium elements have not as yet been obtained.

However, if one follows the course of the variation of half-lives with increasing atomic weight for odd isotopes in the region $Z = 84$–96 (and these isotopes have been studied in this region in a complete detail), he will also observe a decrease in the half-lives of the transuranium isotopes (see Table 32 and Fig. 25). The increased half-life of the first odd emitter, AcC′, is connected with the fact that it lies close to the 126-neutron shell region. Farther on, there is a regular increase in the half-life with increasing atomic weight, an increase which is especially large for the elements containing two odd isotopes. A too rapidly increasing charge—i.e., a small number of odd isotopes in the element —retards the half-life increase and even reverses the direction of the trend. The number of odd isotopes in the transuranium region (Np–Fm) is small (ten isotopes for eight elements). And it is probable that, because of this, the half-life here cannot attain the magnitude possessed

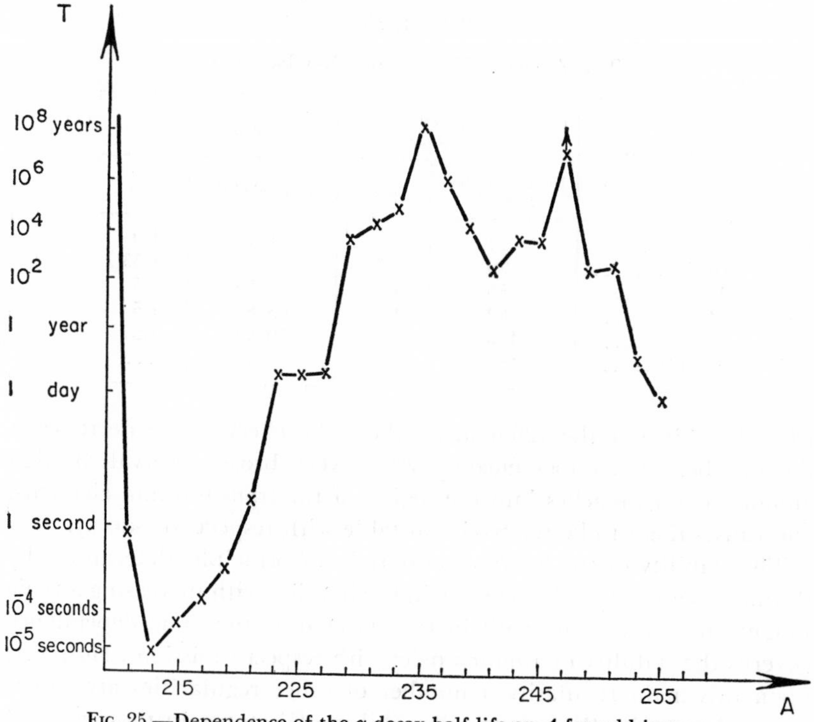

FIG. 25.—Dependence of the α-decay half-life on A for odd isotopes.

by the heavy odd isotopes of thorium or uranium—the elements with a large number of isotopes.

The average number of odd isotopes per element, which, according to equation (11.15), is

$$I_{\text{odd}} = \frac{1}{2}\frac{dA}{dZ} = 1 + \frac{5}{6}\frac{A - 2Z}{Z},$$

generally increases with increasing atomic weight but diminishes in the vicinity of the closed neutron shells.

Table 33 and Figure 13 (see p. 131) give an average value of I_{odd} for the individual sectors of elements. A notable decrease in the number of odd isotopes is observed, relative to the theoretical value, in the shell regions with 20, 50, 82, and 126 neutrons. A closed shell adds neutrons reluctantly; and the number of neutrons varies considerably more slowly than would be expected from statistical theory. Therefore, the number of odd isotopes in the region of closed shells is

$$I_{\text{odd}} = \frac{1}{2}\frac{dA}{dZ} = \frac{1}{2}\frac{d(A - Z)}{dZ} + \frac{1}{2} \approx \frac{1}{2},$$

which is too low. Here lie the elements which do not have odd isotopes: argon ($A - Z = 20$), technetium ($A - Z = 50$), cerium and promethium

TABLE 33

THE AVERAGE NUMBER OF ODD ISOTOPES

INTERVAL OF Z	REGIONS OF CLOSED NEUTRON SHELLS		INTERMEDIATE REGIONS	
	No. of Neutrons in Shell	I_{odd}	Interval of Z	I_{odd}
...	...	...	1–15	1.0
16–20........	20	1.2	21–35	1.33
36–43........	50	1.0	44–53	1.5
54–62........	82	1.22	63–81	1.5
82–89........	126	1.25	90–92	1.57
93–100.......	156	1.25	...	...

($A - Z = 82$). For the 126-neutron shell, the effect of the decrease in the number of isotopes encompasses a very broad interval of high atomic weights, reaches into the region of the transuranium elements, and causes them to be relatively unstable with respect to α-decay.

The stability of the heavy α-emitters is, in principle, determined by the main regularity—the increase in the half-life with increasing atomic weight and its decrease with increasing charge (the same dependence governs the stability of atomic nuclei with respect to fission). However, upon this main regularity a number of other regularities are superimposed, namely, (1) an unusual stability of isotopes in the region of the 126-neutron shell; (2) a large number of isotopes in even elements, causing a particular stability of the heaviest among these isotopes, which enter into pairs of isobars of the first kind as the components of lower charge (U^{238}, Th^{232}); (3) great stability of odd isotopes of high atomic weight in the elements which have two odd isotopes (AcU^{235}); (4) greater stability of odd isotopes in comparison with the neighboring even isotopes; (5) stability of those α-emitters whose decay products are β-active; and (6) decrease in the average number of isotopes per element in the α-decay region. This probably contributes to the relatively low stability of the transuranium elements.

A combination of the indicated conditions determines the fact that in nature there exists only three isotopes as independent heavy α-emitters: Th^{232} and the isotopes of uranium, UI^{238} and AcU^{235}. All remaining elements possess decay periods that are much shorter than the time of the existence of the earth's crust, and they could not have been preserved as independent isotopes in the course of its history. Some of them are formed in the process of decay of the long-lived radioelements, and others can be obtained only artificially.

In view of the exponential nature of the law of radioactive decay (rapid decrease with time), the unstable elements are either practically preserved during the time t_e of the existence of the earth (if the half-life $T_{1/2} > t_e$) or are completely destroyed (if $T_{1/2} < t_e$). Only in rare cases (when $T_{1/2} \approx t_e$) is there observed a considerable decrease in the radioactive element, but complete destruction does not occur. Such dying radioelements are AcU^{235} and K^{40}.

14. STABILITY OF ATOMIC NUCLEI AGAINST FISSION

We have already seen in the preceding section that the increase in the number of protons and the strengthening of the Coulomb field of the heavy atomic nuclei favor α-decay. These conditions also favor another nuclear process—the fission of atomic nuclei into two fragments of comparable size.

The energy of the heavy atomic nuclei is independent of their type, and, as was shown in Section 11, the very heavy nuclei are indifferent toward the conservation of spherical symmetry. This leads to important consequences. The deviation of the atomic nucleus from spherical shape causes the possibility of fission of atomic nuclei, if

$$\frac{E_{\text{Coul}}}{E_{\text{surf}}} > 2 \quad \text{or} \quad \frac{Z^2}{A} > 40. \tag{14.1}$$

The criterion of stability against fission was first obtained by Frenkel' [229] and then by other authors immediately following the experimental discovery of fission. Criterion (14.1) is very simple. At the basis of the explanation of the fission mechanism lies the macroscopic concept of instability of a spherical drop carrying too high a charge. Now it seems astonishing how such a simple and readily explainable (even from the viewpoints of classical physics) effect has escaped the detection by theoreticians for many years after the development of α- and β-decay theories, until the chemists Otto Hahn and Strassmann, following a laborious and indirect path, discovered the fission of uranium under the action of neutrons.

Classical Condition of Fission

The classical condition for a complete division of the atomic nucleus into two equal fragments was also given by Frenkel' [229]. We shall give this derivation. Let the nucleus with atomic weight A and charge Z break up into two equal fragments with atomic weights $A_1 = A_2 = A/2$ and charges $Z_1 = Z_2 = Z/2$. In this process, the Coulomb, $E_{\text{Coul}} = \frac{3}{5} Z^2e^2/A^{1/3}r_0$, and the surface energy $E_{\text{surf}} = sA^{2/3}$ of the nucleus undergo a change. For the fragments, obviously,

$$E_{\text{Coul}}(1) = E_{\text{Coul}}(2) = \frac{3}{5}\frac{(Z/2)^2e^2}{(A/2)^{1/3}r_0} = \frac{2^{1/3}}{4}E_{\text{Coul}},$$

$$E_{\text{surf}}(1) = E_{\text{surf}}(2) = s(A/2)^{2/3} = 2^{-2/3}E_{\text{surf}}.$$

In addition to this, the energy of the electrostatic repulsion at the moment of the division is

$$U = \frac{Z_1 Z_2 e^2}{R_1 + R_2} = \frac{2^{1/3} Z^2 e^2}{8A^{1/3} r_0} = \frac{5 \cdot 2^{1/3}}{24} E_{\text{Coul}}.$$

Fission of the nucleus is feasible if energy is liberated in the process, that is, if the energy difference between the initial and the final state is greater than zero:

$$E_{\text{Coul}} + E_{\text{surf}} - [E_{\text{Coul}}(1) + E_{\text{Coul}}(2) + E_{\text{surf}}(1) + E_{\text{surf}}(2) + U] > 0$$

or

$$\Delta_0 = E_{\text{surf}}(1 - 2^{1/3}) + E_{\text{Coul}}\left(1 - \frac{17}{24} 2^{1/3}\right)$$

$$\approx 0.11 E_{\text{Coul}} - 0.26 E_{\text{surf}} > 0. \tag{14.2}$$

For a limiting case on the threshold of stability,

$$\frac{E_{\text{Coul}}}{E_{\text{surf}}} = \frac{2^{1/3} - 1}{1 - \frac{17}{24} 2^{1/3}} \approx 2.4, \tag{14.3}$$

which is very close to expressions (14.1). The difference is probably explained by the fact that, in the derivation of equation (14.3), too crude a concept of the classic division of the nucleus into two touching fragments of spherical shape has been used.

At the instant of the fission of fragments, their kinetic energy can equal zero, so that the total energy is equal to the energy of the electrostatic repulsion U. During the separation of fragments the potential energy of interaction between them decreases rapidly, i.e., it is converted into kinetic energy. In the case of the fission of uranium, the electrostatic energy of repulsion $U \approx 200$ Mev. In reality, the energy of fragments is somewhat smaller (165 Mev). The possible causes of this discrepancy will be examined later.

The energy of fission has a maximum value when the mass and charge of the fragments are equal. Suppose that the fragments are not equal, but the ratio A/Z for them is the same. Let us also assume that $A_1 = A/2(1 + \zeta)$, $A_2 = A/2(1 - \zeta)$. It is not difficult to show that, in this case,

$$\Delta - \Delta_0 = \frac{4}{45} U \zeta^2 \left(1 + \frac{5}{72} \zeta^2\right). \tag{14.4}$$

In the fission of the uranium nuclei, $\zeta = 0.2$ and $\Delta_\zeta - \Delta_0 \approx 0.7$ Mev, so that the dependence of the inequality of fragments on the energy is not too great.

The fission of heavy nuclei is energetically feasible because the Coulomb energy of the fragments, even if the energy of their interaction is taken into account, is considerably smaller than the Coulomb energy of the initial nucleus. The surface energy increases during the fission, but the decrease in the Coulomb energy compensates for this increase, and the total energy of the final system turns out to be smaller than the energy of the initial system. It is readily shown that fission into three fragments is energetically much less favorable than fission into two fragments. The reason for this lies in the increase in the potential energy of fragments at the instant of fission, which in this case consists of three members of the type $Z_1Z_2/R_1 + R_2$ (Z_1, Z_2 and R_1, R_2 are, respectively, the charges and the radii of the fragments) whose sum is approximately equal to 400 Mev.

Let us turn to the case when the total energy of fragments is smaller than the energy of their Coulomb repulsion U at the instant of fission. Here the fragments have to pass through a mutual potential barrier, so that the probability of fission in this quantum case should be much smaller than in classical fission. In the limiting case, the energy of fragments is equal to zero (the passage of particles in the lower part of the mutual potential barrier) and the stability criterion,

$$E_{\text{Coul}} + E_{\text{surf}} - [E_{\text{Coul}}(1) + E_{\text{Coul}}(2) + E_{\text{surf}}(1) + E_{\text{surf}}(2)] \approx 0, \quad (14.5)$$

has a numerical expression,

$$E_{\text{Coul}}\left(1 - \frac{2^{1/3}}{2}\right) + E_{\text{surf}}(1 - 2^{1/3}) = 0, \quad (14.6)$$

from which

$$\frac{E_{\text{Coul}}}{E_{\text{surf}}} = \frac{2^{1/3} - 1}{1 - 2^{1/3}/2} \approx 0.8, \qquad \frac{Z^2}{A} = 16. \quad (14.7)$$

Condition (14.7) is fulfilled for all atomic nuclei heavier than strontium. In other words, the capability of spontaneous fission is possessed by all atomic nuclei, beginning with the intermediate atomic weights. Indeed, for many isotopes of this region examples can be found where the fission is energetically feasible,

$$E(A,Z) > E(A_1,Z_1) + E(A_2,Z_2).$$

The subscripts 1 and 2 denote the fragments; $A = A_1 + A_2$ and $Z = Z_1 + Z_2$. Examples of fission reactions are given in Table 34.

TABLE 34

POSSIBLE FISSION REACTIONS FOR ATOMIC NUCLEI HEAVIER THAN STRONTIUM

Original Nucleus	Z^2/A	Possible Reaction	Decay Energy Q (Mev)
Zr^{96}..........	16.7	${}_{40}Zr^{96} = 2\,{}_{20}Ca^{48} + Q$	4.3
Mo^{92}..........	19.2	${}_{42}Mo^{92} = {}_{20}Ca^{44} + {}_{22}Ti^{48} + Q$	0.8
Mo^{92}..........	19.2	${}_{42}Mo^{92} = {}_{20}Ca^{42} + {}_{22}Ti^{50} + Q$	1.2
Mo^{94}..........	18.8	${}_{42}Mo^{94} = {}_{20}Ca^{44} + {}_{22}Ti^{50} + Q$	4.6
Ru^{96}..........	20.2	${}_{44}Ru^{96} = 2\,{}_{20}Ti^{48} + Q$	10.2

The heavier atomic nuclei possess a still greater energy of spontaneous fission, but the probability of the process is everywhere extremely small. It can be easily shown that the transparency coefficient of the potential barrier in this case is

$$D = \exp\left(-\frac{\pi}{8}\frac{e^2}{\hbar}\sqrt{\frac{2M}{Q}}\,Z^2\right), \tag{14.8}$$

where M and Z are, respectively, the mass and charge of the initial nucleus and Q is the disintegration energy. In the decay of ruthenium the fission energy is greater than the α-decay energy of the shortest-lived α-emitters, but even in this example $\ln D \sim 800$, which means that the process is practically impossible. The probability that one ruthenium atom has disintegrated in the entire Galaxy during the earth's existence is $\sim 10^{-260}$. The accuracy of this estimate is low, but under any premises the probability remains negligible. Thus the nuclei of this region can be considered as practically stable. This serves as an example of the circumstance that is so common in the nuclear realm: the energetic feasibility of a nuclear transmutation does not necessarily determine the observable extent of the process.

As a very weak process, spontaneous fission of natural isotopes was discovered only in the heaviest nuclei—the isotopes of thorium and uranium. Before we turn to this effect, let us examine the main characteristics of induced fission, which has been studied in much greater detail. Historically, even until the present time, the former process—the fission of uranium with neutrons—is practically the most important case.

Neutron-induced Fission of Uranium

While the light isotope AcU^{235} breaks up when irradiated with slow neutrons, the fission of the main uranium isotope, U^{238}, takes place if the energy of the neutrons is not less than 0.35 Mev. For thorium, the energy threshold of the reaction is still greater—1.1 Mev.[8]

If during the period of the order of the lifetime of the excited nuclei (10^{-15} sec.) fission does not occur, the energy is emitted as γ-quanta. In the capture of slow neutrons by actinouranium, the probability of the latter process is sufficiently high ($\sim$15 per cent). Fission under the action of neutrons proceeds almost instantaneously in competition with such a rapid process as the emission of γ-rays. Consequently, during the fission of an excited nucleus the leakage through the potential barrier cannot take place because this would strongly reduce the fission probability. The absence of this quantum effect permits, within

[8] Fission of the lighter elements is possible upon irradiation with particles of higher energies. [Author's footnote.]

certain limits, the consideration of fission of the excited nuclei as a classical event.

The different behavior of uranium-I and actinouranium in the fission with slow neutrons is explained by Bohr in terms of the dependence of the process on the type of isotope. He starts with the concept that the binding energy of even nuclei is greater than that of odd nuclei. This reasoning was incorporated into many translated textbooks on nuclear physics. However, fission of atomic nuclei is feasible exactly for those isotopes which lie close to the stability limit (14.1) and for which the energy does not depend on isotope type. In fact, the mass-spectrometric data have shown that the binding energy of actinouranium is somewhat greater than the energy of uranium-I. The fission of AcU during slow-neutron capture is evidently explained by the fact that, for this lighter isotope, the ratio Z^2/A is larger than for UI.

During the fission of uranium, fragments are produced which differ in both mass and energy. The atomic weight of fragments varies from 72 to 160, i.e., fission takes place in approximately 45 different ways. The fragments produced in the process of fission turn out to be excited, and, while passing into the ground state, they emit neutrons. Their number can change during fission into fragments of different masses. On the average, the uranium nucleus which is fissioned with slow neutrons emits 2.5 neutrons. The expulsion of neutrons during fission represents a remarkable characteristic which distinguishes this process from other cases of the splitting of atomic nuclei. Namely, because of this, it is possible to realize a chain reaction of fission and to utilize in practice the fission energy—the so-called atomic energy.

Spontaneous Fission

Immediately after the discovery of fission of uranium upon interaction with neutrons, K. A. Petrzhak and G. N. Flerov discovered the spontaneous fission of uranium. The probability of this process is very small—one uranium fission in approximately two million decay acts. Nonetheless, the neutrons from the spontaneous fission of the heavy radioelements constitute one of the major components of the neutron flux of the earth's crust, which causes diverse artificial transmutations of atomic nuclei of the earth.

The instantaneous fission of uranium is accomplished by capturing a neutron which contributes an energy of the order of 10 Mev. Spontaneous fission, in the absence of excitation energy, takes place as a penetration of fragments through a mutual potential barrier of about 200 Mev. The particles pass through the barrier at a height lower by 10 Mev, i.e., in the uppermost part of the barrier. As a result of high

TABLE 35

SPONTANEOUS FISSION OF HEAVY ISOTOPES

Z	A	Z^2/A	Element, Isotope	Effective Half-Life of Spontaneous Fission T_f	α-Decay Half-Life $T\alpha$	$T_f/T\alpha$
90...	232	34.91	Th	$>10^{21}$ years	1.39×10^{10} years	$>7 \times 10^{10}$
	230	35.22	Io	$\geqslant 1.5 \times 10^{17}$ years	8.0×10^4 years	$\geqslant 1.9 \times 10^{12}$
91...	231	35.59	Pa	$\geqslant 10^{16}$ years	3.4×10^4 years	$\geqslant 3 \times 10^{11}$
92...	238	35.58	UI	8.0×10^{15} * years	4.5×10^9 years	1.8×10^6
	236	35.87	U	2×10^{16} years	2.4×10^7 years	8.3×10^8
	235	36.02	AcU	1.9×10^{17} years	7.1×10^8 years	2.7×10^8
	234	36.18	UII	2×10^{16} years	2.5×10^5 years	8×10^{10}
	233	36.33	U	$\geqslant 3 \times 10^{17}$ years	1.6×10^5 years	$\geqslant 2 \times 10^{12}$
	232	36.48	U	8×10^{13} years	7.4 years	1.1×10^{12}
93...	237	36.49	Np	$\geqslant 4 \times 10^{16}$ years	2.2×10^6 years	$\geqslant 1.8 \times 10^{10}$
94...	244	36.21	Pu	2.5×10^{10} years	7.6×10^7 years	330
	242	36.51	Pu	7.1×10^{10} years	3.8×10^5 years	1.8×10^5
	240	36.82	Pu	1.2×10^{11} years	6.6×10^3 years	1.8×10^7
	239	36.97	Pu	5.5×10^{15} years	2.4×10^4 years	1.3×10^{11}
	238	37.12	Pu	4.9×10^{10} years	90 years	5.4×10^8
	236	37.43	Pu	3.5×10^9 years	2.7 years	1.3×10^8
95...	241	37.45	Am	$\geqslant 1.4 \times 10^{13}$ years	458 years	$\geqslant 3 \times 10^{10}$
96...	250	36.86	Cm	2×10^4 years	...	<1
	248	37.16	Cm	4.6×10^6 years	4.7×10^5 years	10
	246	37.46	Cm	2.0×10^7 years	6600 years	3×10^3
	244	37.78	Cm	1.4×10^7 years	18 years	8×10^5
	242	38.18	Cm	7×10^6 years	180 days	1.4×10^7
	240	38.41	Cm	7.9×10^5 years	26.8 days	1×10^7
97...	249	37.79	Bk	6×10^8 years	314 days	7×10^8
98...	254	37.81	Cf	0.15 years	...	<1
	252	38.11	Cf	66 years	2.2 years	30
	250	38.42	Cf	1.5×10^4 years	10.9 years	1.4×10^3
	249	38.57	Cf	1.5×10^9 years	360 years	4×10^6
	248	38.73	Cf	$\geqslant 1.5 \times 10^4$ years	350 days	$\geqslant 1.5 \times 10^4$
	246	39.04	Cf	2×10^3 years	35 hours	5.1×10^5
99...	254	38.59	E	>2 years	480 days	>1.5
	253	38.74	E	7×10^5 years	20 days	1.3×10^7
100...	256	39.06	Fm	3–4 hours	?	0.04(?)
	255	39.22	Fm	>60 years	21.5 hours	$>2 \times 10^4$
	254	39.37	Fm	246 days	3.24 hours	2.1×10^4
	252	39.68	Fm	>8 years	22.7 hours	$>3 \times 10^3$

* E. K. Gerling and Yu. A. Shukoliukov (*Radiokhimiya*, 1: 212–22, 1959), and E. K. Gerling, Yu. A. Shukoliukov, and B. A. Makarochkin (*Radiokhimiya*, 1: 223–26, 1959) report a new value of $(5.8 \pm 0.5) \times 10^{15}$ years for the spontaneous fission half-life of U^{238}.

charges of the reacting particles, the barrier penetration probability, even at this high level, is very small.

Experimental data on spontaneous fission probability are given in Table 35 [239]. For convenience, the probability is expressed in terms of the effective value of the half-life, T_f. Such a half-life would be possessed by the given isotope if there were no natural α-decay, which is more probable for the nuclei of this region than is spontaneous fission, and therefore determines the real lifetime of the atomic nucleus.

In general, the probability of spontaneous fission, like that of α-decay, increases with increasing charge and decreasing atomic weight of the isotope (i.e., with increasing Z^2/A). The ratio T_f/T_α decreases, on the average, with increasing atomic weight. For uranium, one spontaneous fission act occurs in almost two million α-transmutations and for Cf^{252} in only 30 such transmutations. In the isotopes Cf^{254} and Fm^{256} no α-radiation has been detected. Apparently, the elements of the far transuranium region decay primarily by fission.

It is clearly seen that for odd isotopes the fission probability is, on the average, three to four orders of magnitude smaller than for the neighboring even isotopes, this being similar to greater stability of odd than of even isotopes with respect to α-decay. For the natural isotopes of uranium the ratio $T_f(\text{AcU})/T_f(\text{UI}) \approx 23$. Obviously, this does not contradict the fact that, of these two isotopes, only the odd one, AcU^{235}, is capable of being fissioned with slow neutrons. The energetic feasibility of fission is determined by the ratio Z^2/A, which happens to be greater for the lighter isotope, AcU^{235}. However, under the condition of the feasibility of fission, the probability of the spontaneous process depends on the fission mechanism—on the probability of the intranuclear separation of fragments as well as of their penetration through the mutual potential barrier. Apparently, the release of fragments, like the release of α-particle, in the interior of an odd nucleus is hindered more than for even atomic nuclei.

For the same type of isotope and for a close value of Z^2/A, the heavy isotope is always less stable with respect to fission than the light one (compare Pu^{242} and U^{232}, Cm^{240} and Cf^{250}, Cm^{242} and Cf^{252}, Cf^{246} and Fm^{256}). Some isotopes (the heaviest among those investigated for a given element—U^{238}, Cf^{254}, Fm^{256}, and, to a lesser degree, Pu^{242}) are distinguished by a large probability of spontaneous fission. For U^{238} this leads to important geochemical consequences (see Sec. 5, p. 45). According to Swiatecki [250], the decrease in the spontaneous fission half-life with increasing atomic weight for the heavy isotopes of californium is associated with the existence in that region of a closed neutron shell with $A - Z = 152$. Possibly, this is the "subshell" $6a$ (see Table 21, p. 123), which contains 154 particles. In the closed shell region with 126 neutrons the most stable isotopes of the heavy elements possess a smaller number of neutrons ($A - Z = 123$–25).

Asymmetry of Fragments

At low excitation energies an asymmetry effect is observed—fission into unequal fragments. Thus, in the slow-neutron fission of actino-uranium, out of 45 possible transmutation paths, the breakup into fragments with $A = 96$ and $A = 140$ occurs most frequently. A departure from these values leads to a decrease in the fission probability and to a yield of equal fragments of only 0.01 per cent. In the limiting case of fragments with the greatest mass difference, the yield is reduced to 1.5×10^{-5} per cent. The asymmetry is conveniently described by the ratio of the yield of the most probable fragments to the yield of the equal fragments. This ratio (the asymmetry coefficient) in the slow-neutron fission of AcU is approximately 600.

With increasing energy of impinging particles, i.e., at high excitation of the nucleus, the ratio decreases, and finally the fission becomes symmetrical, as can be seen from Table 36. The data in the table are merely of illustrative nature.

TABLE 36

ASYMMETRY OF FISSION FRAGMENTS

Type of Fission	Asymmetry Coefficient	
	For Uranium	For Thorium
Spontaneous fission	$\sim 10^4$	...
Slow-neutron fission	600	120
Fast-neutron fission	...	10
Fission with 37-Mev α-particles	...	2
Fission with 45-Mev α-particles	1.2	1.2
Fission with 50-Mev α-particles	1	1

Asymmetry is found in the fission of both uranium and thorium. In the fission of bismuth with fast deuterons, the following phenomenon is observed. At the beginning, a large number (approximately 12) of neutrons are consecutively emitted. At the same time, the value of Z^2/A for the excited nucleus increases from 33.4 to 35.5, that is, it achieves the same order of magnitude as for U^{238}. Then, as is usual at high-excitation energies, symmetrical fission takes place.

Spontaneous fission, on the contrary, is distinguished by greater asymmetry. Some spontaneous fission products—namely, the isotopes of the rare gases krypton and xenon—have been investigated by Macnamara and Thode [90]. The ratio of the yields of the xenon isotopes Xe^{136} and Xe^{129} in the slow-neutron fission of uranium is 6, whereas in spontaneous uranium fission it is 68 (compare with Table 10, p. 61). As is common for nuclear transmutations, with decreasing energy the discriminatory nature of the process becomes more intensely manifested, so that only the individual most probable reactions take place.

The asymmetry effect is especially pronounced in the case of the nuclear excitation-energy deficiency. This means that asymmetric fission evidently is energetically more favorable. We have shown that, from the viewpoint of the simplest gas model, fission into equal fragments is favorable, but at the same time we have not taken into consideration those deviations from the general binding-energy trend that are observed in the region of isotopes with closed neutron shells. For the first isotopes of each shell, the binding energy is greater than the expected energy. In reality, the most probable is fission into fragments whose masses lie near the closed shell region: $A - Z = 50$ and $A - Z = 82$. The energy gain in this process is not large, but, in general, the change in the energy during an asymmetric fission is, according to the simplest model (14.4), very small. In the case of high excitation of the fissioned nuclei, the energy factors do not prove decisive, and, in principle, equal-sized fragments are formed.

We note that this explanation of the asymmetry of nuclear fission is not generally accepted. In a survey of the fission problems, Hill and Wheeler [240] explain the effect by hydrodynamic instability. Later, Hill [241] expressed the assumption that asymmetry is connected with the formation of fragments with closed shells in the interior of the fissioned nucleus. Apart from the general asymmetry of the fission fragments, a "fine structure" is observed—the predominance of fragments of a definite mass which evidently with all certainty gravitate toward states of closed shells.

Excitation of Fragments

The principal characteristic of fission is the excitation of fragments, amounting to 30 Mev and leading to the emission of several neutrons. In addition to neutrons, the excited nuclei can emit α-particles and even heavier nuclei, for example, Li^8. The yield of α-particles is 0.2–0.25 per cent, and that of Li^8 is of the order of 10^{-4} per cent. Probably these rare modes of decay occur when the greater part of the excitation energy is concentrated in one of the fragments and is capable of exciting a heavy charged particle, so that it is thrown over the potential barrier of the atomic nucleus. It is obvious that emission of particles with penetration of the barrier during the short lifetime of the excited nucleus is wholly excluded, that is, the decay takes place in the "classical" manner. The height of the potential barrier in the emission of an α-particle from the fragment is of the order

$$U = 2\frac{Z}{2}\frac{e^2}{(A/2)^{1/3}r_0} = 18 \text{ Mev}, \qquad (14.9)$$

and in the emission of a Li^8 particle it is 27 Mev. The transfer to the particles of energy of such magnitude is permissible, inasmuch as the total excitation energy is of the order of 30 Mev. In practice, α-particles are observed with energies ranging from 15 to 20 Mev, which is in agreement with the concept of the classical α-decay of the fragment. If such a decay took place for the original nucleus, the energy of the particles should be of the order of 30 Mev.

The excitation of fragments is not in the least connected with the excitation-energy excess of the fissioned nucleus, since the excitation is observed in slow-neutron fission near the energy threshold of this reaction and even in spontaneous fission, when the energy deficiency is felt very strongly, a fact that stipulates an exceedingly small probability of the effect. Obviously, the division into the excited fragments is a factor which favors fission. We and also Zel'dovich and Zysin [242] independently expressed the following assumption. During fission, there occurs the "self-excitation of fragments." The energy of self-excitation is used up for the distribution of protons in the fragments in such a way as to decrease the electrostatic energy of the interaction of these fragments,

$$U = \frac{Z_1}{2} \cdot \frac{Z_2}{2} \cdot \frac{e^2}{R_1 + R_2} \approx 220 \text{ Mev}. \qquad (14.10)$$

This can be achieved either during the alteration of the shape of fragments (deformation with increasing mean distance between the fragments); during excitation of the entire system, with an increase of the mean separation between the particles and therefore also of the radii of the fragments; or, finally, during the distribution of protons in such a manner as to concentrate them on the opposite sides of the

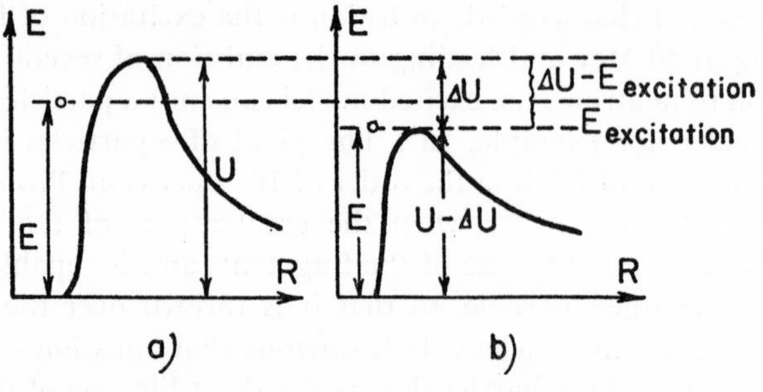

FIG. 26.—Schematic diagram of fission of atomic nuclei. *a*—impossibility of fission of excited nucleus; *b*—fission of self-excited nucleus.

fragments which are removed from each other. In all these cases the deformation is connected with the expenditure of energy for the "self-excitation" of the nucleus and leads to a decrease in the height of the mutual potential barrier, which is the interaction energy (14.10).

At the present level of knowledge of the intranuclear processes there is hardly any point in considering in greater detail the indicated kinds of possible deformation of the fragments. If, for the self-excitation of the fragments, the energy E_{exc} is used and the height of the potential barrier decreases in the process by ΔU, then the relative rise in the energy level of the fragments in comparison with the peak of the barrier is ΔU-E_{exc} (see Fig. 26). In order to make the effect of self-excitation favor fission, it is required that

$$\Delta U - E_{exc} > 0. \tag{14.11}$$

Since $E_{exc} \approx 30$ Mev, the change in the potential barrier is $\Delta U > 30$ Mev, and the barrier height in the case of self-excitation decreases from $U = 200$ Mev to

$$U - \Delta U \leqslant 170 \text{ Mev.} \tag{14.12}$$

In reality, the energy of the fission fragments, on the average, is 165 Mev, which agrees with (14.12).

We have already encountered the self-excitation phenomenon in the α-decay of short-range particles, where this process does not play a decisive role. In fission of heavy isotopes, the self-excitation of fragments is evidently necessary for the disintegration of the nucleus. The probability of fission, like the probability of α-decay, increases with increasing nuclear charge and decreases with increasing atomic weight. The elementary theory of the fission stability of atomic nuclei is very simple. First of all, the stability is determined by the value of Z^2/A. With $Z^2/A \gtrsim 40$, spontaneous fission occurs instantaneously. However, it has already taken place at much lower values of Z^2/A. This is promoted by two mechanisms: the possibility of self-excitation of the fragments and the passage of the fragments through a mutual potential barrier. The upper boundary of the region of α-emitters and the lower boundary of the region of spontaneous fission lie close to each other. This condition is not a principal one but depends on the combination of those parameters which stipulate the stability of nuclei against both fission and α-decay.

β-Instability of Fragments and of α-Decay Products

With increasing weight of atomic nuclei, the ratio between neutrons and protons increases. Therefore, the fission fragments of heavy nuclei contain excess neutrons in comparison with the stable nuclei of their own weight and consequently turn out to be β-active (see Fig. 24). While passing into a stable condition, each of the fragments experiences three to four β-transmutations. Thus, for 45 different modes of fission, there arise about 300 different β-emitters.

In nature, there exist or are produced many β-unstable nuclei which are capable of the emission or absorption of light particles. These isotopes can be classified in the following manner:

1. Independent β-active isotopes. Here belong (*a*) odd-odd nuclei which, in the process of β-decay or K-capture, form a pair of stable even isobars (these are, as we have pointed out, K^{40}, La^{138}, Lu^{176}); (*b*) components of odd isobars (in nature, only β-unstable isotopes of this type are known: Rb^{87}, In^{115}, Re^{187}); (*c*) components of even isobars of the second kind, capable of a double β-decay (Ca^{48}, Zr^{96}, Te^{130}, and others).

2. Products of radioactive decay: (*a*) daughter nuclei which during α-decay have acquired an excess of neutrons which sooner or later leads to β-decay; (*b*) fission fragments.

3. β-active products of artificial disintegration. On the earth artificial transmutations of atomic nuclei do not possess great significance. The most probable reaction of this type is the disintegration of atmospheric nitrogen by the secondary cosmic-ray neutrons, during which the β-unstable isotopes C^{14} and H^3 are produced.

Of the β-unstable nuclei of the earth's crust, the most active are K^{40} and the β-unstable decay products of thorium and uranium. K-capture —the absorption by the nucleus of an extra-nuclear electron—is, strictly speaking, a consequence of the interaction of the nuclear field with the external environment, that is, K-capture occupies an intermediate position between natural and artificial transmutations of atomic nuclei. It is obvious that the state of the extra-nuclear electron can influence the probability of K-capture. The K-shell, the first electronic shell, lies deep in the atom and is usually only slightly changed by external factors. For the light elements these changes should be the greatest. Recent investigations have shown that, indeed, the K-capture constant of Be^7 varies, depending on whether beryllium is in the ionic, Be^{+2}, form (keeping only the electrons of the K-shell) or in the form of atomic beryllium [243]:

$$\lambda_{BeO} - \lambda_{Be} = -0.15 \pm 0.09 \times 10^{-3}\lambda_{Be},$$

$$\lambda_{BeO} - \lambda_{BeF_2} = 1.375 \pm 0.053 \times 10^{-3}\lambda_{BeO}$$

It was also discovered that the probability of the transition of Tc^{99} from the isomeric into the ground state is different for metallic technetium and for its salt, $KTcO_4$ [244]. The γ-transition for this isotope is forbidden, and there is observed full internal conversion, with the transfer of energy to the outer shell electron.

In the earth's crust, the most active nucleus capable of K-capture is

K^{40}. It is possible that the probability of the process varies, depending on the state of potassium in the crystalline lattice of natural minerals, but the variations cannot be large, and, at the present time, the geochemical consequences of this effect lie outside the sensitivity limits of laboratory techniques.

The study of the principal modes of nuclear instability is necessary in order to be able to analyze the observed regularities in the abundance of atomic nuclei and to approach the question of their origin. This problem cannot be solved at the present level of our knowledge, but it has already advanced from the realm of speculation and into the field of scientific hypotheses, which are subject to further criticism and development.

III

Regularities in the Abundance of Isotopes and the Problem of Formation of Atomic Nuclei

15. DEPENDENCE OF THE ABUNDANCE OF ISOTOPES ON *A* AND *Z*

We shall describe the basic regularities of the abundance of isotopes and the attempts at a theoretical explanation of these regularities, using the data on the cosmic abundance of atoms in the earth's crust, in the sun's atmosphere, and in the meteorites, as presented in chapter I. The fundamental material for this purpose is the abundance of isotopes in the earth's crust. We do not know the isotopic composition of the elements of the sun. Although in most cases there is no basis for supposing that the isotopic composition of solar and terrestrial matter is essentially different, nonetheless we have no right to regard this composition as identical. The ratios of the isotopes of the chemical elements in meteorites are remarkably close (except for radiogenic products) to those of terrestrial isotopes.

Our problem is the investigation of the regularities in the abundance of stable isotopes. The term "stable" as applied to atomic nuclei is somewhat indeterminate. The powerful agents of cosmic space—the cosmic rays—possess sufficient energy to disintegrate any atomic nucleus, to produce new heavy particles, and to cause profound changes in the state of nuclear matter. But even if we restrict ourselves to the spontaneous decay of radioactive nuclei, we still have a large number of unstable elements for which the causes of decay and of lifetime differ very strongly. In the old literature of physics and especially in geochemical literature the idea is encountered that radioactive decay is a general property of atomic nuclei. This is certainly incorrect. Nearly all light elements existing in nature are absolutely stable and incapable of spontaneous decay, which is confirmed by the unequivocal data on their energetics. The majority of the heavy nuclei are unstable. For some isotopes the processes of artificial splitting of the nuclei—of small probability for the elements of the cosmos—are nevertheless of greater intensity than spontaneous decay.

The demarcation of atomic nuclei into stable and unstable isotopes has a conditional character. In practice, those isotopes should be regarded as stable that exist in nature independently and are not the short-lived products of radioactive decay or of artificial transmutation. The number of known radioactive isotopes is now large and will undoubtedly increase with the development of experimental techniques.

The most important regularity of the abundance of atomic nuclei is its dependence on atomic weight. The preponderance in nature of the light elements was noted by Menedeleyev as early as the last century. At the beginning of our century this regularity was expressed quantitatively. The dependence of the logarithm $Q_Z = \log n_Z$ of the abundance of the element on charge for some cosmic objects is given in Table II of the Appendix (p. 269) and in Figure 1 (see p. 31); and the dependence of the logarithm of the abundance Q_A of isotopes of the earth's crust on atomic weight A is given in Table I of the Appendix (p. 265) and in Figure 27.

Goldschmidt [257] supposed that the dependence on charge could be described by the following empirical formula:

$$n_Z = aZ^{-m} \quad (m = 7\text{–}8). \tag{15.1}$$

Since Z is proportional to A to a first approximation, it follows from equation (15.1) that $n_A \sim A^{-m}$. Yet it is impossible to agree with this type of power dependence of the abundance. In reality, a rapid drop in the abundance curve for the light isotopes with increasing atomic weight is changed to a relatively uniform course in the region of the heavy atomic nuclei. The uniform course of the curve is interrupted by many deviations. The most substantial of them is the deficiency of the light metals (Li, Be, B), which are destroyed in thermonuclear reactions of stellar interiors. Some deviations are explained by the secondary processes of element distribution.

The curve of the atomic abundances in the earth's crust shows dips of local origin. They are caused by the impoverishment of the earth's crust in the elements which were partly lost by the earth during its formation and also in those elements (selenium: $A = 76\text{–}82$, tellurium: $A = 124\text{–}30$) which enrich the intermediate layers and the interior

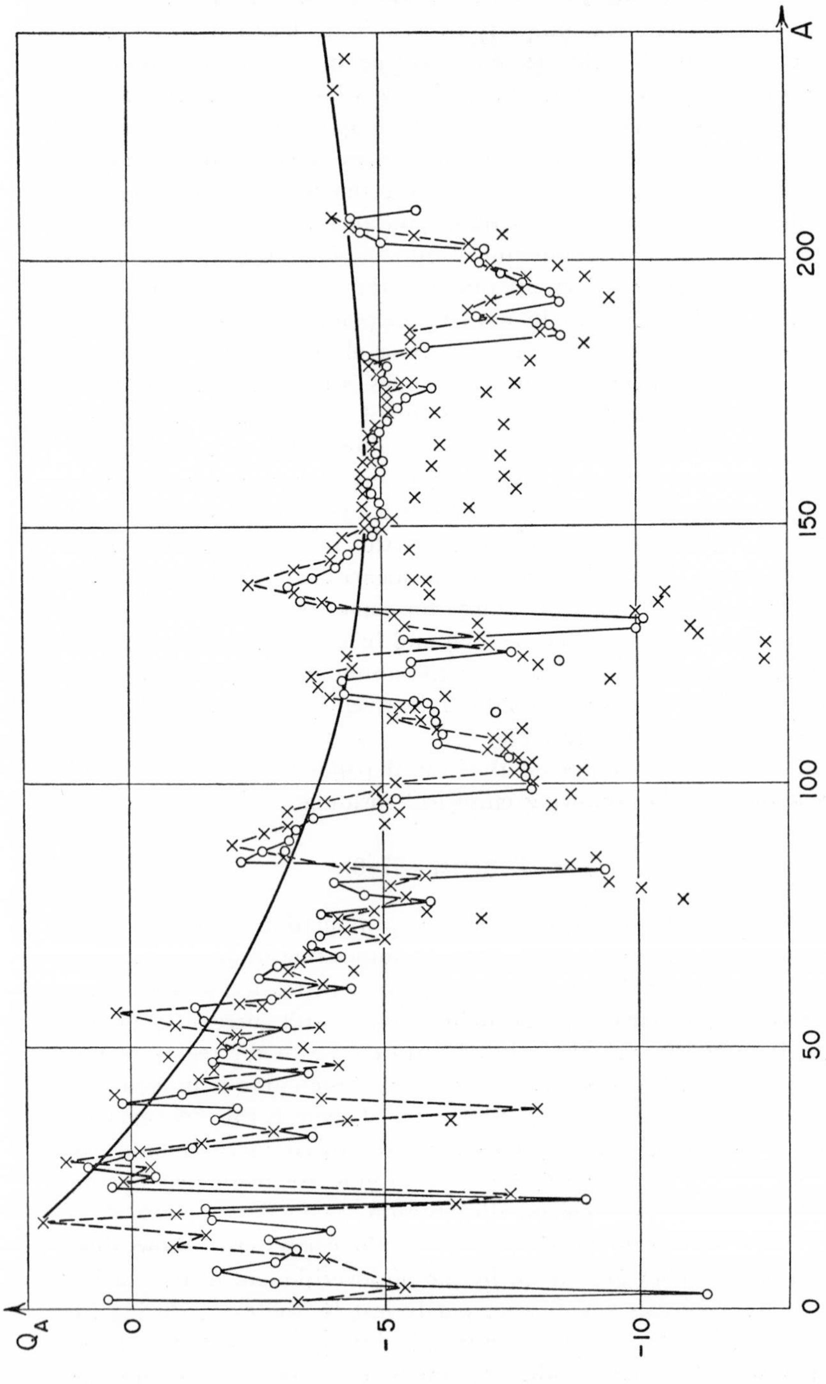

FIG. 27.—Dependence of the abundance of isotopes in the earth's crust on atomic weight. x = even isotopes, o = odd isotopes. The broken curves connect isotopes of different type. The curves are drawn through isobar components of high abundance. The continuous curve shows the theoretical dependence of Q_A on A, according to equations (19.10) and (19.11) (p. 243).

parts of the earth (the platinum-group elements and gold: $A = 100$–106 and 186–204).

However, even if one excludes these sectors, the abundance curve contains regions of excess and deficient elements which lie, respectively, above and below the mean abundance curve. The anomalous abundance of certain elements is detected, although to a different degree, for all cosmic objects studied and probably reflects the peculiarities of the primordial composition of the cosmos. To the deficient elements belong scandium, gallium-germanium, rhodium-indium, and possibly rhenium; and among the excess elements are the regions of iron isotopes, of strontium-yttrium-zirconium, and of barium-lanthanum-cerium isotopes. It is essential to note that elements of different chemical and geochemical properties can belong to one region, so that evidently the departures are indeed connected with the nuclear and not the atomic properties of isotopes.

The atomic abundance curve (see Fig. 27) shows a clear minimum in the region of elements of intermediate atomic weight. However, the position of the minimum is difficult to establish because of the uneven course of the curve.[1] This, to a considerable degree, is caused by the fact that the ratio of the individual elements is altered by the secondary processes of their distribution. In order to convince one's self of the reality of this minimum, it is necessary to utilize such material on the abundance of the elements that does not reflect the migration of the elements, that is, the material on the isotopes of one element. Inasmuch as the abundance depends on the type of isotope (this question will be considered later), it is necessary to take into account only the isotopes of the same type. It is also obvious that one may consider only those isotopes which are neither members of isobar pairs nor radioactive-decay products (as, for example, the lead isotopes). This imposes an extreme limitation upon the investigation possibilities. The available material on the abundance of isotopes of the same type, assembled by taking into consideration the indicated conditions, is shown in Table VII of the Appendix (p. 293) [252].

If there are two isotopes of the same element with atomic weights $A - 1$ and $A + 1$ and the per cent concentrations n_{A-1} and n_{A+1}, then the quantity

$$\zeta = \left(\frac{n_{A-1}}{n_{A+1}}\right)_Z \qquad (15.2)$$

[1] Compare the above statements with conclusions of H. E. Suess (*Zeitschr. f. Naturforsch.*, **2a**: 311–321, 604–8, 1947; *Experientia*, **5**: 266–70, 1949), H. C. Urey (*Phys. Rev.*, **88**: 248–52, 1952), H. E. Suess and H. C. Urey (*Rev. Mod. Phys.*, **28**: 53–74, 1956), and of A. G. W. Cameron (*Astrophys. Jour.*, **129**: 676–99, 1959), all based mainly on the elemental abundances in meteorites and the sun, rather than on the abundances in the earth's crust.

is related to the abundance by the approximate expression

$$\log \zeta = \frac{dQ_A}{dA} \Delta A = 2 \frac{dQ_A}{dA}, \tag{15.3}$$

where $Q_A = \log n_A$ and in our case $\Delta A = 2$. If ζ is known, it is possible to find the tangent of the curve $Q_A = f(A)$ and, from this, to establish the true course of the curve. Obviously, the position of the minimum is determined by the relationship

$$\log \zeta = 0, \qquad \frac{n_{A-1}}{n_{A+1}} = 1. \tag{15.4}$$

The average (geometric) values of ζ for the individual groups of elements are given in Table 37. In Figure 28 is shown the curve of the

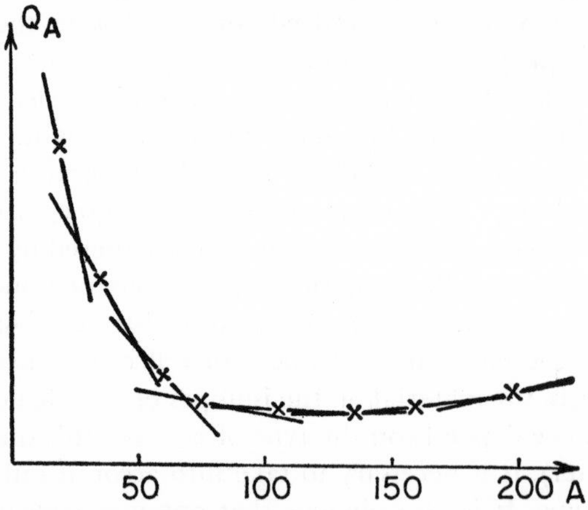

FIG. 28.—Dependence of the abundance of isotopes on atomic weight, taking into account the data on the average ratio of isotopes of the same type.

primordial abundances plotted by using these values. The curve has a clear maximum at $A \approx 140$.

TABLE 37

AVERAGE VALUES OF ζ FOR INDIVIDUAL GROUPS OF ELEMENTS

Z	$\bar{A}$	No. of Isotope Pairs	$\zeta = \frac{n_{A-1}}{n_{A+1}}$
<10.	19	2	71
11–20.	34	6	6.27
21–30.	60	4	2.41
31–40.	75	2	1.24
41–50.	105	4	1.04
51–60.	136	3	1.02
61–70.	158	5	0.91
71–80.	195	5	0.82

On the elemental abundance curve as a function of atomic number (see Fig. 1, p. 31) a minimum (or, in any case, a practically uniform course of the curve beginning from the middle of Mendeleyev's table) for the elements of intermediate weight is observed only for the earth's crust and meteorites. The abundance of the elements in the sun's atmosphere decreases, on the average, uniformly (if one ignores the numerous deviations of the individual points of the curve) with increasing atomic number. This discrepancy we have discussed in Section 4 (p. 39). The primordial abundance curve, as far as it is possible to reconstruct it from the ratio of isotopes, has a minimum in approximately the same region as the abundance curve of isotopes in the earth's crust. Perhaps the composition of the heavy elements of the earth is closer to the primordial composition than for the elements of the sun's atmosphere, and the discrepancy in the composition of these two bodies is caused by the gravitational differentiation of the solar matter.

Abundance of Even and Odd Isotopes

As early as 1914, Addo noticed that even elements are more abundant than odd elements [253]. Later, Harkins [254] showed that even isotopes are also more abundant than odd isotopes. Inasmuch as the number of isotopes for even elements is considerably greater than for odd elements, the latter rule is stronger than the former. We have noted that the preponderance of even isotopes is especially large for the light nuclei and diminishes for the heavy ones [252, 255]. Even a quick survey of the composition of even elements in the table of isotopes (see p. 272) reveals that the abundance of odd isotopes is smaller in the majority of cases than the average abundance of the neighboring even isotopes. In all cases (with the exception of Xe^{129}) the content of the odd isotope is smaller than the sum of the contents of the neighboring even isotopes.

A quantitative description of this effect is connected with some difficulty. Direct comparison of odd isotopes with the neighboring even isotopes of the same element is methodically incorrect, since even isotopes can enter into pairs of even isobars. The abundance of even isobars possesses its own regularities, which will systematically distort such determination of the ratio of even to odd isotopes.

The investigation of the ratio of the abundance of the even (n_{even}) to that of the odd (n_{odd}) isotope of approximately the same atomic weight we shall carry out by three independent methods.

1. The determination of the ratio $n_{\text{even}}/n_{\text{odd}}$ from the average content of odd isotopes in even elements. Let this content be x. On the average, the content of even isotopes for even elements is doubled

because of the instability of odd-odd nuclei and the formation of even isobars. Thus

$$x = \frac{n_{\text{odd}}}{n_{\text{odd}} + 2n_{\text{even}}} = \frac{1}{1 + 2(n_{\text{even}}/n_{\text{odd}})}. \quad (15.5)$$

In Table 38 are given data on the per cent content of odd isotopes

TABLE 38

RELATIVE ABUNDANCE OF EVEN ELEMENTS AND THEIR CONTENT OF EVEN ISOTOPES

Z	ELEMENT	NUMBER OF ISOTOPES		ABUNDANCE OF ODD ISOTOPES (PER CENT)	$Q_Z - \frac{Q_{Z+1} + Q_{Z-1}}{2}$		
		Even	Odd		Sun	Earth's Crust	Meteorites
8....	Oxygen	2	1	0.037	1.0	2.95	...
10....	Neon	2	1	0.257	...	...	...
12....	Magnesium	2	1	10.11	1.32	−0.25	0.85
14....	Silicon	2	1	4.68	1.31	1.45	1.65
16....	Sulfur	3	1	0.750	0.7	−0.2	1.15
18....	Argon	3	0	0.00	...	...	...
20....	Calcium	5	1	0.145	2.33	1.95	2.3
22....	Titanium	3	2	13.26	0.9	2.25	1.65
24....	Chromium	3	1	9.55	0.25	−0.15	0.75
26....	Iron	3	1	2.17	2.25	2.5	1.95
28....	Nickel	4	1	1.25	0.62	0.65	1.95
30....	Zinc	4	1	4.11	1.3	1.3	0.55
32....	Germanium	4	1	7.67	...	0.3	0.45
34....	Selenium	5	1	7.58	...	...	...
36....	Krypton	5	1	11.55	...	...	...
38....	Strontium	3	1	7.02	1.08	0.7	0.7
40....	Zirconium	4	1	11.23	0.7	1.85	1.5
42....	Molybdenum	5	2	25.15	...	...	...
44....	Ruthenium	5	2	29.8	...	...	...
46....	Palladium	5	1	22.6	0.35	0.2	−0.05
48....	Cadmium	6	2	25.01	1.7	1.7	0.6
50....	Tin	7	3	16.49	0.8	2.5	1.3
52....	Tellurium	6	2	7.86	...	...	...
54....	Xenon	7	2	47.62	...	...	...
56....	Barium	5	2	17.91	0.9	1.8	0.75
58....	Cerium	4	0	0.00	1.2	0.7	0.35
60....	Neodymium	5	2	20.50	...	...	...
62....	Samarium	5	2	28.91	...	...	...
64....	Gadolinium	5	2	30.41	...	1.75	0.65
66....	Dysprosium	5	2	43.85	...	0.9	0.6
68....	Erbium	5	1	22.94	...	0.8	0.65
70....	Ytterbium	5	2	30.44	0.25	0.8	0.65
72....	Hafnium	4	2	32.17	−0.1	0.35	0.25
74....	Tungsten	4	1	14.4	...	...	...
76....	Osmium	5	1	17.74	...	...	...
78....	Platinum	5	1	33.7	...	1.35	0.8
80....	Mercury	5	1	30.06	...	0.25	...

for all stable even elements. Excluded from the table are the light elements the isotopic composition of which was caused by thermonuclear reactions in stellar interiors and also lead, which is strongly enriched in the earth's crust with radioactive-decay products. The average values of x taken over the groups of elements are shown in Table 39. This table also gives the values of the ratio $n_{\text{even}}/n_{\text{odd}}$ according to equation (15.5).

TABLE 39

AVERAGE VALUES OF x, $-\log y$ AND $n_{\text{even}}/n_{\text{odd}}$ FOR INDIVIDUAL GROUPS OF ELEMENTS

Z	A	Av. Odd Isotope Abundance in Even Elements (According to Table 38) (Per Cent)	Av. Value of $Q_Z - \frac{Q_{Z+1} + Q_{Z-1}}{2}$ from Table 38	Av. Value of $n_{\text{even}}/n_{\text{odd}}$ from Formula		
				(15.5)	(15.8)	(15.9)
To 20.....	32	2.282	1.32	22	10	7
21–30.....	59	6.06	1.25	7.8	8.4	5.3
31–40.....	83	9.01	0.91	5.0	3.6	2.2
41–50.....	110	23.81	0.71	1.6	2.1	2.9
51–60.....	139	18.78	0.95	2.2	4.0	...
61–70.....	163	31.31	0.78	1.1	2.5	2.0
71–80.....	189	25.61	0.48	1.5	1.0	1.8

2. Determination of $n_{\text{even}}/n_{\text{odd}}$, using the abundance ratio y of even and odd elements. It is obvious that

$$\log y = \frac{Q_{Z+1} + Q_{Z-1}}{2} - Q_Z, \tag{15.6}$$

where Z is even and Q_Z is the logarithmic abundance of the element. Considering that the number of even isotopes for even elements is doubled, on the average, we find

$$y = \frac{\bar{n}_{\text{odd}}}{n_{\text{odd}} + 2n_{\text{even}}}. \tag{15.7}$$

The numerator of this ratio contains the average abundance of the neighboring odd elements, and the denominator contains the sum of the abundances of odd and even isotopes of the even element.

On the average $\bar{n}_{\text{odd}} = n_{\text{odd}}$, i.e., the average abundance of odd isotopes is the same for the neighboring even and odd elements, so that

$$\log\left(2\frac{n_{\text{even}}}{n_{\text{odd}}} + 1\right) = Q_Z - \frac{Q_{Z+1} + Q_{Z-1}}{2}. \tag{15.8}$$

In Table 38 are given values of the relative abundance of even elements [the right part of eq. (15.8)], according to the data of Table II (p. 269), for the sun, the earth's crust, and the meteorites. Table 39 gives the average values taken over the individual groups of the elements for the indicated objects and also the ratio $n_{\text{even}}/n_{\text{odd}}$ computed from these values.

3. The determination of $n_{\text{even}}/n_{\text{odd}}$ from the ratio of the abundance of the neighboring even and odd isotopes which can belong to different elements. In determining the ratio $n_{\text{even}}/n_{\text{odd}}$ it is necessary to consider the fact that even isotopes often enter into even isobars, so that one has to add up the abundance of all isobars of different atomic number:

$$\log \frac{n_{\text{even}}}{n_{\text{odd}}} = Q_A - \frac{Q_{A+1} + Q_{A-1}}{2}, \tag{15.9}$$

where A is even and Q_A is the logarithmic abundance of the isotope

$$Q_A = \log \sum_Z n_{A,Z}.$$

In Table 39 are shown the average values of $n_{\text{even}}/n_{\text{odd}}$ obtained by this method for the same intervals as the values of this ratio arrived at by other methods. The abundance of isotopes, according to Fersman's data, was taken from Table I of the Appendix (p. 265). Excluded from this calculation were isotopes of the elements which were lost from the earth.

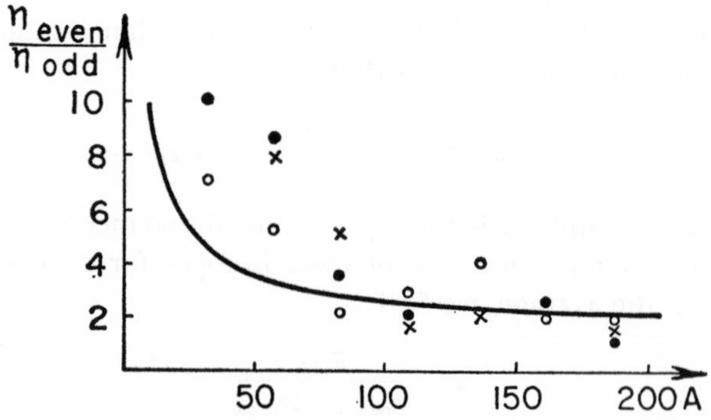

FIG. 29.—Data on the abundance ratio of even to odd isotopes as a function of atomic weight. Determinations of points are based on the odd isotope content of even elements (X), the abundance of even and odd elements (•), and the abundance of even and odd isotopes. (o). A theoretical curve of type (19.20) is also shown.

In Figure 29 is shown the atomic-weight dependence of the average values of $n_{\text{even}}/n_{\text{odd}}$ found by the three different methods. The individual values are strongly discrepant, but, on the whole, a regular drop in the ratio of even to odd isotopes is observed which ranges from approximately 10 for the light elements to 2 for the heavy elements. Since this regularity was obtained by independent methods, it evidently possesses, regardless of the low accuracy of determination, an objective character.

The number of isotopes in even elements is greater than in odd elements, in which (with the exception of the lightest elements) only odd isotopes are present. The ratio of the abundance, n_Z, of even elements to that, n_{Z+1}, of odd elements of approximately the same atomic weight is

$$\frac{n_Z}{n_{Z\pm1}} = \frac{2n_{\text{even}} + n_{\text{odd}}}{n_{\text{odd}}} = 2\frac{n_{\text{even}}}{n_{\text{odd}}} + 1, \tag{15.10}$$

i.e., if there is observed a preponderance of even isotopes, then even elements should also be overwhelmingly preponderant.

Abundance of Even Isobars

The number and arrangement of the energy levels of even isobars can be satisfactorily described in terms of the simplest statistical model of the nuclei. The state of even isobars we have characterized by the expression $\delta = Z - Z_0$, where Z is the average charge of the isobar pair and Z_0 is the optimum charge of the state with a given atomic weight. On the average, the values of δ with opposite signs are equally probable, and the existing departures can be qualitatively explained. The abundance of even isobars is subject to the following regularities:

a) Among even isobars, on the average, the components of lower charge predominate, that is,

$$\kappa = \frac{n_{Z-1}}{n_{Z+1}} > 1. \tag{15.11}$$

b) The ratio κ increases, on the average, for isobars of higher atomic weight.

c) The ratio κ increases with increasing δ. This is understood from energetic considerations, since for the values $\delta < 0$ the energy level of the component of lower charge lies above that of the component of higher charge, i.e., the former state is less stable than the latter (see Fig. 18, p. 142).

These regularities were first shown in our work of 1945 [252]. Regularity *a* was noted in a later work [256–58]. The first indication of the existence of regularities in the abundance of even isobars is due to Weizsäcker [259], who noted that if there is a pair of isobars with atomic weight A and with charges $Z \pm 1$ and if the nucleus of atomic weight $A - 1$ and charge $Z - 1$ is unstable, then the isobar component with charge $Z - 1$ is more abundant. The condition, noted by Weizsäcker, is a specific case of regularity *a*.

We shall use two methods for the determination of the abundance ratio of isobars.

1. We assume that the abundance of the neighboring even elements is the same, on the average. In this case the abundance ratio of isobars

agrees, on the average, with the concentration ratio of these atoms in the isotopic composition of the elements to which they belong. The values of the ratio κ_1 found by this method are given in Table V of the Appendix (p. 282). These concepts we shall call the "abundance according to the isotopic composition."

2. We find the abundance ratio κ_2 of isobars in the earth's crust (see Table V). Since many elements were lost from the crust, some data are so altered that they cannot be used.

TABLE 40

DEPENDENCE OF κ ON δ

δ	N	κ_1	N	κ_2
−1.........	8	0.44	4	0.19
$-\frac{1}{2}$.........	15	1.27	9	2.55
0.........	12	2.04	4	5.75
$+\frac{1}{2}$.........	25	29.6	12	38.3
+1.........	6	36.6	4	98
Av......	...	7.38	...	6.49

In Table 40 is shown the dependence of the average ratio κ on $\delta = Z - Z_0$. The letter N in this, as well as in the following table, denotes the number of isobar pairs. As δ decreases from +1 to −1, the ratio κ drops by a factor of the order of hundreds. This, as already noted, follows from the general energy considerations.

The average values of κ for isobars of different groups of atomic numbers are shown in Table 41 and also in Figure 30 (on a logarithmic scale).

TABLE 41

DEPENDENCE OF κ ON ATOMIC NUMBER

Z	$\delta < 0$		$\delta = 0$		$\delta > 0$		TOTAL		N	κ_2
	N	κ_1	N	κ_1	N	κ_1	N	κ_1		
<30......	2	0.001	3	0.05	3	0.132	8	0.027	6	0.063
30–40......	2	1.22	2	0.89	4	22.1	8	4.70	3	8.65
40–60......	12	1.47	3	4.77	13	30.7	28	6.83	8	28.0
60–80......	7	2.28	4	27.6	11	159	22	30.0	16	16.7
Av.....	..	0.88	..	2.04	..	31.1	..	7.38	..	6.49

With increasing Z, the preponderance of the component of lower charge increases. This is traced for the independent groups of isobars with different δ and thus constitutes a general regularity in the abundance of even isobars. For the first isobars of the periodic table of elements, in contrast to the general rule, the components of higher charge predominate. It is possible that this is, in some measure, explained by the asymmetry of the energy curve as a function of the charge of atomic nuclei.[2] The manifestation of this curve is strongest in the low-atomic-weight region.

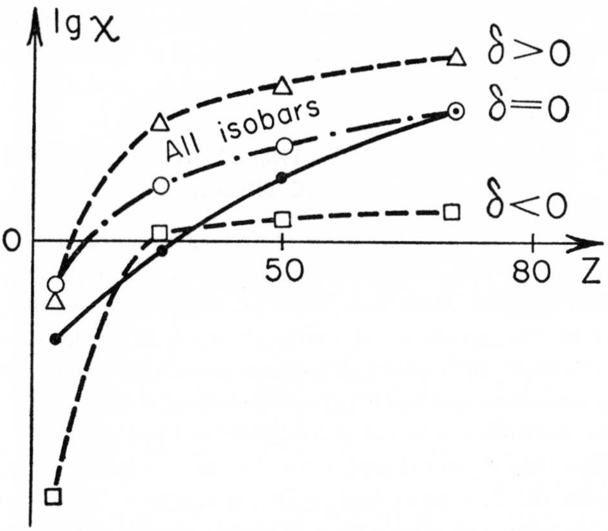

FIG. 30.—Abundance ratio $\kappa = n_{Z-1}/n_{Z+1}$ of even isobars as a function of charge for isobars with different values of $\delta = Z - Z_0$.

In Section 13 (p. 151) we have shown that, for even isobars in the α-decay region, one also observes greater stability of the component with lower charge. The decay period of this component is 10^3–10^8 times longer than for the component of higher charge. However, it should be emphasized that this phenomenon has only a formal resemblance to the preponderance of stable isobars of lower charge. The stability of these components in the α-decay region is explained by the general thesis regarding the high instability of α-emitters with increasing charge (see Sec. 13). For even isobars, both stable and α-emitting, the energy levels of both components are a priori equal. The preponderance of the component of lower charge cannot be explained by the difference in the energy of the nucleus. It is probably associated with the conditions of the formation of isobars and of atomic nuclei in general.

We shall now consider the abundance of odd isobars. The causes

[2] As a result of the asymmetry, the energy of the isobar $Z-1$ is greater, on the average, than that of the isobar $Z+1$, i.e., the latter is more stable. [Author's footnote.]

which determine the existence of these nuclear species are different from those determining the existence of even isobars (see Sec. 12, p. 138), but their abundance is subject to the same regularity; among odd isobars the component of lower charge predominates. This is observed for the pairs of stable isobars, as well as for pairs in which one component is unstable. In all known cases the radioactive odd isobars are β-active, i.e., the component of lower charge is unstable. Although the state of higher charge is consequently energetically more favorable, the abundance of this isotope is always lower than that of the unstable isotope (see Table 30, p. 164).

16. CHARACTERISTICS OF THE ABUNDANCE CURVE OF ATOMIC NUCLEI

It is widely known that the most abundant isotopes are the atomic nuclei of high binding energy in the region of the light nuclei—the "helium-like" isotopes, with $A = 2Z = 4n$, where n is a whole number. In support of this, geochemical literature gives examples of such isotopes as O^{16}, Mg^{24}, Si^{28}, and Ca^{40}, which essentially (about four-fifths by weight) constitute the earth's crust. However, if we make a detailed study of the dependence of the abundance on binding energy, we will be convinced that these examples are due to a secondary effect.

First of all, the dominant isotope of the cosmos is hydrogen, whose nucleus is an unbound elementary particle—the proton. If one turns to the "helium-like" nuclei, he finds that some (C^{12}, S^{32}) among them by no means possess high abundance, let alone the isotopes Ne^{20} and Ar^{36}, which were almost completely lost by the earth. But if we examine the binding energy of the helium-like isotopes, we find that only the lightest nuclei of this type—C^{12}, O^{16}, and S^{32}—possess the greatest binding energy among the isotopes of their elements. For neon, magnesium, silicon, and calcium, the greatest binding energy is possessed by the heaviest even isotopes with $A > 2Z$, although the light isotope with $A = 2Z$ is certainly preponderant in its abundance. In the given region odd isotopes have, as described in Section 11 (p. 125), a smaller binding energy than even isotopes, but sometimes odd states are more abundant—for example, the binding energy of Si^{29} (a content of 4.68 per cent) is smaller than that of Si^{30} (content of 3.05 per cent). It is not difficult to find an opposite example. The odd isotope of nitrogen has a greater binding energy, but its abundance is nearly 300 times smaller than the abundance of the even isotope.

In Figure 31 is shown the binding-energy curve for the light atomic nuclei and the abundance curve for the earth's crust as a function of atomic weight. The odd isotopes in this region, as a rule, possess a lower binding energy as well as lower abundance. However, a quantitative relationship between these parameters cannot be successfully established. In a number of cases, some parallelism of these two curves is observed, but cases of divergence between them are found almost as often. Perhaps the most interesting but, at the same time, nearly the sole example where an isotope differs from its neighbors simultaneously in high binding energy and abundance, is O^{16}.

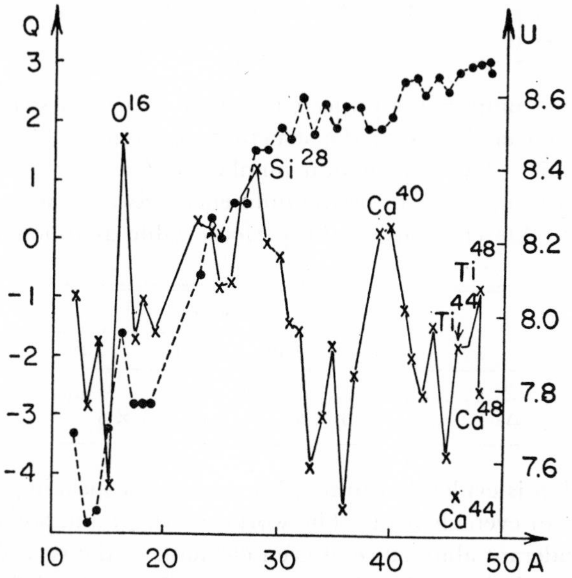

FIG. 31.—Binding energy U and terrestrial abundance Q of light isotopes. Values of U are marked by dark circles and those of Q by crosses.

For the heavy nuclei, the binding energy varies comparatively little and, to a first approximation, obeys the curve with a maximum at $A = 60$, given by the statistical model of the nucleus. The abundance of individual elements undergoes much greater fluctuation. The binding energy of the heavy nuclei is almost independent of their type. At the same time, the difference in the abundance of even and odd isotopes is traced to the end of the sequence of stable elements. Thus a simple and definite relationship between the abundance and the binding energy of isotopes does not exist.

Periodic Deviations in the Abundance of Individual Isotopes

Attempts to discover the periodic properties of atomic nuclei were made as early as the 1920's and were based precisely on the data on the abundance of the elements. Thus Meitner [215] reported high abundance of some helium-like isotopes of type $A = 4n$. In the works of the mineralogists Sonder [216] and Niggli [217] the assumption was expressed that the highest abundance is possessed by the elements with a period of six atomic weight units:

	Element												
	O		Si		Ca		Fe		Sr		Ba		W
Z	8		14		20		26		38		56		74
ΔZ		6		6		6		2×6		3×6		3×6	

The authors compare the projected periodicity with a space structure of atomic nuclei similar to the structure of the ionic lattices of minerals, in which the co-ordination number 6 occurs very often. Also a multiple of 6 turns out to be the difference between the atomic numbers of unstable elements of the periodic table as follows:

	Element						
	K		Rb		Tc		Pm
Z	19		37		43		61
ΔZ		3×6		1×6		3×6	

This relation is evidently illusory. We have been speaking of the high abundance of even elements. The works of Niggli and Sonder confirm the preponderant abundance of even elements of the type $Z = 6n + 2$, where n is a whole number. Let us examine the region of the relatively light elements, up to the element iron. Of these elements, neon ($Z = 10$) and argon ($Z = 18$) were almost completely lost from the earth, and the abundance of magnesium ($Z = 12$) and sulfur ($Z = 16$) in the earth's crust is significantly reduced. The predominance of oxygen over carbon and of calcium over magnesium is caused by the peculiarity of the distribution of the elements in the earth's crust and possibly does not reflect the primordial abundance of the elements. A high abundance of tungsten has also been recorded for the earth's crust only. Apparently, a high cosmic abundance of iron, strontium, and barium is real, but the abundance of the elements adjacent to strontium (zirconium and the odd rubidium) and barium (cerium and the odd lanthanum) is also extremely high. In some cosmic objects (in meteorites and especially in the atmospheres of the S-type red giants) there is more zirconium than strontium. In any case, we should speak of the segments of isotopes with increased abundance and not of the exceptional abundance of the individual elements.

The periodicity of unstable odd elements is undoubtedly fortuitous, since it links the elements for which the individual isotopes are unstable, the instability being of quite different nature (in potassium the even isotope K^{40} is radioactive; in rubidium, the odd isotope Rb^{87}, while technetium and promethium do not have a single stable isotope). Of the elements of the type $Z = 6n + 2$, germanium ($Z = 32$), on the contrary, has a low abundance in all cosmic objects, whereas samarium and erbium ($Z = 62$ and $Z = 68$) do not differ in abundance from the neighboring rare-earth elements. The content of ruthenium ($Z = 44$) in the earth's crust is exceedingly low, as is also the content of all platinum-group metals, but even in the sun this element is not prominent in comparison with its even neighbors.

The primordial abundance is a nuclear property. It is difficult to suppose that this property depends on nuclear charge, i.e., that, abundance-wise, it is possible to single out groups of different atomic nuclei which are united by the common criterion of an atomic number.

In an excellent four-volume treatise on geochemistry, Fersman [4] notes, along with the preponderance of even isotopes, a high abundance of isotopes of the type $A = 4n + 3$ (n is a whole number) relative to that of isotopes of the type $A = 4n + 1$. The former include such isotopes as Al^{27}, Na^{23}, K^{39}, Cl^{35}, F^{19}, and others, which comprise about 8 per cent of the total number of atoms of the earth's crust. The most abundant isotopes of the type $A = 4n + 1$ are Si^{29}, Mg^{25}, K^{41}, Cl^{37}, Fe^{57}, and O^{17}, whose total content does not exceed 1 per cent of all atoms of the earth's crust. On the peaks of the abundance curve of even elements of low atomic weight there lie isotopes of the type $A = 4n$ (O^{16}, Si^{28}, Mg^{24}, Ca^{40}).

The regularity noted by Fersman is a specific case of the following regularity. If the even isotope has increased abundance and is located on the peak of the curve, then the most abundant odd isotope is the one whose atomic weight is lower by one unit. This rule is also applicable to the heavy isotopes (where the helium-like nuclei do not occur and even elements, lying on the peaks of the curve, can have the mass of the type $A = 4n$ as well as that of the type $A = 4n + 2$, with A being always greater than $2Z$). The elements which lie on the peaks of the abundance curve are given in Table 42 (according to the data of Vinogradov [2] on the abundance of elements in the earth's crust). It is possible that, for the average cosmic abundance of elements, the group of the most abundant isotopes will change considerably. On the abundance curve for the elements of the sun's atmosphere (see Fig. 1, p. 31) well-expressed maxima are present only for iron, strontium, and barium.

The atomic weight of the most abundant odd isotope is nearly always lighter by one unit than the weight of the even isotope which lies on the peak of the curve.

On the peaks of the abundance curve of the even heavy elements

TABLE 42

MOST ABUNDANT ISOTOPES WHICH OCCUPY PEAKS OF ABUNDANCE CURVE FOR ATOMIC NUCLEI OF EARTH'S CRUST

Even Isotopes				Odd Isotopes				$A_{even} - A_{odd}$
Z	Element	A_{even}	Type of At. Wt.	Z	Element	A_{odd}	Type of At. Wt.	
8	Oxygen	16	$4n$					
12	Magnesium	24	$4n$	11	Sodium	23	$4n + 3$	1
14	Silicon	28	$4n$	13	Aluminum	27	$4n + 3$	1
20	Calcium	40	$4n$	19	Potassium	39	$4n + 3$	1
22	Titanium	48	$4n$	22	Titanium	47	$4n + 3$	1
26	Iron	56	$4n$	25	Manganese	55	$4n + 3$	1
38	Strontium	88	$4n$	37	Rubidium	85	$4n + 3$	3
50	Tin	120	$4n$	50	Tin	119	$4n + 3$	1
56	Barium	138	$4n + 2$	56	Barium	137	$4n + 3$	1

there lie the isotopes Ti^{48}, Fe^{56}, Sr^{88}, and Sn^{120}, which are of the type $A = 4n$. Only one (the sharpest) peak of this curve is represented by the isotope Ba^{138} of the type $A = 4n + 2$. It is difficult to say whether the preponderance of heavy isotopes of the type $A = 4n$ over those of the type $A = 4n + 2$ is fortuitous or whether this regularity, while unconditional for certain light, helium-like nuclei, is also traced in the heavy isotope region.

Abundance of Atomic Nuclei with Closed Nucleonic Shells

We shall consider the dependence of the abundance of atomic nuclei on the completeness of nucleonic shells. The nuclei with closed proton shells enter the following elements:

$Z =$	2	8	14	20	28	50	82
	He	O	Si	Ca	Ni	Sn	Pb

All of them, except helium and nickel, are located on the peaks of the terrestrial abundance curve for elements; but this is probably caused by the peculiarities of the distribution of terrestrial matter, a fact which we have pointed out for oxygen, silicon, and calcium. It is possible that the high abundance of tin and lead is also a phenomenon caused by the impoverishment of the earth's crust in the neighboring elements (the platinum-group elements, the elements of the sulfide field, and also tellurium and mercury). In the atmosphere of the sun no abundance maximum is observed for the indicated elements, except for helium, which, by contrast, was almost completely lost by the earth.

Thus the atomic nuclei with closed proton shells are not unique from the standpoint of the abundance criterion.

The most abundant isotopes are usually those with closed neutron shells or with the number of neutrons closely approximating that of a closed shell. Many of these isotopes also predominate in the isotopic

TABLE 43

ABUNDANCE OF ISOTOPES WITH CLOSED NEUTRON SHELLS

$A - Z$	Z	Isotope*	Fractional Occurrence in Element (Per Cent)	Abundance in Earth's Crust (Atom Per Cent) (According to Table III)
8	7	N^{15}	0.365	1.8×10^{-4}
	8	O^{16}	99.759	53.2
14	12	Mg^{26}	11.29	0.194
	13	Al^{27}	100	4.80
	14	Si^{28}	92.97	14.87
20	16	S^{36}	0.017	8.5×10^{-6}
	17	Cl^{37}	24.6	0.025
	18	Ar^{38}	0.063	...
	19	K^{39}	93.08	0.98
	20	Ca^{40}	96.97	1.37
28	20	Ca^{48}	0.185	2.4×10^{-3}
	22	Ti^{50}	5.34	0.012
	23	V^{51}	99.76	7×10^{-3}
	24	Cr^{52}	83.76	7.5×10^{-3}
	26	Fe^{54}	5.84	0.076
50	36	Kr^{86}	17.37	...
	37	Rb^{87}†	27.85	5.5×10^{-4}
	38	Sr^{88}	82.56	5.8×10^{-3}
	39	Y^{89}	100	1×10^{-3}
	40	Zr^{90}	51.46	2.6×10^{-3}
	42	Mo^{92}	15.86	3.2×10^{-5}
82	54	Xe^{136}	8.87	...
	56	Ba^{138}	71.66	4.3×10^{-3}
	57	La^{139}	99.91	8×10^{-5}
	58	Ce^{140}	88.48	3.5×10^{-4}
	59	Pr^{141}	100	6×10^{-5}
	60	Nd^{142}	27.13	5.4×10^{-5}
	62	Sm^{144}	3.16	2.5×10^{-7}
126	82	Pb^{208}	52.3	5.2×10^{-5}
	83	Bi^{209}	100	8×10^{-7}

* The italic isotopes are located in the maxima of the isotope abundance curve for the earth's crust. [Author's footnote.]

† β-active. [Author's footnote.]

composition of their own elements (see Table 43). To the shell with 14 neutrons belong the isotopes Al^{27} and Si^{28}, both located in the maxima of the abundance curves for odd and even isotopes of the earth's crust. To the shell with 20 neutrons belong isotopes of high abundance: K^{39} and Ca^{40}. For the shell with 28 neutrons, increased abundance in the isotopic composition of the element is possessed only by Cr^{52}, but the cosmic abundance of the element itself is not very high. However, the iron isotope Fe^{56} ($A - Z = 30$), which is exceptionally abundant in all investigated objects of the cosmos, borders on this shell. In the shell with $A - Z = 50$ there are even isotopes of high abundance, Sr^{88} and Zr^{90}. The most abundant isotope of this region is Rb^{85}, with $A - Z = 48$. The shell with 82 neutrons embraces the most clearly expressed maximum on the abundance curve, which is composed of the even isotopes Ba^{138} and Ce^{140} ($A - Z = 82$) and of the odd isotopes Ba^{137} ($A - Z = 81$) and La^{139} ($A - Z = 82$). Of the comparatively abundant isotopes, only Pb^{208} belongs to the shell with 126 neutrons. The role of this shell is manifested especially strongly, not in the abundance of the stable isotopes, but in the special stability of some α-emitters (see Sec. 13, p. 151).

The structure of atomic nuclei with closed nucleonic shells permits a description of the regularities in the spin of atomic nuclei. The even nuclei, which have an anomalously high spin (K^{40}, Lu^{176}), are distinguished by a low abundance. For odd nuclei, possibly, there is also a tendency toward a decrease in the abundance of atomic nuclei with high values of the spin. In the minima of the abundance curve for the earth's crust, the sun's atmosphere, and the meteorites there lie Sc^{45} ($j = 7/2$), isotopes of indium, Ge^{73}, Bi^{209},[3] and Cs^{133} ($j = 9/2$).

Exceptionally high abundances are possessed by the isotopes of iron (in particular Fe^{56}), rubidium, strontium, zirconium (in particular, Rb^{85}, Sr^{88}, Zr^{90}), and those of barium, lanthanum, and cerium (in particular, Ba^{137}, Ba^{138}, Ce^{140}). For some isotopes the number of neutrons corresponds to that of the closed shell (Sr^{88}, Y^{89}, and Zr^{90}: $A - Z = 50$; Ba^{138}, La^{139}, and Ce^{140}: $A - Z = 82$); for others it has a value approximating that of the closed shell (Fe^{56}, $A - Z = 30$). There seems to be a rule that a maximum in the abundance curve occurs for odd isotopes at a lower value of atomic weight than for even isotopes (Mn^{55}-Fe^{56}, Rb^{85}-Sr^{88}, Ba^{137}-Ba^{138}, and others). Many even isotopes with closed shells are also the main isotopes of their elements. The content of these isotopes is higher than 50 per cent, which is rarely found for elements heavier than sulfur. Such isotopes are Ca^{40}, Cr^{52}, Sr^{88}, Zr^{90}, Ba^{138}, Ce^{140}, and Pb^{208}.

Dips in the Abundance Curve

The position of some isotopes deviates strongly from the mean course of the abundance curve. This is sometimes associated with the

[3] There are no data on the abundance of bismuth in the sun's atmosphere, but apparently the abundance of this element is not high. [Author's footnote.]

migration of elements in the investigated system but often also with fluctuations in the primordial abundance of the individual isotopes. In addition, the abundance curve has sharp dips in the region of light ($A = 5$–11) and heavy metals ($A > 208$) (see Fig. 32).

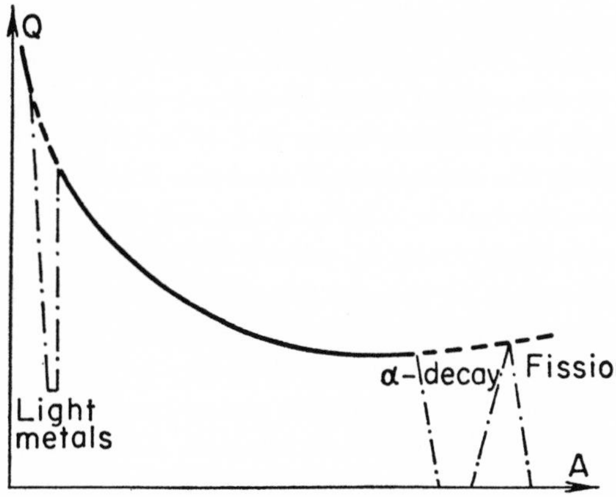

FIG. 32.—Schematic diagram of dips in the abundance curve of atomic nuclei.

The deficiency of the light metals is explained by their burning in stellar interiors, which was first assumed by Goldschmidt in 1928 [30]. Later we [252] noted that, in addition to an anomalous abundance, the light metals also have an anomalous isotopic composition. For lithium and boron the odd heavy isotope predominates ($Li^7 = 92.48$ per cent; $B^{11} = 81$ per cent), whereas for the other light elements (up to calcium) the light isotope always predominates, and for all even elements there is observed a lower content of odd isotopes. Evidently, the anomalous isotopic composition of lithium and boron is connected with the probability of their burning. For beryllium, only the odd isotope, Be^9, is generally stable.

The abundance of the light metals, especially lithium and beryllium, in the bodies of the solar system is considerably higher than in the atmosphere of the sun (see Table II of the Appendix, p. 269). For the earth's crust this could be explained by addition of these metals. Indeed, lithium, beryllium, and boron are the strongly pronounced lithophile elements which have an affinity for the pegmatitic and pneumatolytic derivatives of the acidic magma. However, enrichment of the light metals relative to the sun is also observed for meteorites on a scale that is only slightly smaller than their excess in the earth's crust. In terrestrial hydrogen there is also observed increased concentration of deuterium—the isotope which nearly burned out in the sun.

Perhaps the excess of deuterium and of the light metals in the composition of the earth is explained by the separation of the matter of the solar system from the sun at the time when its content of these light isotopes was much greater than it is today.[4]

Beyond Bi^{209} there is a region of α-unstable nuclei, three of which (Th^{232}, U^{238}, and AcU^{235}) occur in nature as independent isotopes and are the progenitors of the three (out of the possible four) series of radioactive elements. The heavier nuclei decay by spontaneous fission, which finally terminates the series of the natural isotopes. The decay of the independent α-emitters gives rise to a large family of active daughter elements whose abundance is wholly determined by the laws of nuclear decay. In nature—for example, in separate sectors of the earth's crust—there is a possibility of migration of radioactive daughter elements, which causes their local departure from the proportion determined by the law of radioactive equilibrium. Some of the characteristics of this migration were considered in Section 9 (p. 94).

The final product of the fourth, the neptunium series, of radioactive elements ($A = 4n + 1$) is long-lived bismuth. Unfortunately, bismuth has only one isotope, so that it is impossible to establish the admixture of products of this series.

The longest-lived isotope of the neptunium series is neptunium proper, but, since its half-life is only 2.2×10^6 years, it had practically decayed during the first tens of millions of years of the earth's existence. However, its abundance could not have been very high because the abundance of bismuth in the earth's crust and meteorites is approximately one-hundreth that of lead.

In recent years the long-lived isotopes U^{236} and Pu^{244} have been produced artificially, both of which decay by α-emission to the main isotope of thorium, Th^{232}. The half-life of Pu (7.6×10^7 years [121]) is the longest for the artificially prepared radioactive nuclei, but it is still too short for the isotope to have been preserved in nature until the present time. When the earth's crust was formed, this progenitor of thorium had already decayed, and it is difficult to assume that traces of its existence could be discovered on the basis of some peculiarities in the geochemistry of thorium.[5]

Along with the dying-away of one type of radioactive nuclei, other types of isotope species—the decay products of unstable nuclei—accumulate. In the earth's crust there has been a noticeable increase (by about one and a half times) in the content of lead and a strong increase in that of Ar^{40}. A common product of nuclear decay is helium, but the helium content of the cosmos is many times greater than the

[4] Instead of saying that the earth and the meteorites contain excess of the light elements, it would have been better to say that the sun is deficient in these elements.

[5] However, some measurable effects due to the spontaneous fission decay branch of Pu^{244} might still be observable.

cosmic content of all heavier elements combined, and, in general, no substantial increase in the abundance of helium, at the expense of the known processes (thermonuclear reactions, radioactive decay), is observed.

Fission Products and Decay Products of Extinct Elements

It is of interest to ask to what extent the heavy nuclei which lie beyond uranium and are unstable against fission could have enriched some isotopes of the intermediate weight with their fragments. The last stable isotopes (lead) of Mendeleyev's table and also the unstable isotopes (thorium and uranium) possess a relatively high abundance. If we assume that the primordial abundance of transuranium elements was of the same order of magnitude, then the total quantity of fragments would be sufficient to increase the abundance of some isotopes.

As we pointed out in Section 14, in the spontaneous and the slow-neutron fission of uranium, unequal fragments are produced whose atomic weights often gravitate toward the region of the closed neutron shells. A number of elements with increased abundance also lie in the region of the closed neutron shells. However, a comparison of the relative yield of isotopes—the fission products—with their content in natural elements does not show any similarity. The yield curve as a function of A has a comparatively smooth course and a sloping, well-defined maximum, but the points on the abundance curve are very much scattered, with the predominance of even isotopes being clearly observed. In addition, isobars of high charge (the "shielded isobars," as they are sometimes called) are generally not formed during fission. The fragments possess an excess of neutrons and are therefore β-unstable. As a result of successive β-decays, the fragments go over into

TABLE 44

ISOTOPES OF XENON

A	Yield in Uranium Fission		Isotopic Composition of Xenon	
	With Slow Neutrons (Per Cent)	Spontaneous Fission (Arbitrary Units)	In Arbitrary Units	In Per Cent
124.........	Absent	Absent	0.066	0.096
126.........	Absent	Absent	0.062	0.090
128.........	Absent	Absent	1.3	1.919
129.........	Absent	Absent	18.2	26.44
130.........	Absent	Absent	2.8	4.08
131.........	2.8	0.74	14.6	21.18
132.........	4.2	3.46	18.5	26.89
134.........	5.5	5.10	7.2	10.44
136.........	6.1	6.1	6.1	8.87

the state of some stable nucleus. If the nuclei of a given atomic weight form isobars, then the final state is obviously the first stable isobar of lower charge, and isobars of higher charge are generally not formed among fission products. However, in the isotopic composition of natural elements, the content of isobars of higher charge can be fairly high (molybdenum, which lies in the region of the 50-neutron shell, contains more of such nuclei than of any other even isotopes).

In Table 44 is given a comparison of the isotopic composition of xenon with the yield of xenon isotopes in spontaneous [90] and slow-neutron fission [260] of uranium.

In Table 45 is shown the fission yield and the abundance of some isotopes of the 82-neutron shell region. The ratio of radiogenic isotopes is totally unlike the corresponding ratio in nature.

TABLE 45

ABUNDANCE AND YIELD OF SOME ISOTOPES OF 82-NEUTRON SHELL REGION DURING SLOW-NEUTRON FISSION OF URANIUM

Element	*A*	Yield of Fragments (Per Cent)	Abundance in Earth's Crust (According to Table III) (10^{-4} Per Cent)
Barium	135	5.9	4
Lanthanum	139	6.3	0.8
Cerium	140	6.1	3.5
Praseodymium	141	5.7	0.6
Neodymium	143	5.4	0.24
Neodymium	144	5.3	0.47
Samarium	147	2.6	0.12
Samarium	149	1.4	0.11
Europium	153	0.15	0.015

Ya. I. Frenkel' [261] and I. P. Selinov [262] assume that in stellar interiors there is a possibility of fission of heavy nuclei which have arisen during neutron capture by atomic nuclei. But the latter process is connected with the impoverishment of atomic nuclei in protons, and this, on the contrary, reduces the fission capability of nuclei. Nonetheless, the general idea of Frenkel' and Selinov about the role of fission products in the formation of isotopes of the region of the abundance-curve peaks deserves attention. The distribution of uranium fragments cannot explain the abundance of isotopes of this region (see Table 45); but uranium anyway could not cause enrichment with its fragments of medium-weight isotopes. The probability of uranium fission is very small, much smaller than the probability of α-decay, and one should expect a great predominance of lead, together with fragments of medium weight. The accumulation of fragments, as a substantial geochemical effect, can be brought about only by the fission of the far transuranium elements, for which the spontaneous fission half-life is short and fission successfully competes with α-decay. On the nature of fragments of these elements, experimental data are not as yet available.[6]

At the present time there have been artificially produced many long-lived β-unstable isotopes which are unknown in nature. Among them, the longest-lived is I^{129} ($T_{1/2} = 1.72 \times 10^7$ years). It decays by β-emission to Xe^{129}, which is the only odd isotope whose abundance is greater than the sum of the abundances of the neighboring even isotopes. The neighboring even isotopes—Xe^{128} and Xe^{130}—enter into even isobar pairs as components of higher charge (the "shielded isobars"). The abundance of such isobars is low, so that the relative content of the interposed odd isotopes, $n_A/(n_{A-1} + n_{A+1})$ (A is odd) generally speaking, increases. For xenon, this ratio achieves an exceptionally high value.

In Table 46 is given the abundance of odd isotopes for those cases in which the neighboring even isotopes are "shielded isobars."

TABLE 46

RELATIVE ABUNDANCE OF ODD ISOTOPES, A, SITUATED BETWEEN "SHIELDED ISOBARS," $A \pm 1$ (n_A IS ABUNDANCE OF ISOTOPE IN PER CENT)

Z	ELEMENT	$A - 1$	n_{A-1}	ODD ISOTOPE A	ODD ISOTOPE n_A	$A + 1$	n_{A+1}	$\frac{n_A}{n_{A+1} + n_{A-1}}$
42.......	Molybdenum	94	9.12	95	15.70	96	16.50	0.61
44.......	Ruthenium	98	2.2	99	12.8	100	12.7	0.86
50.......	Tin	114	0.65	115	0.34	116	14.24	0.023
54.......	Xenon	128	1.919	129	26.44	130	4.08	4.41
56.......	Barium	134	2.42	135	6.59	136	7.81	0.645
62.......	Samarium	148	11.27	149	13.84	150	7.47	0.74

The anomalous position of Xe^{129} needs no explanation. It supports the view (see Sec. 6, p. 66) that Xe^{129} is enriched to a considerable extent in the extinct odd isobar I^{129} [120, 263]. Of course, many unstable nuclei passed into a stable state soon after the formation of atomic nuclei or in the process of their formation. This, however, cannot be ascertained and is apparently of no great significance in the study of the contemporary abundance of isotopes.

[6] Some data on the nature of the fission fragments of the transuranium elements are available. See, for example, Glenn T. Seaborg, *The Transuranium Elements* (New Haven: Yale University Press, 1958).

17. AGE AND COSMIC EVOLUTION OF ATOMIC NUCLEI

Many elements of Mendeleyev's periodic table have radioactive isotopes. This proves conclusively that the chemical elements of the universe that surrounds us have a finite existence. It is obvious that, when considering the genesis of atomic nuclei, it is necessary to explain not only how but also when they were formed. Many radioactive isotopes do not differ in their abundance from neighboring isotopes, and the behavior of radioactive elements is subject to the general regularities of the elemental abundances. Since the processes of transformation of heavy nuclei take place in the surrounding universe only on an insignificant scale, it is necessary to assume that matter, with its modern distribution of A and Z values among the individual heavy nuclei, was put together essentially in a certain "element-forming" system. In this sense it is permissible to speak about the "age" of atomic nuclei.

The data are still insufficient to judge whether the main bulk of the contemporary nuclei of the Galaxy was formed in the system at the same time or at different times. Obviously, the formation could have been accomplished prior to the origin of the Galaxy as well as during its history. The answer to this does not follow from general premises and should be sought by experimental means. Thus the concepts "the age of atomic nuclei" and "the age of the Galaxy" are not identical. In foreign science these concepts, as well as the concepts of the age of the earth and of the solar system, are sometimes interchanged or substituted for each other. Not far behind this is concealed a tacit, or even an open, admission that matter originated several billion years ago—an idealistic concept about the creation of the universe.

We must rigorously distinguish and delimit the following concepts:

The age of atomic nuclei.—Probable, but not proved, is the isochronous formation of atomic nuclei. Strictly speaking, we can attempt to determine only the age of individual elements of the earth's crust—for example, we can speak of the uranium age, the potassium age, and so forth. We assume that the term "the age of atomic nuclei" will not give rise to the erroneous idea that in the history of creation there was an epoch when matter did not consist of atomic nuclei.

The age of the Galaxy.—The kinetics of the astronomical processes permit us to estimate the age of individual formations of the Galaxy. For example, V. A. Ambartsumian [264] proposes the following method of estimating the age of open stellar clusters. The stars of the open clusters, which can be considered as stellar gas, tend, as a result of interaction, toward an equilibrium condition. The gas laws show that in the state of equilibrium all components have the same energy. In this state, the stars with a smaller mass possess a greater velocity and are capable of leaving the clusters. The relaxation time of stellar clusters can be estimated, and, from the contemporary state of these systems, it is possible to determine their age. At the present time there exists interesting material on the age of individual astronomical objects, but the accuracy of these determinations is not high, and a complete answer to the question of the age of the Galaxy has not yet been obtained.

In the history of the cosmos, certainly, the processes of redistribution of the entire nuclear matter according to atomic weights and charges took place. In the present Galaxy two main processes occur which change the composition of the chemical elements: (1) conversion of hydrogen into helium by way of nuclear reaction, with participation of nitrogen and carbon; (2) spontaneous decay of radioactive elements.[7] In this section we are going to examine those possibilities offered for the explanation of the age of the cosmogonic processes by experimental material on radioactive elements.

The age of the earth's crust.—This age is, of course, younger than the age of the Galaxy and of atomic nuclei, inasmuch as the formation of heavy isotopes did not take place in the bodies of the solar system. It is obvious that the maximum age of the minerals of the earth's crust represents the lower limit of the age of the crust, and certainly that of the age of atomic nuclei.

The question of the age of individual objects of the earth's crust and of the solar system was considered in the last sections of chapter i. The age of the oldest minerals of the earth's crust is evidently not greater than 2.6 billion years. The oldest ore leads with an "ancient" isotopic composition possess a similar age of about 3 billion years. This age is determined from the rate of accumulation of radiogenic lead in the crust of the earth. The age of the meteorites is much higher. Similar considerations about lead accumulation show that the isotopic composition of lead from iron meteorites corresponds to that which existed on the earth about 4 billion years ago. From the ratio of the radiogenic leads Pb^{207} and Pb^{206} in the stony meteorites, the age of these objects is 4.4–4.6 billion years.[8] The argon method gives an age for the stony meteorites up to 4.5–4.8 billion years.[9] There is a gap

[7] The possibility of continuous synthesis of heavy elements in stars should also be included in this list. In this connection see, for example, the discussions by W. A. Fowler, G. R. Burbidge, and E. M. Burbidge (*Astrophys. Jour., Suppl. Ser.,* **2**: 167–94, 1955); W. A. Fowler and J. L. Greenstein (*Proc. Nat. Acad. Sci.,* **42**: 173–80, 1956); E. M. Burbidge, G. R. Burbidge, W. A. Fowler, and F. Hoyle (*Rev. Mod. Phys.,* **29**: 547–650, 1957).

[8] C. Patterson (*Geochim. et Cosmochim. Acta,* **10**: 230–37, 1956) in more recent summary of his work gave an age of 4.55 ± 0.07 billion years for the stony meteorites.

[9] The potassium-argon age interval quoted in this paragraph has been criticized in footnotes on p. 72.

observed between the ages of the oldest minerals of the earth's crust and the meteorites. The "first billion" years of the earth's history did not leave observable manifestations in its crust. It is not known how much younger the earth's crust is than the solar system, but, obviously, the formation proceeded as follows: the solar system—the earth—the earth's crust.

Upper Limit of the Age of the Earth's Crust

Russell [265] first proposed the determination of the age of the earth from the ratio between the content of lead and that of the radioactive elements of the earth's crust. This method is known to give low results, inasmuch as the earth's crust is relatively enriched in uranium and thorium. More substantiated data are obtained by comparing the ratios of the radiogenic isotopes of lead. I. E. Starik [126] used the ratio of Pb^{206} to Pb^{207} for the determination of the age of the earth, according to equation (8.2) (p. 89). From the accumulation of radiogenic lead it is possible to establish (see Sec. 8) that the age of the earth's crust is not greater than 5.2 billion years.

These data may be used also to estimate the age of the atomic nuclei of the solar system. First of all, we shall attempt to define more precisely the upper limit of the age of the earth's crust. This limit has been obtained on the assumption that Pb^{206} and Pb^{207} in the earth's crust are wholly of radiogenic origin. This, of course, is not true; but, for an accurate solution of the problem, information is needed on the original isotopic composition of lead, which is unknown. However, using the data on the neighboring elements of the periodic table, it is possible to estimate the lower limit of the ratio of the isotopes of the original lead [136]. In the present epoch,

$$\gamma = \frac{2Pb^{207}}{Pb^{206} + Pb^{208}} = 0.550. \qquad (17.1)$$

Using data on the change of the isotopic composition of lead [see eq. (8.1)], it is possible to represent γ as a function of time (see Fig. 8, p. 93). The value of γ never exceeded 0.645. In Table 47 are given values of

$$\gamma = \frac{2n_A}{n_{A+1} + n_{A-1}}$$

(A is odd) for the last ten even elements (from samarium to mercury) of Mendeleyev's table and for lead. If the element contains two odd isotopes, then only the heavier isotope is taken, since for the light isotope the ratio γ is known to be too high because of the low abundance of the neighboring even isotopes, the "shielded isobars."

TABLE 47

RELATIVE CONTENT OF ODD ISOTOPES FOR HEAVY ELEMENTS

	Element					
	Sm	Gd	Dy	Eb	Yb	Hf
Z.......	62	64	66	68	70	72
γ........	1.48	0.691	0.930	0.759	0.601	0.440

	Element				
	W	Os	Pt	Hg	Pb
Z.......	74	76	78	80	82
γ........	0.505	0.811	1.16	0.500	0.550

The ratio γ varies from 0.440 (hafnium) to 1.48 (samarium), its average value being 0.734. The relative abundance of odd isotopes, generally speaking, increases for the heavy nuclei, so that the value of 0.440 may be accepted as a minimum value for primordial lead. Then the maximum age of the earth's crust turns out to be 4.7×10^9 years. Consideration of the probable isotopic composition of primordial lead permits us to lower this age from 5.2 to 4.7 billion years.

If the recent composition of lead is $Pb^{204} = 1.00$, $Pb^{206} = 18.50$, $Pb^{207} = 15.69$, $Pb^{208} = 38.51$, then 4.7×10^9 years ago this composition was $Pb^{204} = 1.00$, $Pb^{206} = 8.05$, $Pb^{207} = 7.8$, $Pb^{208} = 27.09$. The increase in lead through the accumulation of radiogenic isotopes in the course of the earth's existence was not greater than 67 per cent.

Age of Atomic Nuclei[10]

The geologists constructed their time scale in a chronological perspective in such a manner that the preceding stages of the earth's history become longer with time, from the last Quaternary period, which continued over scarcely 1 million years, back to the Archean, which spans not less than 2 billion years. Naturally, one would expect a still longer time interval for the existence of atomic nuclei prior to the formation of the earth; however, this interval appears to be relatively small. This is indicated by an abnormally high abundance of Xe^{129}—the decay product of the extinct I^{129} (see p. 80)—in the xenon

[10] This discussion of the age of atomic nuclei should now take into account the recent discovery of excess Xe^{129} in meteorites by J. H. Reynolds (*Phys. Rev. Letters*, **4**: 8–10, 351–54, 1960; *Jour. Geophys. Res.*, **65**: 3843–46, 1960), P. Signer (*Zeitschr. f. Naturforsch.*, **15a**: 748–49, 1960), and J. Zähringer and W. Gentner (*Zeitschr. f. Naturforsch.*, **15a**: 600–602, 1960), and the determination of the iodine content of meteorites by G. G. Goles and E. Anders (*Jour. Geophys. Res.*, **65**: 4181–84, 1960).

of the earth's atmosphere. It is possible that traces of I^{129} still existed at the time of the formation of the bodies of the solar system, thus assuring a several fold increase in the amount of Xe^{129}. In order for such an increase to manifest itself noticeably, it is necessary that the system initially lost the given element, since the abundance of the neighboring isotopes in primordial matter was, on the average, the same; so that the enrichment of a certain isotope with the decay products of the neighboring radioelement cannot substantially change its concentration.

If the radioactive isotope I^{129} were preserved prior to the formation of the earth and meteorites, the enrichment in the radiogenic isotope would be greater for the meteoritic than for terrestrial xenon, inasmuch as meteorites lost the rare gases to a larger extent than did the earth. However, xenon isolated from stony meteorites [183, 186] does not show an excess content of Xe^{129}. If this xenon is not a terrestrial impurity, then an important conclusion follows. The present isotopic composition of xenon, which is the same for the earth and meteorites, was evidently produced in the dust cloud from which, in the opinion of the majority of cosmogonists, the bodies of the solar system were formed. The dust cloud had already lost the bulk of the volatile components (the rare gases, iodine), but their traces could have been retained in the solid phase of the primordial substratum. Naturally, in the course of the evolution of this substratum, including the formation of the massive bodies of the solar system, the loss of the volatile components could have continued; for example, even until the present time He^3 is being rapidly lost from the atmosphere of the earth.

We shall estimate the time interval between the formation of atomic nuclei and the dust cloud, using the data on the abundance of Xe^{129}. Let us assume that there was no further loss of the rare gases, i.e., we shall equate the relative xenon content of the dust cloud to that of the earth. It is obvious that the age estimate will be too high. The earth's content of xenon relative to that of the neighboring elements decreased by a factor of 10^5 (see Table 4, p. 33), whereas the content of iodine decreased by approximately a factor of 10. The amount of radiogenic Xe^{129} is probably not less than a factor of 5 greater than the primeval abundance of this isotope (see Table 46). Assuming that the abundances of I^{129} and I^{127} were approximately equal at the instant of the formation of atomic nuclei—a common occurrence for the elements of the central region of Mendeleyev's table—we shall find that the amount of I^{129} preserved at the time of the formation of the dust cloud decreased by hundreds of times in comparison with the initial amount, I_0. Taking into consideration $T_I = 1.72 \times 10^7$ years, we find from

$$I^{129} = I_0^{129} e^{-\lambda} \tag{17.2}$$

that the time t is 0.1–0.15 billion years. This value represents the upper limit of the given time interval.

The age of atomic nuclei is the sum of the duration of three periods:

1. The time between the formation of atomic nuclei and the evolution of the dust cloud ($\leqslant$ 0.15 billion years).

2. The time of the existence of the dust cloud prior to the formation of the planets. This time cannot be measured by radioactive methods, but, according to the data of modern cosmogony, it is apparently short.

3. The age of the earth's crust. The maximum value of this age, from the given calculations, is 4.7 billion years.

Thus the probable age of atomic nuclei is about 4.8 billion years.

More rigorous and reliable is the estimation of this age proposed by Rutherford [266] as early as 1929 (this was the first attempt in the history of science to determine the age of atomic nuclei). Rutherford started from the basic regularity in the abundance of atomic nuclei, according to which the abundance of odd isotopes is, on the average, lower than that of even isotopes, and assumed that in the first instant of the existence of atomic nuclei the abundance of odd actinouranium, AcU^{235}, did not exceed that of even U^{238}. If the present ratio of these isotopes is AcU/U and the original ratio was $(AcU/A)_0$, then it is obvious that

$$\frac{AcU}{U} = \left(\frac{AcU}{U}\right)_0 e^{-(\lambda_{AcU} - \lambda_U)t},$$

whence the age of the system is

$$t = \frac{1}{\lambda_{AcU} - \lambda_U} \ln \left[\frac{U}{AcU}\left(\frac{AcU}{U}\right)_0\right]. \tag{17.3}$$

Assuming that at the first instant the ratio $(AcU/U)_0$ could not have been greater than 1, Rutherford estimated that the upper limit of the uranium age is 3.4 billion years.

This method was proposed at a time when not only precise information on actinouranium was lacking but the element had not yet been discovered. There existed only a hypothesis concerning the origin of the actinium series from a certain unknown isotope of uranium [267]; and on the basis of indirect assumptions it was possible to estimate the abundance and the half-life of this isotope. Using the new data (see Table VI, p. 286), we obtain $t = 5.52$ billion years.

On the average, even isotopes are more abundant than odd isotopes, but in some cases the opposite is observed. Actually, it is necessary to take into account the position of isotopes in the composition of the element. Actinouranium and uranium are, respectively, the heaviest odd and the heaviest even isotopes of uranium. In Table 48 are given data on the abundance and the ratio of isotopes of this type for the heavy even elements.

TABLE 48

HEAVIEST ODD AND EVEN ISOTOPES FOR HEAVY EVEN ELEMENTS

Z	ELEMENT	ABUNDANCE OF HEAVIEST ISOTOPE (PER CENT)		$\frac{n_A}{n_{A+3}}$
		Odd n_A	Even n_{A+3}	
74	Tungsten	14.4	28.4	0.501
76	Osmium	16.1	41.0	0.39
78	Platinum	33.7	7.23	4.66
80	Mercury	13.22	6.85	1.93
Av.	...	...	...	1.16

The ratio n_A/n_{A+3} is subject to considerable fluctuation—in fact, so large that the average value is not legitimate. One can assume that the primeval ratio AcU/A lay within the possible limits 0.39–4.66 of values for the heavy elements. According to Table 48, these limiting values are possessed by osmium and platinum. For all even elements heavier than cerium (which has no odd isotopes) the abundance ratio of the heaviest odd to heaviest even elements falls within these limits. The data on the lighter elements need not be given, since the abundance ratio of odd to even isotopes is known to be smaller for them than for the heavy elements.

If we assume that the primeval relative abundance of actinouranium lay within the indicated limits, then, according to equation (17.3), we obtain

$$\text{A minimum value:} \quad t = 4.47 \times 10^9 \text{ years}; \left(\frac{\text{AcU}}{\text{U}}\right)_0 = 0.39;$$

$$\text{A maximum value:} \quad t = 7.24 \times 10^9 \text{ years}; \left(\frac{\text{AcU}}{\text{U}}\right)_0 = 4.66.$$

The probable age of the uranium nuclei is within the interval 4.5–7.2 billion years.

The singular regularities which govern the abundance of atomic nuclei support the assumption that all heavy nuclei were formed at the same time in a single system. Unfortunately, age determination from the content of other radioactive isotopes is somewhat difficult. The decay probability for most of these isotopes is so small that their abundance did not decrease in any observable manner within the time of the existence of atomic nuclei.

The radioactive odd isobars In^{115} and Re^{187} are the most abundant isotopes in the respective elements. The content of Rb^{87} is smaller than that of the non-radioactive light isotope:

$$\frac{Rb^{85}}{Rb^{87}} = 2.67. \tag{17.4}$$

The ratio of isotopes of the same type (see Table VII of the Appendix, p. 293) decreases, on the average, with increasing atomic weight. It is larger than 2.67 only for some elements lighter than rubidium, and for the elements heavier than nickel it is always smaller. However, the difference is not so large as to affirm the decrease in the content of Rb^{87} at the expense of radioactive decay.

The abundance of odd-odd radioactive nuclei in the isotopic composition of their elements is very low (see Table 26, p. 140). This is not connected with the decay of these nuclei because the decay rate for most of them (with the exception of K^{40}) is so slow that their abundance did not decrease substantially within the time of the existence of the earth. The small probability of β-decay in these isotopes is determined by the forbidden nature of the transmutation due to a large angular momentum of the nuclei. Obviously, not only did this condition inhibit the decay, but in the due course of time it also interfered with the formation of odd-odd nuclei which survived in nature.

In conclusion we shall give the age estimate for the system of the galactic nebulae that surrounds us. The age was obtained from the data on the Hubble effect—the red shift in the spectral lines of distant galaxies. The shift increases in direct proportion to the distance. According to the elementary theory of the Doppler effect, this shift indicates that the nebulae move away from us with velocities which increase in the direction of the outer fringes of the universe, so that at some stage back in time the density of the matter now accessible to observation was very high. According to some cosmologic theories, the expansion of the universe is a consequence of its geometry. We shall not consider the speculative concepts which are unavoidable in the attempts to explain one of the most important and difficult problems of theoretical astrophysics, but from the experimental data we shall be able to estimate the time interval needed for the system of galaxies to expand to their present condition. On the basis of recent data [295] this age of the universe is 5.4 ± 1.1 billion years.[11] Thus we have the following cosmic age values:

[11] The revised astronomical estimate for the age (the reciprocal of the Hubble constant H) of the universe is $(13 \pm 7) \times 10^9$ years (A. Sandage, *Astrophys. Jour.*, **127:** 513–26, 1958). There is close agreement between this value and the value of $(11 \pm 6) \times 10^9$ years derived for H^{-1} by W. A. Fowler and F. Hoyle (*Ann. Phys.*, **10:** 280–302, 1960) from the thorium-uranium ratio in meteorites, assuming addition of new material to the Galaxy from time to time. The assumption of the Autonomous Galaxy gave the age of $15_{-3}^{+5} \times 10^9$ years.

The age of atomic nuclei from the lead and xenon isotope data...... 4.8 ± 0.5 billion years

The age of atomic nuclei from the uranium method of Rutherford ...... 5.9 ± 1 billion years

The age of the system of galaxies from the Hubble effect data...... 5.4 ± 1 billion years

The practical agreement of all these ages is hardly accidental. Probably, 5 billion years ago, there occurred a powerful cosmic revolution, in the course of which the structural units of the microcosm—the atomic nuclei—and the largest units of the macrocosm—the galaxies—came into existence.

Cosmic Evolution of Atomic Nuclei

Let us consider the problem of the evolution of a nuclear assemblage. The principal factor in the change of its composition and in the release of the energy of the cosmos are thermonuclear reactions. The probability of the reaction upon collision in stellar interiors of fast particles with a relative velocity v is given by the expression

$$dw = n_1 v \sigma \, dn_2(v),$$

where n_1 and n_2 are the stellar concentrations of the reacting particles. Under conditions of thermodynamic equilibrium in the environment, a Maxwellian distribution is established:

$$dn_2(v) = n_2 \frac{mv}{kT} e^{-mv^2/2kT} \, dv \tag{17.5}$$

(T is the temperature of the environment), i.e., the number of particles with a high velocity is very small.

The cross-section of the reaction is

$$\sigma = \sigma_0 D, \tag{17.6}$$

where

$$D \sim \exp\left(-\frac{2\pi e^2 Z_1 Z_2}{\hbar v}\right)$$

is the transparency of the mutual potential barrier during the collision of particles with charges Z_1 and Z_2. The cross-section, σ, is large only for particles with high velocities. As a result, thermonuclear reactions are feasible only in a narrow range of velocities for which the number of particles with high velocity is not yet too small and the cross-section of the reaction is already large. Calculation [268] shows that the probability of the thermonuclear reaction is

$$w = c_1 n_1 n_2 e^{-c_2(Z_1^{2/3} Z_2^{2/3}/T^{1/3})}, \tag{17.7}$$

where c_1 and c_2 are certain numerical constants. It is seen that the probability depends very strongly (exponentially) on the charges of the active nuclei and the temperature of the medium.

A star begins its existence from a cold, rarefied gas cloud whose density increases under the action of gravitational forces. The released energy causes the heating of the interior layers of the star. When an adequate temperature is reached, thermonuclear reactions begin which provide sufficient gas pressure, opposed to gravitational pressure, that the star attains a certain stationary condition. The first thermonuclear reactions which take place at sufficiently low temperatures are the reactions of irreversible burning of light metals, with the capture of protons and the final production of helium—the (p, α) reactions. The duration of such a condition is hardly longer than 10^6–10^7 years. After these light nuclei have been destroyed, there is a further contraction and heating of the star, and the proton reactions, with participation of carbon and nitrogen (and also of deuterium), set in.[12]

The special characteristics of the binding energy of the light atomic nuclei leads to the energetic infeasibility of proton capture and of subsequent α-emission by C^{12}, C^{13}, and N^{14}, inasmuch as in these reactions B^9, B^{10}, and C^{11} should be produced. These nuclei and even their stable decay products, Be^9 and B^{11}, possess a much smaller binding energy than helium or the isotopes of carbon and nitrogen. But upon proton capture by the N^{15} nucleus, the reaction (p, α) leads to the formation of the C^{12} nucleus, with a large binding energy, and proves to be energetically feasible. Thus a small binding energy of the nuclei of light metals causes repeated proton capture by carbon, which proceeds as far as the formation of N^{15}, according to the catalytic reaction of Bethe (5.2) (see p. 47).

The course of this reaction in the stars is determined not by the carbon and nitrogen reserves (in the course of the reaction these elements remain almost undepleted) but by the content of hydrogen. Therefore, the energy release at the expense of the Bethe reaction and the proton reaction (5.3) continues for a long time. If one assumes that the star will continue its radiation with the same energy as at the present time until the exhaustion of its hydrogen reserves, then the lifetime of the star will be

$$t = \frac{C_H V_H M}{m_H L}, \tag{17.8}$$

where $C_H \approx 0.5$ is the relative concentration of hydrogen, $V_H \approx 8$ Mev

[12] For a detailed analysis of the element-building processes in stars see E. M. Burbidge, G. R. Burbidge, W. A. Fowler, and F. Hoyle (*Rev. Mod. Phys.*, **29**: 547–650, 1950).

is the energy released during the burning of one hydrogen nucleus, m_H is the mass of the hydrogen atom, and the letters M and L denote, respectively, the mass and luminosity of the star. For the sun,

$$t_\odot \approx 5 \times 10^{10} \text{ years.}$$

Introducing the relationship between the mass M and the luminosity L of the stars,

$$L \sim M^n, \tag{17.9}$$

where $n = 3$–4, we find that

$$t = t_\odot \left(\frac{M_\odot}{M}\right)^{n-1} \tag{17.10}$$

($M_\odot$ is the mass of the sun).

The time of the exhaustion of the energy supplies decreases with the mass of the star, and for a star with $M = 10M_\odot$ it is only 10^7–10^8 years, i.e., of the order of the duration of geologic epochs.[13] For the majority of the stars the duration of thermonuclear reactions is about 10^{11} years. Since the age of the sun is probably of the order of 5×10^9 years, the sun is still at the beginning of its evolutionary path.

The stars for which the carbon-nitrogen and proton reactions play an essential role during the release of their energy comprise the so-called main sequence, to which belongs the overwhelming majority of stars. For the main-sequence stars, the temperature and luminosity are related by means of the following approximate formula:

$$L \sim MT^i \quad (i \gg 1). \tag{17.11}$$

Outside the main sequence, there is a branch of red giants which have low temperatures and high luminosity. For one type of these stars (class N red giants) G. A. Shain [72] discovered an anomalous isotopic composition of carbon—an increased C^{13}/C^{12} ratio which varies for individual objects. This suggests that the red giants are young stars just entering the carbon-nitrogen stage of the main sequence. However, in astrophysics, up to this day, there is no generally accepted theory of red giants.[14]

The rapid burning of light metals in thermonuclear reactions determines the low abundance of these metals in all cosmic objects, with the possible exception of cosmic rays. The reverse processes of the

[13] In fact, the lifetime of the giants is still shorter because the massive stars emit considerable corpuscular radiation. [Author's footnote.]

[14] There is some consensus on this subject. See, for example, A. G. W. Cameron (*Astrophys. Jour.*, **121**: 144–60, 1955); W. A. Fowler, G. R. Burbidge, and E. M. Burbidge (*Astrophys. Jour.*, **122**: 271–85, 1955; *Astrophys. Jour. Suppl. Ser.*, **2**: 167–94, 1955); E. Anders (*Astrophys. Jour.*, **127**: 355–62, 1958). Note, however, more recent observations of H. L. Helfer, G. Wallerstein, and J. L. Greenstein (*Astrophys. Jour.*, **129**: 700–719, 1959) on the metal-deficient K giant stars.

creation of light metals are exceedingly limited. The formation of the heavy isotope of lithium can take place according to the reaction

$$He^4 + He^3 = Be^7 + \gamma; \quad Be^7 \xrightarrow{\beta^+} Li^7;^{15} \qquad (17.12)$$

but the duration of this process for the sun ($\tau \approx 3 \times 10^7$ years) is much longer than the time of the burning of Li^7, which is approximately equal to 1 minute. The destruction of Li^7 proceeds according to the equation [269]

$$Li^7 + H^1 = 2He^4 + \gamma. \qquad (17.13)$$

The small probability of lithium production is explained by the fact that reaction (17.12) proceeds during the combination of two helium nuclei; and during the collisions of helium with atomic nuclei the barrier height is doubled in comparison with that for the proton reactions. The content of lithium during the equilibrium state of reactions (17.12) and (17.13) is negligible. These reactions determine not so much the accumulation of lithium as the formation of the stable isotope He^4 from He^3.

The energies of natural radioelements in stellar energetics can be neglected. The greatest spontaneous decay energy in the sun is probably released by K^{40}. Assuming the potassium content of the mass of the sun to be the same as that of its atmosphere and the isotopic composition of potassium the same as that on the earth, we find that K^{40} liberates about 10^{-11} erg/sec/gm of the solar matter, whereas the energy of thermonuclear reactions supplies 2 ergs/sec/gm.

The elements heavier than nitrogen practically do not change their concentration and isotopic composition even at as late a stage as the exhaustion of the hydrogen sources in the stars. After the bulk of hydrogen has burned up, the star collapses, and its temperature rises. At $T = 2 \times 10^8$ deg. C., which is one order of magnitude higher than the temperature of the central regions of the ordinary stars, thermonuclear reactions of the helium nuclei become possible. The heavy atomic nuclei can be formed from helium by way of the endothermic Salpeter reaction [296]:

$$He^4 + He^4 + Q = Be^8 + \gamma$$

($Q = 0.095$ Mev). Be^8 is unstable at low densities and temperatures, and, by capturing helium, it can form heavier nuclei:

$$Be^8 + He^4 = C^{12} + Q, \text{ etc.}$$

The energy yield of such reactions cannot be large because the participating nuclei are saturated, with the binding-energy difference being relatively small. In a number of studies [297–99] the possibilities of synthesis of the heavy nuclei at the expense of helium capture have

[15] Be^7 decays to Li^7 by electron capture.

been investigated. The astrophysical premises of these studies cannot be reliable, inasmuch as our knowledge of the stars of the later stage of evolution is debatable and inaccurate.

In the systems which have achieved a high density, the degeneracy of the stellar gas becomes possible. The criterion of the degeneracy of particles with mass m is the increase in the energy W of the degenerate gas relative to the energy of the thermal motion of the particle:

$$W = \frac{h^2}{2\overline{m}^{2/3}m}\left(\frac{3}{8\pi}\rho\right)^{2/3}, \tag{17.14}$$

where ρ is the density of the gas and $\overline{m}$ is the mean mass of the gas particles. The value of W increases for the light particles, so that degeneracy of the electron gas occurs first. With increasing density, the energy of the degenerate gas can achieve a critical value W_{cr} at which a reverse β-process is feasible—the capture of electrons by protons, with the formation of neutrons according to the equation

$$p + e + W_{cr} = n + \nu. \tag{17.15}$$

In vacuum a direct reaction takes place:

$$n = p + e + \nu + W_\beta, \tag{17.16}$$

with the release of energy $W_\beta = 0.7823$ Mev. Assuming that $W_\beta = W_{cr}$, we find

$$\rho_{cr} = 2 \times 10^6 \text{ gm/cm}^3.$$

L. D. Landau [270] in 1937 showed that, at high densities of stellar matter, conversion of protons into neutrons can take place. The assumption that this reaction is the main source of stellar energy was not confirmed, but the reaction should manifest itself regularly during the depletion of the energy resources of the star. At this stage the abundance of hydrogen is low, so that reaction (17.15) does not proceed with free protons but with protons as the component particles of the heavy nuclei, thus leading to the relative enrichment of the latter in neutrons and to the formation of neutron-rich nuclei.

Neutron-rich Nuclei

Let us examine the energetic conditions of the possibility of the existence of nuclei with a large mass which are enriched in neutrons. We shall follow the scheme worked out by us in 1939 [271]. The atomic weight and charge of the nuclei are related, according to the simplest statistical theory, by means of equation (11.12) (p. 128):

$$\left(1 + \frac{A - 2Z}{A}\right)^{2/3} - \left(1 - \frac{A - 2Z}{A}\right)^{2/3} = \frac{6}{5}\frac{c}{\epsilon}\frac{Z}{A^{1/3}}. \tag{17.17}$$

For the light nuclei, the ratio $(A - 2Z/A)$ is small, and the left side of equation (17.17) can be expanded into a power series of this ratio. With increasing atomic weight, the ratio Z/A decreases. Setting $Z = xA$, where $x < 1$, we find

$$x = \frac{\xi}{A^{2/3}}\left[1 - \left(\frac{\xi}{A^{2/3}}\right)^{2/3} - \frac{2}{3}\frac{\xi}{A^{2/3}} - \cdots\right],$$

where

$$\xi = \frac{5}{6}\,2^{2/3}\,\frac{\epsilon}{c} \approx 30.$$

For the very heavy neutron-rich nuclei the relative number of protons is small,

$$Z = \xi A^{1/3}, \tag{17.18}$$

and the neutron-rich nuclei of a sufficiently large mass turn out to be fission-stable. The upper limit of atomic nuclei capable of fission according to equation (14.1) is determined from the relation

$$\frac{Z^2}{A} = \xi^2 A_f^{-1/3} \geqslant 2, \tag{17.19}$$

whence $A_f \approx 10^8$. From equation (11.3) we find that the mean kinetic energy of the heavy neutron-rich nuclei is $2^{2/3}\varepsilon$, whereas the binding energy [compare eqs. (11.8) and (11.18), p. 133] is

$$U_A = v' - |v'|A^{-1/3}, \tag{17.20}$$

where the coefficient of the volume energy $v' = u - 2^{2/3}\varepsilon \approx 5$ Mev. At large values of A,

$$U_A \approx v' \approx 5 \text{ Mev}, \tag{17.21}$$

i.e., the binding energy tends to a constant value that is half the value of the binding energy of the existing atomic nuclei. The accuracy of the determination of this value is, of course, not great. The dependence of the charge upon atomic weight, which embraces the region of the light as well as of the neutron-rich nuclei, can be given approximately in the form

$$Z = \frac{A/2}{1 + (A^{2/3}/2\xi)}. \tag{17.22}$$

The potential of the Coulomb field on the surface of the heavy neutron-rich nuclei converges to a constant value,

$$\frac{Ze}{R} = \frac{\xi_e}{r_0} \approx 30 \text{ Mev}, \tag{17.23}$$

which is twice as large as the surface potential of the heavy atomic nuclei. For the neutron-rich nuclei, the increase in the potential barrier is accompanied by a potential barrier broadening, inasmuch as these entities are sufficiently large. Therefore, the transparency coefficient of the potential barrier for the emission of the charged particles is extremely small. The interaction of the neutron-rich nuclei with the external surroundings, the capture of particles (with the exception of neutrons), and also their emission (for example, α-decay) are practically impossible.

The neutron-rich nuclei can exist regardless of the nuclear processes of stellar interiors. As yet, such nuclei have not been discovered. Evidently, if they exist, they are concentrated, because of high molecular weight, in the central regions of the stars. For the degenerate matter of the fading stars, there is a possibility of the growth of a neutron phase. It can be shown that in the case of a mass of the order of 10^{-5}–$10^{-6}\ M_\odot$ the neutron-rich nuclei can change the thermodynamic conditions of the environment substantially and cause processes which perhaps will be detected through surface manifestations.

The binding energy of the neutron-rich nuclei of very large mass increases at the expense of the increasing gravitational energy of the nucleus:

$$U = v' + \frac{3}{5} g \frac{m^2}{r_0} A^{2/3}, \tag{17.24}$$

where m is the mass of the nucleon and g is the gravitational constant of Newton. When $M \approx 0.01\ M_\odot$, both terms are of the same order of magnitude. When $M \approx 0.1\ M_\odot$, the gravitational attraction of charged particles of the external surroundings by the neutron-rich nuclei becomes greater than the electrostatic repulsion:

$$g \frac{m_1 m A^{2/3}}{r_0} \geqslant \xi \frac{z_1 e}{r_0}$$

(where m_1 and z_1 are, respectively, the mass and the charge of the particle); that is, the neutron-rich nucleus begins actively to absorb the matter of the external surroundings. The growth of the neutron-rich nucleus proceeds very rapidly, and enormous energy is released. The very large neutron-rich nuclei, like the degenerate systems of great mass, turn out to be unstable. The pressure of the degenerate gas in a non-relativistic case is

$$P_f = \frac{2}{3} E_V = \frac{2}{3} \frac{\overline{W}\rho}{m} = \frac{1}{5} \frac{h^2}{m} \left(\frac{3}{8\pi}\right)^{2/3} \left(\frac{\rho}{m}\right)^{5/3} \tag{17.25}$$

(where E_V is the energy of the volume element V and $\rho = M/V$ is the density of the gas), and the gravitational pressure is

$$P_g = -\frac{dU_g}{dV} = \frac{1}{5} \left(\frac{4\pi}{3}\right)^{1/3} g M^2 \rho^{4/3}, \tag{17.26}$$

where $U_g = \frac{3}{5} g M^2/R$ is the gravitational energy of the nucleus.

For a system of relatively low density it is always possible to find such a value of ρ as to satisfy the condition of equilibrium,

$$P_f \gg P_g,$$

under which gravitational contraction is counterbalanced by the oppositely directed gas pressure. However, at very high density the energy of the particles is very large, and the non-relativistic case cannot be used. In the extreme relativistic case ($W \gg mc^2$) the mean energy, according to equation (10.11) (p. 121), is

$$\overline{W} = \frac{3}{8}\left(\frac{3}{\pi}\right)^{1/3} hc\left(\frac{\rho}{m}\right)^{1/3},$$

and the pressure of the degenerate gas is

$$P_{f,r} = \frac{2}{3}E_V = \frac{3}{8}\left(\frac{3}{\pi}\right)^{1/3} hc\left(\frac{\rho}{m}\right)^{4/3}. \tag{17.27}$$

In this case the gas and the gravitational pressure have the same type of dependence on density ($\sim\rho^{4/3}$); so that the condition

$$P_{f,r} > P_g$$

is fulfilled only for the bodies with a mass smaller than a certain critical value.

The precise value of the mass for the degenerate gas is given by the Landau-Chandrasekhar [270, 272] criterion,

$$M = \frac{5.728}{\mu^2} M_\odot, \tag{17.28}$$

where μ is the molecular weight of the gas.

At greater values of the mass there is an infinite contraction of matter. The physical meaning of this is that the system is unstable and instantaneously passes into a new state as a result of explosion, the physical picture of which can now hardly be extrapolated.

It is possible that the flares of certain supernovae, which liberate energy of the order of 10^{40} ergs in the visible portion of the spectrum and a full energy of perhaps several orders of magnitude greater, are caused by the transition of stellar matter into a neutron phase. The supernovae represent an extremely rare phenomenon. In every galaxy there is, on the average, one flare-up in every several hundred years. In our Galaxy such flare-ups were the star of 1054 in the constellation of Taurus, recorded in Chinese chronicles, and the Nova of 1572, the so-called star of Tycho de Brahe. The closest object of this type which flared up within the time of modern astronomy was the Nova of 1885 in the Andromeda Nebula. The hypothesis regarding the connection of the supernovae with the formation of a neutron phase was postulated by Baade and Zwicky [273] in 1938, but it is not generally accepted in astronomy.

There was published in 1956 a remarkable study by G. Burbidge, F. Hoyle, E. Burbidge, R. Christy, and W. Fowler [300], who showed that the flare-ups of certain supernovae were caused by the formation of Cf^{254} in a neutron-rich environment. This idea will be considered in greater detail at the end of this chapter.

The behavior of the neutron-rich nuclei as a specific case of degenerate systems was investigated by Oppenheimer and Volkoff [274], who obtained a solution for the mass of the neutron phase in the interval 0.1–0.7 $M_{\odot}$. The calculations are based on certain specific premises concerning the geometry of nuclear space.

The Problem of White Dwarfs

In conclusion we shall consider the stars which evidently consist of a degenerate electron gas. These are the so-called white dwarfs, differing from the main-sequence stars in high temperature at very low luminosity. The white dwarfs possess an exceptionally high density (up to 10^5gm/cm^3). The nature of nuclear reactions in them is not explained. The presence of hydrogen in the spectra of white dwarfs indicates that the collapse of the stellar gas in this case has not been caused by the exhaustion of the fuel reserves but by some special mechanism, the more so because a time of the order of 10^{11} years is required for the transition of the stars into the state of a degenerate gas. There are no sufficient bases for attributing such a long lifetime to these objects of our Galaxy.

B. V. Kukarkin and P. P. Parenago [275] projected the following evolutionary sequence of unstable stars: the nova—the nova-like star of T Pyxidis type—the star of U Geminorum type—the white dwarf.

The time interval between the flare-ups of the novae is 10^3–10^4 years. As the evolution proceeds down the indicated sequence, the period and amplitude of the luminosity variation decrease until the star has become a stable white dwarf.

Many hypotheses have been proposed to explain the origin of white dwarfs. The very number of these hypotheses characterizes their unreliability. The general features of the effect indicate that the transition of a star into the state of a white dwarf is of a compulsory nature. Perhaps this is connected with the presence in the interior of the star of a neutron-rich nucleus which causes a transition of the surrounding medium into the state of a degenerate gas. A high content of hydrogen in this case assures an intensified release of energy at the expense of thermonuclear reactions. This reverts the star to its original state of ideal gas, the state which is unstable and leads to a flare-up. Considerable energy released during the flare-ups furthers rapid exhaustion of the energy of the star and transition into the state of a white dwarf.

It is doubtful whether the above considerations can solve the complex question of the origin of white dwarfs. However, it is not precluded that the consideration of the possibility of the existence of neutron-rich nuclei will help in the solution of many astrophysical and cosmogonical problems.

Invariability of Universal Constants

We have considered the possible evolution of the stellar universe in association with definite nuclear processes which can be traced for approximately the last 5 billion years. It is legitimate to ask whether or not the laws of nuclear physics and, first of all, the parameters of these laws—the universal cosmic constants—have undergone a change in the course of this time.

The experimental material on the age of some sectors of the earth's crust and of meteorites which has been obtained by different methods (decay of α-emitters—U, Th—and of β-emitters—K, Rb, and others) is in good agreement. The most accurate and free of hypothetical assumptions are the data on the age of old minerals. The detailed investigations by I. E. Starik and his co-workers [140, 141] permitted fixing the age of pegmatites of the White Sea suite of Karelia at 1,700 million years, with a possible error of ± 5 per cent. Evidently, it will be possible to establish the age of the Rhodesian pegmatites with approximately the same accuracy [68, 276].

The concordance of the ages found by different methods indicates the invariability of radioactive-decay constants within the same limits of accuracy, since, in the expressions for age determination, the decay constants λ always appear in the form of the product λt. Yet the significance of this fact is far greater. The expressions for the decay constants given by the theory of atomic nuclei contain the universal constants, with the nature of dependence for α-decay (exponential function) being different from that for β-decay or K-electron capture (power function). The agreement among the ages obtained from the data on the decay of different emitters indicates an approximate invariability of the universal constants. The permissible limits of their variation can be established, with the material on α-decay obviously giving more rigorous conditions for the estimation of the possible variations.

We shall use expressions (13.11) and (13.12) (p. 155) for the probability of α-decay. The nuclear dimensions will be given in the units of r_0—the mean action radius of nuclear forces. Introducing the notation $r = \rho r_0$, we obtain

$$\lambda = Ce^{-(2e\sqrt{m_\alpha r_0}/\hbar)I(z,E,\rho_0)}, \tag{17.29}$$

where m_α is the mass of the α-particle,

$$I = \int_{\rho_0}^{\rho_1} \sqrt{\frac{2z}{\rho} - \frac{Er_0}{e^2}}\, d\rho,$$

and ρ_0 and ρ_1 are, respectively, the inner and outer radii of the potential barrier in nuclear units. The dimensionless exponential factor

$$\frac{2e\sqrt{m_\alpha r_0}}{\hbar} \approx 1.3, \tag{17.30}$$

and the numerical value of the integral for the α-decay of the natural radioelements is 70–80.

The assumed change in the decay constant can be caused by a change in the universal constants m_α, r_0, e, $\hbar$, and in the integral I, that is, in the structure of the nucleus. Let us examine the first case. It is necessary to point out that one cannot expect a change in the universal constants in which the dimensionless factor (17.30) remains invariable. In reality, the expression for the probability of β-decay (12.2) (p. 140) contains the universal constants in a different relationship; so that in this case a systematic change would be observed in the time intervals determined from α- and β-decay of radioactive elements. Thus the invariability of radioactive-decay constants determines the invariability of universal constants.

Let us examine in what limits these constants remain invariable during the investigated intervals of the existence of the universe. Let the change in the radioactive-decay constant take place within the limits from λ to $\lambda + \delta\lambda$. We shall assume that this change is caused by the variation in the value of the Planck constant from $\hbar$ to $\hbar + \delta\hbar$. Obviously,

$$\frac{\delta\lambda}{\lambda} = \frac{2e\sqrt{2m_\alpha r_0}}{\hbar} I \frac{\delta\hbar}{\hbar}.$$

Inasmuch as

$$\frac{2e\sqrt{2m_\alpha r_0}}{\hbar} I \approx 100 \quad \text{and} \quad \frac{\delta\lambda}{\lambda} \leqslant 0.05,$$

the relative change in the Planck constant within the interval of 1.7×10^9 years will be

$$\frac{\delta\hbar}{\hbar} \leqslant 5 \times 10^{-4}, \tag{17.31}$$

or, in the interval of 1 billion years,

$$\frac{\delta\hbar}{\hbar} \leqslant 3 \times 10^{-4}. \tag{17.32}$$

Quite the same also is the upper limit of the possible change in the elementary charge. For the mass of α-particles and the radius of nuclear forces this limit is higher by a factor of 2.

The age of old minerals based on α-emitters and on K-electron capture in K^{40} turns out to be the same. The probability of K-capture, according to equation (14.13), also depends, apart from the Planck constant, on the velocity of light and the mass of electrons. The constancy of λ_K indicates, consequently, the constancy of these quantities. The permissible limits of their change are considerably higher than in formula (17.32).

The concordance of the results of absolute age determinations made on old minerals by different methods indicates, aside from the relatively limited problem of the confirmation of the correctness of the radiometric bases of the analysis, the high invariability of the universal constants within the "cosmogonic" time of the order of billions of years.

18. THEORY OF THE ABUNDANCE OF ISOTOPES. FORMATION OF ATOMIC NUCLEI IN A NON-EQUILIBRIUM SYSTEM

Basic Directions of the Abundance Theory

A theory of the abundance of atomic nuclei should be in agreement with the fundamental data of astrophysics and cosmogony. The theory should also explain the main regularities of the abundance of isotopes that are manifested in the experimental material assembled by geochemistry and cosmochemistry. These regularities are as follows:

1. The abundance of atomic nuclei decreases with increasing atomic weight up to the middle of Mendeleyev's table; then, after having passed through a minimum in the vicinity of $A = 140$, the abundance increases. The drop in the curve of the cosmic abundance of the elements from hydrogen to the region of the minimum reaches 10–15 orders of magnitude.

2. The abundance of even isotopes is, on the average, greater than the abundance of odd isotopes of approximately the same atomic weight. With increasing atomic weight, the preponderance of even isotopes is less.

3. For even isobars, the abundance of the isobar of lower charge n_{Z-1} is, on the average, greater than the abundance of isobars of higher charge n_{Z+1}, with the ratio n_{Z-1}/n_{Z+1} increasing as the atomic weight increases.

4. The dependence of the abundance on the binding energy of atomic nuclei is, generally speaking, not observed.

5. Especially high abundance is possessed by the isotopes of the region of closed neutron shells with $A - Z = 28$, 50, and 82.

6. The abundance curve of atomic nuclei as a function of atomic weight is interrupted by "dips" in the regions of light metals, α-decay, and fission, which finally terminates the sequence of isotopes existing in nature.

The theory must explain these aspects. Because of the unique conditions of the development of the science of the abundance of isotopes, the theoretical works linked the abundance primarily with the problems of cosmogony, directing main attention to the astrophysical side of the problem and not to the regularities in the abundance of atomic nuclei. These regularities could not but attract the interest of geochemists. However, scientists in this field usually limit themselves to the confirmation of the regularities. The majority of theoretical studies were aimed at the explanation of only the first of the indicated fundamental regularities—the general course of the abundance curve. At the same time, the important fact of the presence in the curve of a minimum in the region of medium atomic weights was not taken into consideration.

We are not setting ourselves the task of describing all the attempts made in scientific literature to solve the problem of abundance. Many of these attempts are integrally connected with certain cosmogonic models and are more related to astrophysics than to nuclear geochemistry. A detailed review of theoretical works is given in a summary by Alpher and Herman [277]. Our purpose is to give a description of the individual trends of the theory and of the prospects of future investigations. The large number of works devoted to the theory of the origin and abundance of atomic nuclei can be divided into two main groups: (*a*) the theory of the synthesis of atomic nuclei in a non-equilibrium system and (*b*) the theory of the formation of atomic nuclei under conditions of thermodynamic equilibrium in the initial system. The first group we shall consider in this section and the second group in Section 19.

The progress of nuclear physics, on the one hand, and of the theory of the internal structure of the stars, on the other, has led to the natural idea of the synthesis of atomic nuclei in stellar interiors, an idea that was put forth (of course, in a very imperfect form), for example, by Perrin [278] as early as 1920. The birth of quantum mechanics and the application of its apparatus to the problems of the atomic nucleus permitted Atkinson [279] in 1931 to develop a theory of thermonuclear reactions and apply it to the problem of nuclear transmutations in stellar interiors. The conditions of matter in the stars at that time were already sufficiently well known. Simple calculations have shown that in the deep regions of the stars only nuclear reactions of the lightest elements are possible. In order to explain the formation of the heavy elements, Atkinson introduced a hypothetical process of fusion of the nuclear matter without the passage of particles through a mutual potential barrier. After the discovery of neutrons, this assumption appeared to have found real support. The further development of the concept of synthesis belongs to Weizsäcker [259]. However, later on, this author gave up his original scheme and considered as more probable the formation of atomic nuclei in an equilibrium system [280].

The chief difficulties of the theory of synthesis are as follows:

1. There are no bases for the assumption that in the interior of the stars there can be present a sufficiently powerful source of neutrons.

2. During the capture of neutrons, α-particles are often emitted, that is, not only the creation of atomic nuclei but also their destruction take place. In the course of this, helium is formed in quantities larger than those which can be correlated with experiment. The states of atomic nuclei $A = 5$ and $A = 8$ are unstable, so that it is necessary to introduce additionally an assumption of a path that would by-pass these states.

3. The hypothesis of synthesis is unable to explain the genesis of the long-lived radioactive elements. On the way toward their formation, atomic nuclei must pass through a broad region of short-lived isotopes, the half-life of which is so short that, at any permissible concentration of free neutrons in the initial system, it is impossible to obtain synthesis of the long-lived α-emitters.

4. The process of synthesis, as is common for nuclear reactions, should go along the most probable paths and should terminate at a limited number of products. For example, in the region of the heavy nuclei, the feasibility of α-decay and of fission leads to the condition that in the earth's crust there exist only three isotopes. In the region of the light nuclei the operation of thermonuclear reactions has caused almost complete destruction of the light isotopes (up to carbon), with the formation of one stable state (helium). In nature, however, all isotopes are evidently present, stable as well as unstable, for which the decay period is sufficiently long. The course of the abundance curve, in spite of the scatter of individual points, is subject to definite regularity, this being in better agreement with the idea of the thermodynamic equilibrium of the initial system.

5. The process of capture of particles by atomic nuclei does not, generally speaking, depend on the type of nuclei, and for this reason the theory of synthesis cannot explain the difference in the abundance of even and odd isotopes.

The α-β-γ Theory

In the first works on the theory of synthesis there were considered the possibilities of capture by atomic nuclei of both protons and neutrons. Alpher, Bethe, and Gamow [281], beginning in 1948, systematically developed the idea of the formation of atomic nuclei in a neutron-capture process under non-equilibrium conditions of the system. This is the so-called α-β-γ theory.

Suppose that a neutron-capture process takes place in a system containing neutrons, protons, and atomic nuclei. The relative concentration ξ_A of the heavy nuclei with the atomic weight A changes according to the law

$$\frac{d\xi_A}{dt} = P_{A-1}\xi_n\xi_{A-1} - P_A\xi_A\xi_n - \psi^{\xi_A/t}. \tag{18.1}$$

The symbol ξ_n denotes the concentration of neutrons; $P_A = pc/\lambda$, where c is the concentration of matter, λ is the decay constant of the neutron, and p is the probability of neutron capture by the given atomic nucleus in unit time per volume element:

$$p \sim \int_0^\infty \sigma(A,E)Ee^{-E/kT}\,dE, \tag{18.2}$$

where σ is the capture cross-section, E is the energy of neutrons, T is the temperature of the medium, and ψ is the parameter that determines the dependence of the density of the system on time. The concentration ξ_A increases during neutron capture by atomic nuclei with weight $A - 1$ and decreases during that by nuclei with weight A.

The hypothesis is based on the concept of the formation of atomic nuclei in an expanding universe within the first instants of its existence, when the primordial neutron concentration has not yet decreased too greatly at the expense of β-decay with the formation of protons, that is, within the time comparable to the half-life of a neutron (12.8 minutes). The initial state of the system is, of course, unknown. Speaking more precisely, this state should be determined from the data on the abundance of atomic nuclei.

The most important idea of the α-β-γ theory is the connection between the abundance curve of atomic nuclei (see Fig. 27, p. 190) and the curve of neutron capture by atomic nuclei (see Fig. 11, p. 125) as a function of atomic weight. If one takes into consideration the fact that the capture of neutrons causes a decrease in the abundance of a given isotope, then the first curve appears as if it were a mirror image of the second curve. The positive consequence of the theory is that it can explain why the atomic nuclei with an anomalously small fast-neutron-capture cross-section—namely, the isotopes with closed neutron shells (Rb^{87}, Sr^{88}, Y^{89} in the region of the 50-neutron shell; Ba^{138}, La^{139}, Ce^{140} in the region of the 82-neutron shell; Pb^{208}, Bi^{209} in that of the 126-neutron shell)—also possess an anomalously high abundance. However, quantitative agreement between the theory and experiment is lacking. Thus the capture cross-section of Rb^{85} is much larger than that of Rb^{87}, but the abundance ratio of these isotopes is inverted. The neutron-capture cross-sections of Pb^{208} and Bi^{209} are similar, but the abundance in nature of Pb^{208} is greater than that of bismuth by many tens of times. The authors assume that the initial system is an expanding gas cloud with a density of about 10^{-8} gm/cm^3 and a temperature of 10^9 deg. C. The theoretical curve plotted upon these assumptions falls off with increasing atomic weight, rapidly at the beginning and more slowly farther on. The curve has the smoothest slope if the duration of the process is assumed to be infinitely long, but even in this case a minimum in the abundance curve does not appear. This is connected with the fact that the curve of cross-sections for the fast-neutron capture, upon which the α-β-γ theory is based, has no maximum.

The experimental data on fast-neutron capture by atomic nuclei are incomplete, but a greater capture probability for odd nuclei (which should assure a higher abundance of even nuclei) is, generally speaking, not observed. Smart [282] presents considerations in favor of a relatively greater change in the binding energy of the last neutron of even nuclei as compared with that of odd nuclei. Hence, according to Smart, there follows greater probability of the formation of even states. This is unconvincing because in the α-β-γ theory the ratio of isotopes is determined by the probability of neutron capture and not by energy considerations.

It is obvious that, during neutron capture by atomic nuclei, out of two stable isobaric states, only the state of the lower charge is formed. The possibility of the formation of isobars of a higher charge ("shielded isobars") Smart explains by means of the nuclear photoeffect. Gamma rays, by knocking out nuclear electrons, can lead to the formation of "shielded isobars." In a large number of cases, this requires repeated operation of the same mechanism.

The theory of the formation of the elements during neutron capture in a non-equilibrium environment is far from a quantitative formulation. The theory is open to criticism in its separate segments, which is natural in view of the unfinished status of the theory. However, the essential defect of the theory is that the basic regularities of the abundance of atomic nuclei cannot be satisfactorily explained. As to the mechanism of the formation of atomic nuclei, there is the unsurmounted difficulty common to all hypotheses that assume the formation of nuclei in a non-equilibrium system—the difficulty of building up the light isotopes (in the region of $A = 5$ and $A = 8$) and the heavy radioactive nuclei.

L. E. Gurevich [283] notes that in the element-forming system, assumed by the authors of the α-β-γ theory, there is a large probability of the photodisintegration of atomic nuclei with γ-quanta, so that the synthesis of the heavy isotopes should not occur. In general, the light nuclei, when irradiated with neutrons, usually disintegrate but do not capture neutrons. The authors of the theory do not explain why in the system, together with free neutrons, there are present fully formed atomic nuclei with a normal proton-to-neutron ratio. And, unless this is true, the theory loses its winning argument—the connection of high abundance with small probability of neutron capture for atomic nuclei with closed neutron shells.

Theory of L. E. Gurevich

Recently L. E. Gurevich [283] worked out a scheme of the origin of the elements, using the cosmogonic ideas of the Soviet school of astrophysicists. Gurevich considers that it is impossible to accommodate the formation of atomic nuclei within the limits of a single astrophysical process. The formation proceeds in the cosmos continuously, and there are put together in the course of this formation in different systems the individual characteristics of the observed abundance of atomic nuclei.

In the electromagnetic fields generated during the motion of the Galaxy, fast cosmic protons are produced, which, upon collision with nuclei, generate deuterons. The deuterons, in turn, combine with helium atoms to produce Li^6. (The concept of such a process offers the possibility for by-passing the unstable system with $A = 5$, that is, it eliminates the difficulty present in the early theories of the synthesis of atomic nuclei). This stage of the process takes place in the interstellar and perhaps even in the intergallactic diffuse medium. The buildup of more complex nuclei is realized by way of capture by the nuclei of the slow "near-barrier" protons with energies not much greater than the potential barrier height of the Coulomb interaction of atomic nuclei and protons. In the systems of low density ($\rho < 10^{-12}$ gm/cm^3), such as the diffuse nebulae, the neutrons cannot be an active instrument of the synthesis of the heavy nuclei, since they have sufficient time to be converted into protons by natural β-decay, prior to their collision with atomic nuclei. The formation of heavy nuclei at the expense of neutron capture begins at the "protostellar" stage of contraction of the nebula and continues in the interior regions of the developing star. Gurevich explains the presence of the light metals in the sun's atmosphere by the fact that these elements and also deuterium are continuously being formed in the interstellar medium and are subsequently absorbed by the celestial bodies.

The merit of Gurevich's conception is its flexibility. If the process is interrupted at one of its stages in the given system, it can continue in another of the many systems of the developing Galaxy. In the course of the combined operation of the reactions of disintegration and synthesis of atomic nuclei, the cosmogonic processes bring the nuclear realm into the observed condition.

Gurevich subjects to criticism the α-β-γ theory as well the hypotheses of the formation of heavy nuclei in the superdense systems.

The drawback of Gurevich's theory is that it does not set out to explain the regularities in the abundance of atomic nuclei but considers only the possibility of nuclear transmutation in interstellar space and in the process of the formation of the stars. No consideration is given to the fact that, upon irradiation of atomic nuclei with fast cosmic particles, the concentration ratio of the nuclei will be subject to the observed regularities of the abundance of isotopes.

The studies of the isotopic composition of rare gases produced under the action of cosmic rays in meteorites show profound differences from the normal isotopic composition of these elements (for neon, the preponderance of the odd isotope; for argon, that of the heavy even isotope).

It seems to us that the most vulnerable point in Gurevich's and other theories based on synthesis is the difficulty of explaining the formation of the heavy elements. In the atomic-weight interval $A =$ 215–17, not a single atomic nucleus lives longer than a fraction of a second. Inevitably, one has to assume the existence of the system in which the synthesis of atomic nuclei (by capture of neutrons or of other particles) proceeds so rapidly that the formation of the heavy nuclei can be completed within seconds.

One should agree with Gurevich that it is not necessary to postulate the process of the formation of the heavy nuclei completely within a single system. The individual links of the process (for example, the formation of Li^6 from helium) can be sought under different conditions. However, the cosmogonic idea of Gurevich does not indicate where the fundamental system is formed or what properties it possesess so that, within a very short time, there can be accomplished the formation of the elements.

19. FORMATION OF ISOTOPES UNDER CONDITIONS OF THERMODYNAMIC EQUILIBRIUM OF ATOMIC NUCLEI

The first works which considered the conditions of thermodynamic equilibrium of atomic nuclei attempted to bring into agreement the observed relationship among the chemical elements of the sun and of other stars with the reactions under thermodynamic conditions of stellar interiors [284]. It is not difficult to show that the temperature of 10^6–10^7 deg. C. attained there is not sufficient for the formation of the heavy nuclei. For this, in the interior regions of the stars, a temperature of the order of $T \approx 10^{10}$ deg. C., $kT \approx n$ Mev would be required. Some scientists attempted to increase the temperature of the stellar interiors to these values, but this is not allowed by the theory of stability and equilibrium of the gaseous stars. The author of the theory, Eddington, once suggested to these scientists "to look for a warmer place." Later on it was clear that the formation of the heavy nuclei could not be accomplished in the interiors of the ordinary representatives of the stellar universe. In 1931, G. I. Pokrovskii [285] for the first time correctly formulated the problem of the formation of atomic nuclei under conditions of thermodynamic equilibrium of a certain initial system. In the following years his ideas were developed by a number of authors [286, 287]. Further on, the calculations of the theory of thermodynamic equilibrium were made on the basis of much experimental material on the binding energy and the abundance of atomic nuclei which up to this day is being continuously accumulated.

Pokrovskii put forth the following important concepts which underlie the later works in this direction:

1. The initial system is characterized by high values of thermodynamic parameters. The temperature is of the order of the nuclear temperature ($kT \approx n$ Mev), and the density is close to the nuclear density ($\rho \approx 10^{14}$ gm/cm^3).

2. The atomic nuclei formed in the initial system were rapidly commutated to other conditions, namely, to those of low temperature and pressure, under which the probability of nuclear reactions is very small. That is why the atomic nuclei kept in a "frozen" condition the same mass and charge distribution that were established in the initial system.

3. It is possible that the heavy elements (starting approximately with iron) were formed under the action of a mechanism different from that which produced the light elements.

The last assumption was later used by a number of authors [288–90], who developed the idea of the formation of light and heavy nuclei at different stages of the evolution of the cosmos. The studies were not based on any definite astrophysical scheme of the evolution of the stars but, on the contrary, were using selected conditions required for obtaining the necessary ratio of the elements of the first and second halves of Mendeleyev's table.

The assumption of different conditions for the formation of these elements is not supported by the general regularities of the abundance of atomic nuclei. The abundance ratios of isotopes of the same type, the ratios of even and odd atomic nuclei, those of the components of even isobars, and the general abundance curve, all have, on the average, in spite of considerable deviation of individual points, a smooth course without those major disturbances that are observed when a new mechanism of nuclear transmutation comes into effect. Really, there are, in the region of α-emitters, separate rules for the abundance of isotopes as a function of atomic weight, of the type of A and Z, etc. For the light metals, together with a sharp decrease in their abundance, an anomalous isotopic composition is observed—the predominance of the heavy odd isotope.

Evidently, the bulk of atomic nuclei originated in a single initial system under the action of a steady, or at least gradually changing, mechanism of nuclear transmutation.

Many works investigate the effect on the distribution of nuclear matter under conditions of thermodynamic equilibrium of such factors as the presence of excited states [288], of the degenerate electron field [289], and of the operation of the gravitational field [288, 290]. The consideration of these effects, under certain premises, leads to an increase in the relative abundance of the heavy elements; but too rapid a drop of the abundance curve with increasing A remains the principal difficulty of this trend of the theory. In order to achieve agreement with experiment, Geheniau and others [291] arbitrarily assume that the statistical weight of the heavy nuclei should be multiplied by $(A!)^2$. Such an attempt to circumvent the indicated difficulty obviously has a speculative character.

Foundations of the Theory of Dissociation Equilibrium of Atomic Nuclei

The concentration of particles of a given kind and with atomic weight A under conditions of thermodynamic equilibrium is described by the equation of M. N. Saha [13],

$$n_A = \frac{(2\pi m_A kT)^{3/2}}{h^3} e^{(F_A - E_A)/kT}, \tag{19.1}$$

where m_A is the mass of the particle, F_A and E_A are, respectively, the free and the internal energy of the particle, and T is the temperature of the system.

Let the nuclear reaction of the type

$$R^{A-1} + H^1 \rightleftarrows R^A$$

take place.

In the state of equilibrium of this reaction, the free energies of the reacting substances obey the relation

$$F_{A-1} + F_1 = F_A \tag{19.2}$$

From equations (19.1) and (19.2) we have

$$n_A = n_{A-1} n_p \left(\frac{h^2}{2\pi m_{\text{eff}} kT}\right)^{3/2} e^{(E_1 + E_{A-1} - E_A)/kT}, \tag{19.3}$$

where $m_{\text{eff}} \approx m$ is the reduced mass of the system and n_p is the concentration of protons.

Examining the state of equilibrium of the nucleus $A - 1$ with the nuclei $A - 2$ and 1 (the proton), we find an expression for n_{A-1} which is similar to equation (19.3). Substituting this expression on the right side of equation (19.3), we obtain the condition of equilibrium of the nuclei A and $A - 2$:

$$n_A = n_{A-2} n_p{}^2 \left(\frac{h^2}{2\pi m_{\text{eff}} kT}\right)^{3/2 \cdot 2} e^{(2E_1 + E_{A-2} - E)/kT}.$$

In a similar manner, passing to the equilibrium of the nucleus A with the nucleus $A - 3$, $A - 4$, etc., and repeating the substitution $(A - 2)$ times, we finally obtain the expression that describes the dissociation equilibrium of atomic nuclei of type A with protons:

$$n_A = \left(\frac{n_p{}^{2/3} h^2}{2\pi m_{\text{eff}} kT}\right)^{3/2(A-1)} n_p e^{(AE_1 - E_A)/kT}. \tag{19.4}$$

For protons,

$$E_1 = mc^2,$$

and, for the atomic nuclei (see Sec. 11, p. 125),

$$E_A = Amc^2 - AU = Amc^2 - Av + sA^{2/3} + cZ^2A^{-1/3}. \tag{19.5}$$

Substituting these expressions in equation (19.4), we find the logarithm of the relative concentration of atomic nuclei, that is, the quantity Q with the accuracy of the addition constant:

$$Q = \log n_A = \log n_p + (A - 1)\frac{3}{2}\log\left(\frac{n_p{}^{2/3} h^2}{2m_{\text{eff}} kT}\right) + \frac{Av - sA^{2/3} - cZ^2A^{-1/3}}{kT}\log e \tag{19.6}$$

or

$$Q = c_1 \pm c_2 A - c_3 A^{2/3} - c_4 Z^2 A^{-1/3}, \tag{19.7}$$

where c_1, c_2, c_3, and c_4 represent certain coefficients which include thermodynamic parameters. The sign of c_2 depends on the numerical values of n and T.

In Figure 33 are plotted the curves $Q = f(A)$, according to equation (19.7), for certain values of the independent parameters.

Curve *I*: $kT = 9.3$ Mev, $n \approx 5 \times 10^{36}$ cm$^{-3} \approx 0.05n^*$, where n^*

corresponds to the nuclear density. The curve is traced through the sectors of light and heavy nuclei. In the central region of the atomic weights, the values of Q are intolerably high, and in the region of high atomic weights the course of the theoretical curve does not agree with that of the experimental curve, which it intersects at a large angle.

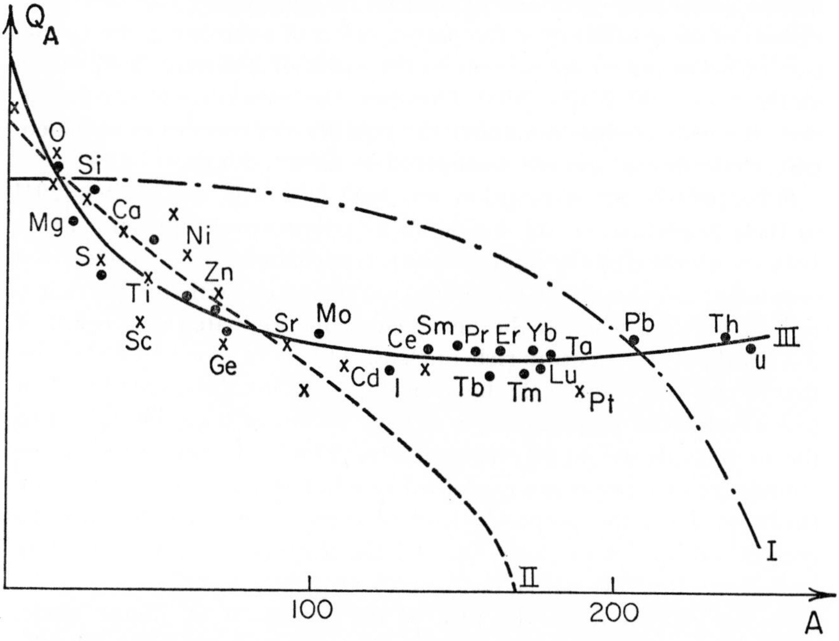

FIG. 33.—Abundance of isotopes in the earth's crust (•) and in the sun's atmosphere (x) and theoretical curves assuming formation of atomic nuclei under conditions of thermodynamic equilibrium of the system of charged particles (curves *I* and *II*) and of the system of neutron fragments (curve *III*). The parameters of the curves are given in the text.

Curve *II*: $kT = 2.5$ Mev, $n = 2 \times 10^{36} \approx 0.02n^*$. The curve describes satisfactorily the position of the light atomic nuclei but falls off rapidly with increasing atomic weight.

Examples show that it is impossible to achieve satisfactory agreement between expressions of the type (19.6) and the experimental curve. The interference lies in the "heavy elements difficulty"—a sharp fall in the theoretical abundance curve in the region of high atomic weights. A rational method of overcoming this difficulty of the theory has not yet been found. This promoted the development of another trend of the theory, namely, a hypothesis of the formation of atomic nuclei during neutron capture in a non-equilibrium system. In the works of physicists abroad this hypothesis is closely tied in with the assumption of an expanding universe.

Formation of Atomic Nuclei in a Neutron Environment

In 1940 we proposed a hypothesis of the formation of atomic nuclei under the conditions of thermodynamic equilibrium of a neutron environment [255, 271, 292]. The hypothesis, as it seems to us, possesses certain advantages over the hypothesis of Pokrovskii. The first indications of the possibility of the participation of neutrons in the formation of heavy nuclei are present in the works of Atkinson [268], Weizsäcker [259], and Walke [293]. However, the possibility of the formation of chemical elements under the equilibrium conditions of a neutron environment was not considered by these authors.

Subsequently our assumption was used by Mayer and Teller [294] in their hypothesis of the fission of a "polyneutron" nucleus. These authors assume that the light elements (approximately up to selenium) originated as a result of thermonuclear reactions with the participation of protons, whereas the heavy elements originated as a result of the breakup of a neutron-rich nucleus. This is supported by the fact that in the heavy nuclei the heavy isotopes are usually more abundant (the above-noted preponderance of even isobars of lower charge). The theory is not based on geochemical data. The basic regularities of the abundance of isotopes are explained qualitatively and not always conclusively. Thus the preponderance of even isotopes is explained by greater stability of the four- than of the three-neutron configuration. It is clear that this aspect itself needs an explanation.

In the general form, the idea of the formation of atomic nuclei during the interaction of neutrons with matter is also utilized in the α-β-γ theory.

Let us turn to the question of the formation of atomic nuclei in an equilibrium neutron environment. We shall examine the conditions of the dissociation equilibrium of neutron fragments (the nuclei made up almost entirely of neutrons).

Substituting in equation (19.4) the expression for the energy of the neutron-rich nuclei [see eq. (17.20)],

$$E_n(A) = Amc^2 - Av' + sA^{2/3}, \tag{19.8}$$

we find the relative concentration of the neutron-rich nucleus with atomic weight A under conditions of thermodynamic equilibrium of the system:

$$Q = \log n_n + \frac{3}{2}(A-1)\log\left(\frac{n_n^{2/3}h^2}{2\pi m_{\text{eff}}kT}\right) + \frac{Av' - sA^{2/3}}{kT}\log e, \tag{19.9}$$

where n_n is the concentration of neutrons in the initial system. We shall write equation (19.9) in a manner similar to that in equation (19.7),

$$Q = c_1 \pm c_2 A - c_3 A^{2/3}. \tag{19.10}$$

This expression differs from equation (19.7) only in that it does not contain the Coulomb energy term and the coefficients have different values. It is not difficult to show that the presence of the Coulomb energy in the expression for Q for the equilibrium of the environment of charged particles is exactly the factor that causes the "heavy elements difficulty," that is, a rapid fall in the curve $Q = f(A)$ at high values of atomic weight.

In Figure 33 curve *III* is the theoretical curve (19.10) of the abundance of isotopes which were formed under the equilibrium conditions of the neutron environment. Curve *III* is traced through the points O^{16}, Nd^{150}, and Th^{232}. The values of the parameters are

$$c_1 = 0.981, \qquad c_2 = +0.134, \qquad c_3 = +1.115, \tag{19.11}$$

whence $kT \approx 3.6$ Mev. The concentration of neutrons enters into the relation

$$\frac{v'}{kT}\log e + \frac{3}{2}\log\left(\frac{h^2 n_n{}^{2/3}}{2\pi mkT}\right) = 0.134. \tag{19.12}$$

The value of v' cannot be determined accurately, and therefore the error in the determination of n_n is large. Roughly, it amounts to $n_n \approx 0.001$ of the nuclear concentration of particles. For the indicated values of the coefficients c_1, c_2, and c_3, curve (19.10) agrees well with the experimental curve (see Fig. 27, p. 190). The minimum in the curve, as is readily seen, is found from the expression

$$A = \left(\frac{2}{3}\frac{c_3}{c_2}\right)^3 \approx 170, \tag{19.13}$$

which is somewhat larger than the value obtained in the study of the ratio of isotopes of the same type (see Sec. 15, p. 188).

In the examination of the dissociation theory of equilibrium we have assumed that the system can be considered as a non-degenerate gas. We shall test the correctness of this assumption. The criterion for the absence of degeneracy is the condition that

$$E(T) \gg W, \tag{19.14}$$

where $E(T)$ is the mean kinetic energy of the gas particles at a given temperature, and

$$W = \frac{3}{10}\frac{h^2}{m^{5/3}}\left(\frac{3}{8\pi}\rho\right)^{2/3}$$

is the mean kinetic energy of particles with the mass m at a temperature of absolute zero and of a given density. It is obvious that, since the neutrons possess the smallest mass and the largest concentration in the initial system, it is sufficient to test the correctness of formula

(19.14) for neutrons only. Taking the neutron concentration to be equal to $0.001n^*$, we find that $W \approx 1$ Mev and $E(T) = 3/2\,kT \approx 5$ Mev, that is, criterion (19.14) is sufficiently valid for the neutrons and is unconditionally fulfilled for the heavier nuclei.

A relationship between the binding energy of the existing atomic nuclei and their abundance, generally speaking, does not exist, this being the major argument against the theory of the formation of isotopes under conditions of equilibrium of the charged particles. For the theory of the formation of atoms in a neutron environment this circumstance is immaterial. On the contrary, it is possible to attempt the solution of the reverse problem, namely, the determination of the binding energy of the neutron-rich nuclei from the abundance of the atomic nuclei which exist in nature.

Dependence of the abundance of isotopes on their type (even-odd effect) during formation in a neutron environment.—As in Section 11, we shall consider an odd particle as an excess particle on the surface of the nucleus which alters its spherical symmetry. From (11.23) (p. 137), the additional energy of an odd isotope is

$$\Delta E = \frac{2E_{\text{surf}} - E_{\text{Coul}}}{3A}\Delta A = \frac{2sA^{2/3} - cZ^2}{3A}\Delta A, \tag{19.15}$$

where $\Delta A \approx 1$. The ratio of isotopes of different type has, according to equation (19.4), the form

$$\frac{n_{\text{even}}}{n_{\text{odd}}} = e^{\Delta E/kT}. \tag{19.16}$$

For the heavy nuclei, ΔE tends to zero, so that the theory of the formation of atomic nuclei in the environment of charged particles cannot explain the predominance of even over odd isotopes, which is also observed for the heavy isotopes, although in a smaller degree than for the light isotopes.

For the neutron-rich fragments,

$$\Delta E = \frac{2s\Delta A}{3A^{1/3}}, \qquad \frac{n_{\text{even}}}{n_{\text{odd}}} = e^{(2s\Delta A/3A^{1/3})(1/kT)} \tag{19.17}$$

or

$$\frac{n_{\text{even}}}{n_{\text{odd}}} = 10^{(\Delta A/A^{1/3})}, \tag{19.18}$$

where the numerical value of $b \approx 1$. The shape of curve (19.18) is in good agreement with the trend of the even-to-odd isotope ratio (see Fig. 29) if one assumes $\Delta A \approx 2$–3.

Conditions of the initial system.—The general shape of the abundance curve of isotopes and the regularity of even and odd isotopes can be satisfactorily described by the theory of thermodynamic equilibrium only upon the assumption of the formation of atomic nuclei in a neutron environment. In order to preserve the distribution according to atomic weights, which was established in the initial system, it is required that the system be "frozen," that is, be rapidly switched over to other thermodynamic conditions, where the artificial transmutations of heavy elements practically do not occur. If one takes into consideration the high energy of the particles and the density of the system, then the starting conditions for the formation of atomic nuclei correspond to the explosion of a neutron-rich nucleus. The possibility of such a process as the final stage in the evolution of the stars was examined in Section 17.

The time between the collisions of the fragments under thermodynamic conditions of the initial system is

$$t = (\sigma v n_A)^{-1} \approx 10^{-15}\text{–}10^{-22} \text{ second} \tag{19.19}$$

($\sigma \approx 10^{-24}$ cm^2 is the collision cross-section, and v is the mean velocity of the fragments). Since the particles do not carry a charge and the potential barrier for them does not exist, each collision leads to some nuclear reaction, and the time for the establishment of thermodynamic equilibrium in this system is very short. The neutron-rich fragments formed during the explosion are rapidly converted into ordinary atomic nuclei by successive β-transitions, and the free neutrons are transformed into protons. The probability of nuclear reactions upon collision of charged particles of low energy is very small, so that the beginning β-decay at once "freezes" the established distribution of matter according to atomic weights. This is also favored by the energy and density decrease during the explosion.

We have been considering a "pure" case of neutron-rich nuclei, a case which is probably unreal. It is more plausible to conclude that the initial system contains, besides neutrons, a known number of protons and that the heavy fragments of this system also possess a certain number of protons. This will somewhat increase the time needed for the establishment of equilibrium in the system but will not change the general considerations regarding this process. If one considers that the fragments of the primordial system possess the charge $Z(A) \leqslant Z_0$ (Z_0 is the optimum charge at a given atomic weight), then the abundance of isotopes can be given in the following general form:

$$Q = c_1 \pm c_1 A - c_3 A^{2/3} + c_4 Z^2(A) A^{-4/3}\,. \tag{19.20}$$

The relative number of protons $Z(A)/A$ probably increases for the heavy nuclei, and this in turn decreases the abundance of these nuclei. Equation (19.20) is in better agreement with experiment than is equation (19.10). With a pure neutron character of the initial system, too great a number of isotopes of the transuranium elements would be produced, which are generally unstable against fission and α-decay. The former leads to an increase in the abundance of certain isotopes of intermediate atomic weight (primarily of isotopes with closed neutron shells) and the latter to an increase in the abundance of the lead and bismuth isotopes. A high abundance of many isotopes with closed neutron shells is indeed observed, but a noticeable excess of lead and bismuth isotopes is not observed.

Formation of even isobars.—The regularity in the abundance of even isobars—the predominance of the component of lower charge—cannot be explained by the theory of the formation of atomic nuclei in the system of charged particles, because isobars possess, on the average, equal energy levels and should consequently have the same abundance.

If one assumes that the initial system was impoverished in neutrons, then the predominance of isobars of lower charge can be qualitatively explained. The β-decay of neutron fragments leads to the formation of the charged nuclei. For isotopes which form isobars, the first stable state is the isobar of the lower charge, $Z - 1$. The excitation energy at this point of the existence of the system can still be so high that a certain number of isotopes of isobaric type $Z - 1$ pass into the unstable state of odd charge Z. Later, this isotope breaks down into even isobars with charges $Z - 1$ and $Z + 1$, with an equal a priori probability. If the energy level of the state $Z - 1$ lies higher than that of the state $Z + 1$, that is, if $\delta = Z - Z_0 < 0$, then this favors the transition of the former state into the latter. Indeed, with decreasing δ, the relative content of the component of lower charge also decreases.

For the heavy elements the time of the transition into a stable condition is longer than for the light elements. For this reason the isobars of this region reach the first stable state $Z - 1$ later, when the energy of the system has already been dissipated to a considerable degree. This encumbers the transition into the intermediate state of odd charge, that is, it diminishes the possibility of the formation of the stable state $Z + 1$. In accordance with the experiment, the ratio n_{Z-1}/n_{Z+1} should increase with increasing atomic weight and, on the average, be greater than 1 (see Fig. 30). For odd isobars there is also observed the predominance of the component of lower charge, which can be explained by similar considerations. The time of the transition of a quasi-neutron fragment into a stable condition is not too short, roughly of the order of hours or days, that is, it is by many orders of magnitude longer than the time of the establishment of the equilibrium of neutron fragments. It should be concluded that the fragments thrown out by the explosion remain for a long time in an excited state, possibly because of the action of the radiation emitted from the central zone of the system. However, at this stage of the existence of the system, the thermodynamic equilibrium of nuclear matter is already absent, and artificial splitting of atomic nuclei with change in their atomic weight does not occur.

This scheme of the formation of atomic nuclei in a neutron environment proposes that the distribution of matter according to atomic weight occurs almost instantaneously under the conditions of thermodynamic equilibrium of the initial stage of the explosion of the neutron system. The distribution of atomic nuclei according to charges is attained later under non-equilibrium conditions of the extinction of the initial system. In this case, the average content of the components of even isobars is not equal, as would be expected from the energy considerations. A greater proportion of atomic nuclei remain in the state of the lower charge. After the original neutron fragments have increased their charge and turned into ordinary atomic nuclei, the processes of α-decay and of fission of the heavy isotopes set in, giving rise to dips at the end of the abundance curve.

The time of the passage of all atomic nuclei into the equilibrium state under the usual conditions of the cosmos is very long. Even the reactions of transmutation of the light elements in the stellar interiors continue without any appreciable change for billions of years. Only in the environment consisting almost entirely of neutrons—in any case, a very rare and probably a momentary fact in the life of the cosmos—thermodynamic equilibrium is attained almost instantaneously. It is possible that in this particular moment there takes place formation of atomic nuclei and rejuvenation of the matter of the system.

The proposed hypothesis is far from a detailed elaboration, but at present it can evidently better explain the observed regularities of nuclear geochemistry than can other variants of the theory of the abundance of atomic nuclei.

Here we shall not touch upon the astrophysical possibilities of the theory, possibilities which, in any event, are not very clear. If one limits himself to the physical and geochemical considerations, the hypothesis gives rise to the following objections:

1. The abundance of isotopes with closed neutron shells is not understood. It is difficult to admit that the nuclei of the same weight, consisting almost entirely of neutrons, also possessed an especially great stability. It is possible that the effect is explained by the fission of certain transuranium elements with the formation of stable isotopes, but direct confirmation of this does not exist.

2. The binding energy of the neutron-rich nuclei has been found from the simplest statistical theory applied to the case where the atomic nuclei do not carry a charge. Direct proof of the stability (that is, of a positive binding energy) of neutron fragments is not available.

Californium-254 and Supernovae

Burbidge and others [300] entitled their work "Californium-254 and Supernovae"; it is one of the most interesting investigations in astrophysics in recent years. The supernovae can be classified into two types [301]. Type I supernovae, during their explosion, release 10^{49}–10^{50} ergs. Type II supernovae are distinguished by a considerably greater (one order of magnitude) energy. A remarkable property of the former is that their light curve [302] falls off in a strictly exponential manner, decreasing to half its value in 55 ± 1 days. For the star IC 4182 [16] this was successfully traced for more than 600 days after the explosion maximum. Borst [303] pointed out that the exponential course of the light curve is difficult to explain other than by decay of some radioactive substance produced during the explosion. Borst assumed that the radioactive isotope is Be^7, made in the following reaction:

$$He^4 + He^4 = Be^7 + n^1$$

However [300], the decay energy of Be^7 is small (57 kev), so that the total quantity of Be^7 in the supernova would be inadmissibly high (1.3×10^{31} gm). Among other isotopes, a similar half-life is possessed by Sr^{89} and Cf^{254}. But the decay of strontium should also lead to an intolerably high accumulation of Y^{89} in the cosmos. In addition, together with Sr^{89} there should be formed a large quantity of the neighboring isotopes, the decay of which would seriously distort the strictly exponential course of the energy curve.

Burbidge and others [300] substantiated the bold idea that the substance which supplies the energy of the fading type I supernova is Cf^{254}.[17] During the explosion the temperature in the interior of the star rises so high that thermonuclear reactions with participation of helium become possible. Reactions of this type,

$$Ne^{21} + He^4 = Mg^{24} + n^1,$$
$$C^{13} + He^4 = O^{16} + n^1,$$

are powerful sources of neutrons. Capture of neutrons by the heavy nuclei, predominantly by iron, leads to the formation of heavy nuclei as far down as the transuranium elements. Among them, Cf^{254} occupies a special position (see p. 181). This nucleus decays only by spontaneous fission whose half-life is sufficiently long.[18] The neighboring nuclei,

[16] The object IC 4182 is a galaxy.

[17] E. Anders (*Astrophys. Jour.*, **129**: 327–46, 1959) proposes that 45-day Fe^{59} rather than Cf^{254} supplies the energy of an average supernova.

[18] A recent determination of the Cf^{254} half-life by J. R. Huizenga and H. Diamond (*Phys. Rev.*, **107**: 1087–90, 1957) gives a value of 56.2 ± 0.7 days.

capable of fission only, decay too rapidly, and the energy of the trans-uranium α-emitters is too low to support the brightness of the supernova—the fading star. During the decay of californium a large number of different fragments are produced and the accumulation of each of them is not too great.[19]

The formation of Cf^{254} is the most powerful nuclear process in the cosmos recorded at the present time. The thermodynamic conditions of supernovae are insufficient for the development of a neutron phase needed for the formation of atomic nuclei, according to the scheme presented above. However, substantial support for this scheme is the fact that in the high-temperature region the leading role is transferred to the reactions under the action of neutrons. It is possible that in type II supernovae, whose energy is greater than that of type I, the growth of the neutron phase proceeds farther yet and approaches those conditions of thermodynamic equilibrium under which, according to our ideas, the atomic nuclei of the cosmos were formed. It is not known whether this process can take place today or whether perhaps the energy output of contemporary cosmic catastrophes is not sufficient.

We have briefly examined the basic trends and results of the theory of the abundance of atomic nuclei without quite nearly touching upon the cosmogonic material. Unfortunately, up to the present time, there is no unified point of view on the origin and evolution of the stars and other astronomical objects. Naturally, the majority of works on the abundance theory were based on certain astronomical ideas, but never had an astronomical model been worked out in such detail that agreement or disagreement with it was absolutely necessary for the support of the conclusions regarding the origin of the elements. We do not speak of the works on thermonuclear reactions in the stellar interiors. In this case, the development of the theory of the internal constitution of the stars, on the one hand, and of nuclear physics, on the other, has led to the condition where one of the most difficult questions long unanswered by science—the question of stellar energy—is now becoming a scientific theory. However, thermonuclear reactions transform only the light isotopes. This process in the investigation of the chemical composition of the cosmos constitutes a secondary phenomenon which superimposes itself upon and alters the primeval abundance of atomic nuclei.

The difficulties of solving the problem of the abundance of atomic

[19] For additional discussions of the supernova synthesis of the heavy elements see the appropriate sections of papers by E. M. Burbidge, G. R. Burbidge, W. A. Fowler, and F. Hoyle (*Rev. Mod. Phys.*, **29:** 547–650, 1957); W. A. Fowler (*Stellar Populations: Proc. Conf. Pontifical Acad. Sci., May 20–28, 1957*, pp. 269–77); A. G. W. Cameron (*Ann. Rev. Nuclear Sci.*, **8:** 299–326, 1958; *Astrophys. Jour.*, **129:** 676–99, 1959); R. A. Becker and W. A. Fowler (*Phys. Rev.*, **115:** 1410–14, 1959).

nuclei (the physical aspect of the problem) and of the properties of the initial system (the astronomical aspect) are complicated by the fact that the heavy atomic nuclei are not formed in the ordinary and most studied cosmic objects—the stars. It should be hoped that, in the further progress of science in these two directions, definite success will be achieved, as has been the case for the problem of stellar energy.

At the present time, most probable is the idea of the formation of atomic nuclei during interaction with neutrons. In this case, the independent and alternate hypotheses are (1) the assumption of the formation of atomic nuclei under conditions of thermodynamic equilibrium and (2) the assumption of their formation under non-equilibrium conditions during the process of the capture of neutrons. The former hypothesis agrees satisfactorily with the experimental material on the abundance of isotopes. The latter theory in its present state can offer only some qualitative considerations of the possibility of the formation of atomic nuclei in the environment irradiated with protons, neutrons, γ-rays, and other particles.

The first hypothesis assumes the formation of nuclei during the explosion of neutron systems, which links the hypothesis with astrophysical ideas about the instability of the neutron phase—the terminal stage of the existence of the massive stars after the exhaustion of their energy sources, that is, after the burning-out of hydrogen. The explosion causes the regeneration of matter rich in light nuclei, which are subsequently burned up during the slow thermonuclear process of the gaseous stars. It is possible that the intermediate position between these processes and the reactions of the neutron phase is occupied by the explosions of type I supernovae, which evidently are accompanied by the formation of Cf^{254} through neutron capture by nuclei of medium atomic weight. Probably many intermediate processes are as yet unknown.

The problem of the origin of atomic nuclei awaits its completion. In its development it must be based on the geochemical and cosmochemical material on the abundance of atomic nuclei. The atomic nuclei have originated under conditions very much removed from the ordinary conditions of the present cosmos. In the distribution according to weight and charge, the nuclei have retained the regularities of the original system, and from these regularities it will perhaps be possible to peruse the first pages of the "paleontology" of atomic nuclei.

Bibliography

[1] Vavilov, S. I. *Vestnik AN SSSR* ("News Herald, Acad. Sci. U.S.S.R."), No. 3, 1944.

[2] Vinogradov, A. P. *Geokhimiya redkikh i rasseyanykh khimicheskikh elementov v pochvakh.* Izd. AN SSSR. *The Geochemistry of Rare and Dispersed Elements in Soils.* Acad. Sci. U.S.S.R., 1950. Transl. from Russian. New York: Consultants Bureau, 1959.

[3] Vernadskii, V. I. *Ocherki geokhimii,* GIZ ("Outlines of Geochemistry"). 1926. 4-e izd. ONTI. 4th ed. 1934.

[4] Fersman, A. E. *Geokhimiya.* Vols. I–IV. ONTI ("Geochemistry"). 1933–39.

[5] ———. *Geokhimicheskiye i mineralogicheskiye metody poiskov poleznykh iskopayemykh,* izd. AN SSSR ("Geochemical and Mineralogical Methods of Prospecting for Useful Deposits"). Acad. Sci. U.S.S.R., 1940.

[6] Noddack, I., und Noddack, W. *Zeitschr. f. phys. Chem.,* **154**: 207, 1931.

[7] ———. *Naturwiss.,* **18**: 757, 1930.

[8] Hevesy, G. von. *Jour. Chem. Soc., London,* **1**: 1, 1931.

[9] Clarke, F. W. *Bull. Phil. Soc., Washington,* **11**: 135, 1889; *The Data of Geochemistry.* (U.S. Geological Survey Bull. 770.) 5th ed. 1924.

[10] Goldschmidt, V. M. *Naturwiss.,* **10**: 918, 1922.

[11] Brown, H. *Rev. Mod. Phys.,* **21**: 625, 1949; *UFN* ("Advances of Physical Sciences"), **41**: 226, 1950.

[12] Urey, H. C. *Phys. Rev.,* **88**: 248, 1952.
Suess, H. E., and Urey, H. C. *Rev. Mod. Phys.,* **28**: 53, 1956.

[13] Saha, M. N. *Phil. Mag.,* **40**: 472, 809, 1920; **41**: 267, 1921; *Proc. Roy. Soc. London,* **99**: 135, 1921.

[14] Russell, H. N. *Nature* (London), **148**: 647, 1941.
Russell, H. N., Dugan, R. S., and Stewart, J. Q. *Astronomy,* Vol. **2**. Boston and New York: Ginn & Co., 1938.

[15] Payne, C. H. *Proc. Nat. Acad. Sci.* (Washington), **11**: 192, 1925.

[16] Merrill, P. W. *Astrophys. Jour.,* **72**: 98, 1930.

[17] Bowen, I. S., and Wyse, A. B. *Lick Obsv. Bull.,* Vol. **19**, No. 495, 1939.

[18] Aston, F. W. *Isotopy.* GIZ, 1923. Orig. *Isotopes.* 1st ed. New York: Longmans, Green & Co., 1922; *Mass-spektry i izotopy.* IL, 1948. Orig. *Mass Spectra and Isotopes.* New York: Longmans, Green & Co., 1933.

[19] Shmidt, O. Yu. *Chetyre lektsii o teorii proiskhozhdeniya Zemli,* izd. AN SSSR ("Four Lectures on the Theory of the Origin of the Earth"). Acad. Sci. U.S.S.R., 1950.

[20] Krat, B. A. *Trudy pervogo soveshchaniya po voprosam kosmogonii,* izd. AN SSSR ("Proceedings of the First Conference on the Problems of Cosmogony"). Acad. Sci. U.S.S.R., 1951.

[21] Goldschmidt, V. M. *Kristallokhimiya, khimteoretizd* ("Crystal Chemistry"). Publishing House of Theoretical Chemical Literature, 1937.

[22] Evans, R. D., and Goodman, C. *Bull. Geol. Soc. America,* **52:** 59, 1941.

[23] Arrol, W. J., Jacobi, R. B., and Paneth, F. A. *Nature* (London), **149:** 235, 1942.

[24] Dalton, J. C., Paneth, F. A., Reasbeck, R., Thomson, S. J., and Mayne, K. I. *Nature* (London), **172:** 1168, 1953.

[25] Belousov, V. V. *Izv. AN SSSR, ser. geog. i geofiz.* ("Bull. Acad. Sci. U.S.S.R., geog. geophys. ser."), p. 553, 1940; *Obshchaya geotektonika* ("General Geotectonics"). State Geological Publishing House, 1948.

[26] Cherdyntsev, V. V. *Vestnik Kazfiliala, AN SSSR* ("News Herald, Kazakh Branch Acad. Sci. U.S.S.R."), No. 5, p. 9, 1946.

[27] Fersman, A. E. *Pegmatity,* Part 1, izd. AN SSSR ("Pegmatites," Part 1). Acad. Sci., U.S.S.R., 1940.

[28] Vinogradov, A. P. *Geokhimiya zhivogo veshchestva,* izd. AN SSSR ("Geochemistry of Living Matter"). Acad. Sci. U.S.S.R., 1932.

[29] Clarke, F. W., and Washington, H. S. *U.S. Geol. Survey Professional Papers,* **127:** 1, 1924.

[30] Goldschmidt, V. M. *Geochemische Verteilungsgesetze der Elemente.* Oslo: I Kommisjon Hos Jacob Dybwad, 1938.

[31] Rankama, K., and Sahama, Th. G. *Geochemistry.* Chicago: University of Chicago Press, 1952.

[32] Zavaritskii, A. N. *Meteoritika,* AN SSSR ("Meteoritics"), Vol. 4. Acad. Sci. U.S.S.R., 1948.

[33] Greenstein, J. L. *Astrophys. Jour.,* **107:** 151, 1948.

[34] Goldberg, L., and Aller, L. H. *Atoms, Stars, and Nebulae.* Philadelphia: Blakiston Co., 1943.

[35] Unsöld, A. *Zeitschr. f. Astrophys.,* **24:** 306, 1948; **21:** 1, 22, 1942.

[36] Ambartsumian, V. A., Mustel', E. R., Severnyi, A. B., and Sobolev, V. V. *Teoreticheskaya astrofizika,* Gostekhizdat ("Theoretical Astrophysics"). State Technical Publishing House, 1952.

[37] Freier, P., Lofgren, E. J., Ney, E. P., Oppenheimer, F., Bradt, H. L., and Peters, B. *Phys. Rev.,* **74:** 213, 1818, 1948.

[38] Kaplon, M. F., Noon, J. H., and Racette, G. W. *Phys. Rev.,* **96:** 1408, 1954.

[39] Dainton, A., Fowler, P., and Kent, P. *Phil. Mag.,* **43:** 729, 1952.

[40] Stix, T. H. *Phys. Rev.,* **95:** 782, 1954.

[41] Bradt, H. L., and Peters, B. *Phys. Rev.,* **80:** 943, 1950.

[42] Kuiper, G. P. *The Atmospheres of the Earth and Planets.* Chicago: University of Chicago Press, 1952.

[43] Aller, L. H. *Astrophys. Jour.,* **109:** 244, 1949.

[44] ———. *Astrophysics.* New York: Ronald Press, 1953.

[45] STRUVE, O. *Proc. Nat. Acad. Sci.* (Washington), **31**: 217, 1941.

[46] SAUKOV, A. A. *Geokhimiya rtuti,* izd. AN SSSR ("Geochemistry of Mercury"). Acad. Sci. U.S.S.R., 1946.

[47] ZAVARITSKII, A. N. *Trudy pervogo soveshchaniya po voprosam kosmogonii,* izd. AN SSSR ("Proceedings of the First Conference on the Problems of Cosmogony"). Acad. Sci. U.S.S.R., 191, 1951.

[48] CHERDYNTSEV, V. V. *Vestnik Kazfiliala, AN SSSR* ("News Herald, Kazakh Branch Acad. Sci. U.S.S.R."), No. 5, p. 10, 1945.

[49] EDDINGTON, A. S. *The Internal Constitution of the Stars.* Cambridge: Cambridge University Press, 1926.

[50] HOLLANDER, J. M., PERLMAN, I., and SEABORG, G. T. *Rev. Mod. Phys.,* **25**: 469, 1953.

[51] WHITE, F. A., COLLINS, T. L., and ROURKE, F. M. *Phys. Rev.,* **97**: 566, 1955.

[52] VALLEY, G. E., and ANDERSON, H. H. *Jour. Amer. Chem. Soc.,* **69**: 1871, 1947.

[53] CRANE, W. W. T., HIGGINS, G. H., and THOMPSON, S. G. *Phys. Rev.,* **97**: 242, 1955.

[54] RIK, G. R., and SHUKOLIUKOV, YU. A. *DAN SSSR* ("Repts. Acad. Sci. U.S.S.R."), **94**: 668, 1954.

[55] SHMONIN, L. I., CHERDYNTSEV, V. V., KASHKAROV, L. L., and TANEEVA, G. G. *Byuleten' Komissii po opredeleniyu absolutnogo vozrasta geologicheskikh formatsii,* Vol. **1**, izd. AN SSSR ("Bulletin of the Commission on the Determination of the Absolute Age of Geologic Formations," Vol. 1). Acad. Sci. U.S.S.R., 1955.

[56] BOATO, G. *Phys. Rev.,* **93**: 640, 1954; *Geochim. et Cosmochim. Acta,* **6**: 209, 1954.

[57] VINOGRADOV, A. P. *Vestnik AN SSSR* ("News Herald, Acad. Sci. U.S.S.R."), No. 5, p. 26, 1954.

[58] ALDRICH, L. T., HERZOG, L. F., HOLYK, W. K., WHITING, F. B., and AHRENS, L. H. *Phys. Rev.,* **89**: 631, 1953.

[59] CHERDYNTSEV, V. V. (jointly with P. I. CHALOV, M. E. KHITRIK, D. M. MAMBETOV, and G. Z. KHAIDAROV). *Trudy III sessii komissii po opredeleniyu vozrasta geologicheskikh formatsii,* izd. AN SSSR ("Proc. of the III Session of the Commission on Determination of the Absolute Age of Geologic Formations"), p. 175. Acad. Sci. U.S.S.R., 1955.

[60] VERNADSKII, V. I. *DAN SSSR* ("Repts. Acad. Sci. U.S.S.R."), p. 215, 1926.

[61] TROFIMOV, A. V. *DAN SSSR* ("Repts. Acad. Sci. U.S.S.R."), **85**: 169, 1952.

[62] UREY, H. C., LOWENSTAM, H. A., EPSTEIN, S., and MCKINNEY, C. R. *Bull. Geol. Soc. America,* **62**: 399, 1951.

[63] *Sbornik "Izotopy v geologii,"* IL (collected volume "Isotopes in Geology"). 1954.

[64] VINOGRADOV, A. P., and DONTSOVA, E. I. *DAN SSSR* ("Repts. Acad. Sci. U.S.S.R."), **85**: 341, 1952.

[65] SILVERMAN, S. R. *Geochim. et Cosmochim. Acta,* **2:** 26, 1951.

[66] TROFIMOV, A. V. *DAN SSSR* ("Repts. Acad. Sci. U.S.S.R."), **66:** 181, 1949.

[67] THODE, H. G., MACNAMARA, J., and FLEMING, W. H. *Geochim. et Cosmochim. Acta,* **3:** 235, 1953.

[68] HOLMES, A., *Nature* (London), **173:** 612, 1954.

[69] DOLE, M., LANE, G. A., RUDD, D. P., and ZAUKELIES, D. A. *Geochim. et Cosmochim. Acta,* **6:** 65, 1954.

[70] GRAHAM, R. P., MACNAMARA, J., CROCKER, I. H., and MACFARLANE, B. *Canad. Jour. Chem.,* **29:** 89, 1951.

[71] RANKAMA, K. *Isotope Geology.* London: Pergamon Press, 1954.

[72] SHAIN, G. A. *DAN SSSR* ("Repts. Acad. Sci. U.S.S.R."), **35:** 99, 1942.

[73] SHAIN, G. A., and HAZE, V. F. *UFN* ("Advances of Physical Sciences"), **43:** 3, 1951.

[74] CLAAS, W. *Rech. Astr. Obs. Utrecht,* **12:** 1, 1951.

[75] BAUER, C. A. *Phys. Rev.,* **72:** 354, 1947; **74:** 225, 501, 1948.

[76] PANETH, F. A., REASBECK, P., and MAYNE, K. I. *Geochim. et Cosmochim. Acta,* **2:** 300, 1952.

[77] CHERDYNTSEV, V. V., KOZAK, L. V., and STROEVA, M. N. *Trudy I sessii Komissii po opredeleniyu absolutnogo vozrasta geologicheskikh formatsii,* izd. AN SSSR ("Proc. of the I Session of the Commission on Determination of the Absolute Age of Geologic Formations"), p. 55. Acad. Sci. U.S.S.R., 1954.

CHERDYNTSEV, V. V., and ABDULGOFAROV, K. K. *DAN SSSR* ("Repts. Acad. Sci. U.S.S.R."), **106:** 311, 1956.

[78] GERLING, E. K. *Byulleten' komissii po opredeleniyu absolutnogo vozrasta geologicheskikh formatsii,* Vol. **1,** izd. AN SSSR ("Bull. of the Commission on Determination of the Absolute Age of Geologic Formations"), **1:** 57. Acad. Sci. U.S.S.R., 1955.

[79] TROFIMOV, A. V., and RIK, K. G. *DAN SSSR* ("Repts. Acad. Sci., U.S.S.R."), **102:** 911, 1955.

[80] REASBECK, P., and MAYNE, K. I. *Nature* (London), **176:** 733, 1955.

[81] LIBBY, W. F. *Report of the Committee on Measurement of Geologoic Time, 1947–1948.* Washington, 1949.

ARNOLD, J. R., and LIBBY, W. F. *Science,* **110:** 678, 1949; **113:** 111, 1951.

LIBBY, W. F., and ANDERSON, E. C. *Phys. Rev.,* **81:** 64, 1951.

[82] FUNT, B. L., SOBERING, S., PRINGLE, R. W., and TURCHINETZ, W. *Nature* (London), **175:** 1042, 1955.

DEVRIES, H., and BARENDSEN, G. W. *Nature* (London), **174:** 1138, 1954.

[83] GROSSE, A. V., JOHNSTON, W. M., WOLFGANG, R. L., and LIBBY, W. F. *Science,* **113:** 1, 1951.

KAUFMAN, S., and LIBBY, W. F. *Phys. Rev.,* **93:** 1337, 1954.

FIREMAN, E. L., and SCHWARZER, D. *Phys. Rev.,* **94:** 385, 1954.

FALTINGS, V., and HARTECK, P. *Nature* (London), **166:** 1109, 1950.

[84] ALDRICH, L. T., and NIER, A. O. *Phys. Rev.,* **74:** 1590, 1948.

[85] KHLOPIN, V., and GERLING, E. K. *DAN SSSR* ("Repts. Acad. Sci. U.S.S.R."), Vol. **61,** No. 2, 1948.

[86] WETHERILL, G. W. *Phys. Rev.,* **92**: 907, 1953; **96**: 679, 1954.
[87] FLEMING, W. H., and THODE, H. G. *Phys. Rev.,* **90**: 857, 1953.
[88] INGHRAM, M. G., and REYNOLDS, J. H. *Phys. Rev.,* **76**: 1265, 1949; **78**: 822, 1950.
[89] KHLOPIN, V., GERLING, E. K., and BARANOVSKAYA, N. *Izv. AN SSSR, ser. khim.* (Bull. Acad. Sci. U.S.S.R., chem. ser."), p. 599, 1947.
KHLOPIN, V. and GERLING, E. K. *DAN SSSR* ("Repts. Acad. Sci., U.S.S.R."), Vol. **61**, No. 2, 1948.
[90] MACNAMARA, J. and THODE, H. G. *Phys. Rev.,* **80**: 471, 1950.
[91] FLEMING, W. H., and THODE, H. G. *Phys. Rev.,* **92**: 378, 1953.
[92] SEABORG, G. T., *Phys. Rev.,* **85**: 157, 1952.
GHIORSO, A., HIGGINS, G. H., LARSH, A. E., SEABORG, G. T., and THOMPSON, S. G. *Phys. Rev.,* **87**: 163, 1952.
[93] LEVINE, CH. A., and SEABORG, G. T. *Jour. Amer. Chem. Soc.,* **73**: 3278, 1951.
[94] PEPPARD, D. F., STUDIER, M. H., GERGEL, M. V., MASON, G. W., SULLIVAN, J. C., and MECH, J. F. *Jour. Amer. Chem. Soc.,* **73**: 2529, 1951.
[95] PEPPARD, D. F., MASON, G. W., GRAY, P. R., and MECH, J. F. *Jour. Amer. Chem. Soc.,* **74**: 6081, 1952; *Chem. Eng. News,* **30**: 4136, 1952.
[96] MORRISON, P., and PINE, J. *Ann. New York Acad. Sci.,* **62**: 69, 1955.
[97] VERNADSKII, V. I. *Trudy XVII mezhdunarodnogo geologicheskogo kongressa* ("Proc. XVII International Geological Congress"), p. 215, 1938.
[98] KHLOPIN, V. G. *Izvestiya AN SSSR, ser. geog. i geofiz.* ("Bull. Acad. Sci. U.S.S.R., geog. geophys. ser."), No. 2, 1937.
[99] WALDRON, E. C., SCHULTZ, V. A., and KOHMAN, T. P. *Phys. Rev.,* **93**: 254, 1954.
[100] BEARD, G., and WIEDENBECK, M. L. *Phys. Rev.,* **95**: 1245, 1954.
[101] SUTTLE, A., and LIBBY, W. F. *Phys. Rev.,* **95**: 866, 1954.
[102] FARAGGI, H., and BERTHELOT, A. *Compt. rend.,* **232**: 2093, 1951.
RIEZLER, W., and PORSCHEN, W. *Zeitschr. f. Naturforsch.,* **7a**: 634, 1952.
[103] AHRENS, L. H., and EVANS, R. D. *Phys. Rev.,* **74**: 279, 1948.
[104] THOMPSON, F. C., and ROWLANDS, S. *Nature* (London), **152**: 103, 1943.
[105] WEIZSÄCKER, C. F. VON. *Phys. Zeitschr.,* **38**: 623, 1937.
[106] PAGE, T. L. *Nature* (London), **138**: 503, 1936.
[107] GERLING, E. K., TITOV, E., and ERMOLIN, G. *DAN SSSR* ("Repts. Acad. Sci. U.S.S.R."), Vol. **68**, No. 3, 1949.
GERLING, E. K., ERMOLIN, G., BARANOVSKAYA, N., and TITOV, N. *DAN SSSR* ("Repts. Acad. Sci. U.S.S.R."), **86**: 593, 1952.
GERLING, E. K., YASHCHENKO, M. L., ERMOLIN, G. I., and BARKAN, V. G. *Trudy III sessii komissii po opredeleniyu absolutnogo vozrasta geologicheskikh formatsii,* izd. AN SSSR ("Proc. of the III Session of the Commission on Determination of the Absolute Age of Geologic Formations"), p. 16. Acad. Sci. U.S.S.R., 1955.
[108] MOUSUF, A. K. *Phys. Rev.,* **88**: 150, 1952.
[109] GERLING, E. K., and PAVLOVA, T. *DAN SSSR* ("Repts. Acad. Sci. U.S.S.R."), **72**: 85, 1951.

[110] GERLING, E. K., and RIK, K. G. *DAN SSSR* ("Repts. Acad. Sci. U.S.S.R."), **101:** 433, 1955.

[111] WASSERBURG, G. J., and HAYDEN, R. J. *Phys. Rev.,* **97:** 86, 1955.

[112] THOMSON, S. J., and MAYNE, K. I. *Geochim. et Cosmochim. Acta,* **7:** 169, 1955.

[113] HAHN, O., STRASSMANN, F., and WALLING, E. *Naturwiss.,* **25:** 189, 1937.
MATTAUCH, J. *Naturwiss.,* **25:** 189, 1937.

[114] AHRENS, L. H. *Nature* (London), **160:** 874, 1947; *Geochim. et Cosmochim. Acta,* **1:** 312, 1951.

[115] WILSON, J. T., FARQUHAR, R. M., GRETENER, P., RUSSEL, R. D., and SCHILLIBEER, H. A. *Nature* (London), **174:** 1006, 1954.

[116] HINTERBERGER, H., HERR, W., and VOSHAGE, H. *Phys. Rev.,* **95:** 1690, 1954.
HERR, W., and MERZ, E. *Zeitschr. f. Naturforsch.,* **10a:** 613, 1955.

[117] MOORE, C. E., and KING, A. S. *Pub. Astr. Soc. Pacific,* **55:** 36, 1943.
DAVIS, D. N. *Pub. Astr. Soc. Pacific,* **55:** 41, 1943.

[118] ALPEROVITCH, E. A., and MILLER, J. M. *Phys. Rev.,* **98:** 262, 1955; *Nature* (London), **176:** 299, 1955.

[119] HERR, W. *Zeitschr. f. Naturforsch.,* **9a:** 907, 1954.

[120] KATCOFF, C., SCHAEFFER, O. A., and HASTINGS, J. M. *Phys. Rev.,* **82:** 688, 1951.

[121] JAFFEY, A. H., DIAMOND, H., HIRSCH, A., and MECH, J. *Phys. Rev.,* **84:** 785, 1951.
DIAMOND, H., and BARNES, R. F. *Phys. Rev.,* **101:** 1064, 1956.

[122] KHLOPIN, V. G. *Prirodnyye gazy* ("Natural Gases"), p. 61, 1931.

[123] DAVIS, R., and SCHAEFFER, O. A. *Ann. New York Acad. Sci.,* **62:** 105, 1955.

[124] BELOUSOV, V. V. *Problemy sovetskoi geologii* ("Problems of Soviet Geology"), **3:** 81, 1933.

[125] KHLOPIN, V. G. *DAN SSSR* ("Repts. Acad. Sci. U.S.S.R."), p. 195, 1926.

[126] STARIK, I. E. *Radioaktivnyye metody opredeleniya geologicheskogo vremeni.* ONTI ("Radioactive Methods of Determination of Geologic Time"). 1938.

[127] KHLOPIN, V. G., GERLING, E. K., and YOFFE, E. M. *Prirodnyye gazy* ("Natural Gases"), **11:** 105, 1936.

[128] GERLING, E. K. *Doklady XVII mezhdunarodnogo geologicheskogo s'yezda* ("Repts. of the XVII International Geological Congress"), 1937; *DAN SSSR* ("Repts. Acad. Sci. U.S.S.R."), **24:** 273, 572, 1939.

[129] GERLING, E. K., and POLKANOV, A. A. *Izvestiya AN SSSR, ser. geol.* ("Bull. Acad. Sci. U.S.S.R., geol. ser."), **2:** 29, 1946.

[130] STRUTT, R. J. *Proc. Roy. Soc. London, A,* **80:** 572, 1908; **81:** 278, 1908; **84:** 194, 1911.

[131] ———. *Ibid.,* **142:** 370, 1933.

[132] KHLOPIN, V. G. *DAN SSSR* ("Repts. Acad. Sci. U.S.S.R."), **32:** 637, 1941.

[133] KEEVIL, N. B. *Amer. Jour. Sci.,* **237:** 195, 1939; **241:** 277, 1943.

[134] Keevil, N. B., Larsen, E. S., and Wank, F. J. *Amer. Jour. Sci.,* 242: 345, 1944.
Keevil, N. B., Jolliffe, A. F., and Larsen, E. S. *Amer. Jour. Sci.,* **240:** 831, 1942.
[135] Cherdyntsev, V. V., and Kozak, L. V., *DAN SSSR* ("Repts. Acad. Sci. U.S.S.R."), **69:** 829, 1949.
[136] Cherdyntsev, V. V., and Gaidina, E. I. *Trudy I sessii komissii po opredeleniyu absolutnogo vozrasta geologicheskikh formatsii,* izd. AN SSSR ("Proc. of the I Session of the Commission on Determination of the Absolute Age of Geologic Formations"), p. 157. Acad. Sci. U.S.S.R., 1954.
[137] Vinogradov, A. P. *Sessiya AN SSSR po mirnomu ispol'zovaniyu atomnoi energii, 1–5 iyulia 1955 g* ("Session of the Soviet Academy of Sciences on the Peaceful Uses of Atomic Energy, July 1–5, 1955").
[138] Patterson, C. C., Brown, H., Tilton, G., and Inghram, M. *Phys. Rev.,* **92:** 1234, 1953.
[139] Khlopin, V. G., and Vladimirova, M. E. *Izvestiya AN SSSR, ser. khim. nauk* ("Bull. Acad. Sci. U.S.S.R., ser. chem. sci."), **2:** 499, 1935.
[140] Starik, I. E. *Trudy III sessii komissii po opredeleniyu absolutnogo vozrasta geologicheskikh formatsii,* izd. AN SSSR ("Proc. of the III Session of the Commission on Determination of the Absolute Age of Geologic Formations"), p. 7. Acad. Sci. U.S.S.R., 1955.
[141] Avdzeiko, G. V. *Ibid.,* p. 153.
[142] Nier, A. O. *Jour. Amer. Chem. Soc.,* **60:** 1571, 1938.
Nier, A. O., Thompson, R. W., and Murphey, B. F. *Phys. Rev.,* **60:** 112, 1941.
[143] Collins, C. B., Farquhar, R. M., and Russel, R. D. *Phys. Rev.,* **88:** 1275, 1952.
Hurley, P. M., and Fairbairn, H. W. *Bull. Geol. Soc. America,* **64:** 659, 1953.
[144] Vinogradov, A. P., Zadorozhnyi, I. K., and Zykov, S. I. *DAN SSSR* ("Repts. Acad. Sci. U.S.S.R."), **85:** 1107, 1952.
[145] Rik, G. R., and Avdzeiko, G. V. *DAN SSSR* ("Repts. Acad. Sci. U.S.S.R."), **90:** 829, 1953.
[146] Patterson, C. C. *Geochim. et Cosmochim. Acta,* **7:** 151, 1955.
[147] Curie, M. *Radioaktivnost'.* Gostekhizdat, 1947. Orig. *Radioactivité.* Paris: Hermann & Cie, 1935.
[148] Khlopin, V. G., and Pasvik, M. A. *Trudy po izucheniyu radia,* izd. AN SSSR ("Collection of Studies on Radium"), **3:** 109, 1928.
[149] Starik, I. E. *Sbornik "V.I. Vernadskomu—Akademiya Nauk SSSR,"* izd. AN SSSR ("Collected Volume, Dedicated to V.I. Vernadskii, Academy of Sciences of the U.S.S.R."), **1:** 445. Acad. Sci. U.S.S.R., 1936.
[150] Starik, I. E. and Segel', N. M. *Trudy radievogo instituta* ("Proc. of the Radium Institute"), **3:** 218, 1937.
[151] Khlopin, V. G. *DAN SSSR* ("Repts. Acad. Sci. U.S.S.R."), p. 178, 1926.

[152] Kolovrat-Chervinskii, L. S. *Trudy radievoi ekspeditsii rossiiskoi akademii nauk* ("Proc. Radium Expedition Russ. Acad. Sci."), Nos. 9, 10, 1918.

[153] Strassmann, F. *Zeitschr. f. phys. Chem.*, Abt. B, **26**: 362, 1934.

[154] Spitsyn, V. I. *Trudy po izucheniyu radiya i radioaktivnykh rud* ("Collection of Studies on Radium and Radioactive Ores"), **2**: 264, 1926.

[155] Starik, I. E., and Melikova, O. S. *Trudy gosudarstvennogo radievogo instituta* ("Proc. of the State Radium Institute"), **4**: 384, 1938.

[156] Kosov, N. D., and Cherdyntsev, V. V. *Byulleten' komissii po opredeleniyu absolutnogo vozrasta geologicheskikh formatsii,* izd. AN SSSR ("Bull. of the Commission on Determination of the Absolute Age of Geologic Formations"), **1**: 22. Acad. Sci. U.S.S.R., 1955.

[157] Starik, I. E., Melikova, O. S., Kurbatov, V. V., and Aleksandrchuk, V. M. *Ibid.*, p. 33, 1955.

[158] Meyer, S., and Schweidler, E. *Die Radioaktivität.* Leipzig and Berlin: B. G. Teubner, 1927.

[159] Starik, I. E. *Izvestiya AN SSSR, otd. khim. nauk* ("Bull. Acad. Sci. U.S.S.R., sec. chem. sci."), No. 6, p. 435, 1943.

[160] Cherdyntsev, V. V. *DAN SSSR* ("Repts. Acad. Sci. U.S.S.R."), **36**: 223, 1942; *Izvestiya AN SSSR, ser. astr. i fiz* ("Bull. Acad. Sci., astr. and phys. ser."), **2**: 90, 1946; *Vestnik Kazfiliala AN SSSR* ("News Herald, Kazakh Branch Acad. Sci. U.S.S.R."), **10**: 7, 1946.

[161] Salomon, W. *Abhandl. Heidelberg. Akad. Wiss., math. Kl.*, No. 14, 1931.

[162] Nikitin, B. A., and Komlev, L. V. *Trudy radievogo instituta* ("Proc. Radium Institute"), **1**: 157, 1930.
Nikitin, B. A., and Merkulova, M. S. *Ibid.*, **2**: 160, 1933.
Komlev, L. V. *Ibid.*, **2**: 207, 1933.

[163] Cherdyntsev, V. V. *Vestnik AN Kaz. SSR* ("News Herald Acad. Sci. Kazakh S.S.R."), Nos. 16–17, p. 10, 1946.

[164] Merkulova, M. S. *DAN SSSR* ("Repts. Acad. Sci. U.S.S.R."), **31**: 345, 1941.

[165] Popov, A. A., and Cherdyntsev, V. V. *Problemy Turkmenii, SOPS AN SSSR* ("Problems of Turkmenia"), **1**: 227, 1934.
Cherdyntsev, V. V., and Popov, A. A. *Trudy gosudarstvennogo radievogo instituta* ("Proc. State Radium Institute"), **3**: 278, 1937.

[166] Baranov, V. I., and Bobin, P. L. *Ibid.*, **2**: 139, 157, 1933.
Komlev, L. V., and Cherdyntsev, V. V. *Ibid.*, **3**: 137, 1937.

[167] Starik, I. E., Starik, F. E., and Petriayev, E. P. *Byulleten' komissii po opredeleniyu absolutnogo vozrasta geologicheskikh formatsii* ("Bull. of the Commission on Determination of the Absolute Age of Geologic Formations"), **1**: 29, 1955. Acad. Sci. U.S.S.R.

[168] Begemann, F., Geiss, J., Houtermans, F. G., and Buser, W. *Helvet. Phys. Acta,* **27**: 115, 1954; *Nuovo Cimento,* **11**: 663, 1954.

[169] Kurbatov, L. M. *Nature* (London), **137**: 949, 1936.
Kurbatov, L. M., and Ermolayev, M. M. *Izvestiya AN SSSR, ser. geol.* ("Bull. Acad. Sci. U.S.S.R., geol. ser."), **1**: 131, 1948.

[170] Piggot, C. S., and Urry, W. D. *Amer. Jour. Sci.,* **239:** 81, 1941.
Urry, W. D. *Amer. Jour. Sci.,* **246:** 689, 1948.

[171] Isaac, N., and Picciotto, E. *Nature* (London), **171:** 742, 1953.

[172] Picciotto, E., and Wilgain, S. *Nature* (London), **173:** 632, 1954.

[173] Cherdyntsev, V. V., and Meshkov, V. I. *Trudy I sessii komissii po opredeleniyu absolutnogo vozrasta geologicheskikh formatsii,* izd. AN SSSR ("Proc. I Session of the Commission on Determination of the Absolute Age of Geologic Formations"), p. 69, 1954.

[174] Reed, G. W., and Turkevich, A. *Nature* (London), **176:** 794, 1955.

[175] Reed, G. W., Hamaguchi, H., and Turkevich, A. *Geochim. et Cosmochim. Acta,* **13:** 248, 1958.

[176] Hamaguchi, H., Reed, G. W., and Turkevich, A. *Geochim. et Cosmochim. Acta,* **12:** 337, 1957.

[177] Bate, G., Potratz, H., and Huizenga, J. *Geochim. et Cosmochim. Acta,* **14:** 118, 1958.
Stoenner, R. W., and Zähringer, J. *Geochim. et Cosmochim. Acta,* **15:** 40, 1958.

[178] Schwarzschild, M., Spitzer, L., and Wildt, R. *Astrophys. Jour.* **114:** 398, 1951.

[179] Noon, J. H., Herz, A. J., and O'Brien, B. J. *Nuovo Cimento,* **5:** 854, 1957.

[180] Appa Rao, M. V. K., Biswas, S., Daniel, R. R., Neelakantan, K. K., and Peters, B. *Phys. Rev.,* **110:** 751, 1958.

[181] Hoering, T. C., and Moore, H. E., *Geochim. et Cosmochim. Acta.,* **13:** 225, 1958.

[182] Parwel, A., Ubisch, H. von, and Wickman, F. E. *Geochim. et Cosmochim. Acta,* **10:** 185, 1956.

[183] Reynolds, J. H., and Lipson, J. I. *Geochim. et Cosmochim. Acta,* **12:** 330, 1957.

[184] Begemann, F., Geiss, J., and Heiss, D. C. *Phys. Rev.,* **107:** 540, 1957.

[185] Gentner, W., and Zähringer, J. *Geochim. et Cosmochim. Acta,* **11:** 60, 1957.

[186] Wasserburg, G. J., and Hayden, R. J. *Nature* (London), **176:** 130, 1955.

[187] Begemann, F., and Libby, W. F. *Geochim. et Cosmochim. Acta,* **12:** 277, 1957.

[188] Damon, P. E., and Kulp, J. L. *Geochim. et Cosmochim. Acta,* **13:** 280, 1958.

[189] Craig, H. *Phys. Rev.,* **105:** 1125, 1957.

[190] Arnold, J. R., and Al-Salih, H. A. *Science,* **121:** 451, 1955.

[191] Winsberg, L. *Geochim. et Cosmochim. Acta,* **9:** 183, 1956.

[192] Starik, I., Ratner, A., Passvik, M., and Ginsburg, F. *Geokhimiya* ("Geochemistry"), No. 2, p. 146, 1957.

[193] Merrill, P. W. *Astrophys. Jour.,* **116:** 21, 1952.

[194] Kuroda, P. K., Edwards, R. R., Robinson, B. L., Jonte, J. H., and Goolsby, C. *Geochim. et Cosmochim. Acta,* **11:** 194, 1957.

[195] Mather, K. B. *Australian Jour. Phys.,* **9:** 147, 1956.

[196] Cherdyntsev, V. V., and Suyarova, O. *Trudy instituta yadernoi fiziki AN Kaz SSR* ("Proc. Inst. Nuclear Phys. Acad. Sci. Kazakh SSR"), **1:** 166, 1958.

[197] Shmonin, L. I., Cherdyntsev, V. V., Kashkarov, L. L., and Ostapenko, V. F. *Uchenyye zapiski kazakhskogo gosudarstvennogo universiteta im. S. M. Kirova* ("Scientific Notes of the S. M. Kirov Kazakh State University"), **30:** issue 5, 25, 1957.

[198] Kashkarov, L. L., and Cherdyntsev, V. V. *Geokhimiya* ("Geochemistry"), No. 7, p. 632, 1958.

[199] Gerling, E. K., Levskii, L., and Afanas'yeva, L. *DAN SSSR* ("Repts. Acad. Sci. U.S.S.R."), **109:** 813, 1956.

[200] Huizenga, J. R., and Wing, J. *Phys. Rev.*, **102:** 926, 1956.

[201] Gerling, E. K., and Levskii, L. K. *DAN SSSR* ("Repts. Acad. Sci. U.S.S.R."), **110:** 750, 1956.

[202] Abdulgafarov, K. K., and Cherdyntsev, V. V. *Uchenyye zapiski kazakhskogo gosudarstvennogo universiteta, im. S.M. Kirova* ("Scientific Notes of the S.M. Kirov Kazakh State University"), **30:** issue 5, 21, 1957.

[203] Chalov, P. I. *Trudy instituta geologii AN kirgizskoi SSR* ("Proc. Inst. Geol. Acad. Sci. Kirgiz SSR"), issue 9, p. 227, 1957.

[204] Starik, I. E., Starik, F. E., and Mikhailov, B. A. *Geokhimiya* ("Geochemistry"), No. 5, p. 462, 1958.

[205] Baranov, V. I., Surkov, Yu. A., and Vilenskaya, V. D. *Geokhimiya* ("Geochemistry"), No. 5, p. 465, 1958.

[206] Naidenov, B. M., and Cherdyntsev, V. V. *Izvestiya AN SSSR, ser. geol.* ("Bull. Acad. Sci. U.S.S.R., geol. ser."), No. 5, p. 40, 1958.

[207] Zhirov, K. K., Zykov, S. I., and Stupnikova, N. I. *Geokhimiya* ("Geochemistry"), No. 2, p. 147, 1957.

[208] Starik, I. E., Sobotovich, E. V., Lovtsius, G. P., Lovtsius, A. V., and Avdzeiko, G. V. *Geokhimiya* ("Geochemistry"), No. 7, p. 584, 1957.

[209] Tilton, G. R., and Nicolaysen, L. O. *Geochim. et Cosmochim. Acta,* **11:** 28, 1957.

[210] Cherdyntsev, V. V. *Trudy komissii po izucheniyu chetvertichnogo perioda, AN SSSR* ("Proc. of the Commission on the Study of the Quarternary, Acad. Sci. U.S.S.R."), **13:** 437, 1957.

[211] ———. *Sovetskaya arkheologiya* ("Soviet Archeology"), **25:** 64, 1956.

[212] Bethe, H. A., and Bacher, R. F. *Fizika yadra,* Vol. **1**, ONTI. 1938. Orig. *Nuclear Physics,* Vol. **6**. Lancaster, Pa.: American Physical Society, 1936–37.

[213] Bethe, H. A. *Lektsii po teorii yadra,* IL, 1949. Orig. *Elementary Nuclear Theory: A Short Course on Selected Topics Given at the Research Laboratory of the General Electric Company at Schenectady, New York.* New York: John Wiley & Sons, 1947.

[214] Fermi, E. *Yadernaya fizika,* IL, 1951. Orig. Jay Orear, *Nuclear Physics: A Course Given by Enrico Fermi at the University of Chicago.* Notes compiled by Jay Orear, A. H. Rosenfeld, and R. A. Schluter. Rev. ed. Chicago: University of Chicago Press, 1950.

[215] Meitner, L. *Naturwiss.,* **15:** 369, 1927.

[216] SONDER, R. *Zeitschr. f. Kristall.,* **57:** 611, 1923.
[217] NIGGLI, P. *Fennia,* **1:** 1, 1928.
[218] SHCHUKAREV, S. A. *Trudy Mendeleyevskogo s'ezda,* Vol. **2** ("Proc. of the Mendeleyev Conference," Vol. 2), 1937.
[219] SELINOV, I. P. *ZhETF* ("Jour. Exper. Theoret. Phys."), **4:** 666, 1934.
[220] MAYER, M. G. *Phys. Rev.,* **74:** 235, 1948; **75:** 1969, 1949; **78:** 16, 22, 1950.
[221] KEILSON, J. *Phys. Rev.,* **82:** 759, 1951.
[222] BLATT, J. M., and WEISSKOPF, V. F. *Teoreticheskaya yadernaya fizika,* IL, 1954. Orig. *Theoretical Nuclear Physics.* New York: John Wiley & Sons, 1952.
[223] HEISENBERG, W. *Zeitschr. f. Phys.,* **77:** 1, 1932.
[224] FRENKEL', YA. I., and CHERDYNTSEV, V. V. *ZhETF* ("Jour. Exper. Theoret. Phys."), **9:** 899, 1938.
[225] WEIZSÄCKER, C. F. VON. *Die Atomkerne.* Leipzig: Akademischer Verlag, 1937.
[226] CHERDYNTSEV, V. V. *ZhETF* ("Jour. Exper. Theoret. Phys."), **8:** 253, 1938; *Collected Volume: Kazakh Branch Acad. Sci. U.S.S.R., for the year 1944,* p. 50, 1946.
[227] DZHELEPOV, B., and ZYRIANOVA, L., *UFN* ("Advances of Physical Sciences"), **48:** 465, 1952; **49:** 447, 1953.
[228] HALSTED, R. E. *Phys. Rev.,* **88:** 666, 1952.
GEIGER, J. S., HOGG, B. G., DUCKWORTH, H. E., and DEWDNEY, J. W. *Phys. Rev.,* **89:** 621, 1953.
REYNOLDS, G. T., and TREIMAN, S. B. *Phys. Rev.,* **94:** 207, 1954.
[229] FRENKEL', YA. I. *ZhETF* ("Jour. Exper. Theoret. Phys."), **6:** 641, 1939.
[230] MCCARTHY, J. A. *Phys. Rev.,* **97:** 1234, 1955.
[231] JONES, J. W., and KOHMAN, T. P. *Phys. Rev.,* **85:** 941, 1952.
[232] FIREMAN, E. L., and SCHWARZER, D. *Phys. Rev.,* **86:** 451, 1952.
[233] WINTER, R. G. *Phys. Rev.,* **85:** 687, 1952; **99:** 88, 1955.
[234] MCCARTHY, J. A. *Phys. Rev.,* **90:** 853, 1953.
[235] LEVINE, C. A., GHIORSO, A., and SEABORG, G. T. *Phys. Rev.,* **77:** 296, 1950.
[236] STROMINGER, D., HOLLANDER, J. M., and SEABORG, G. T. *Rev. Mod. Phys.,* **30:** 585, 1958.
[237] INGHRAM, M. G., HESS, D. C., and HAYDEN, R. J. *Phys. Rev.,* **73:** 180, 1948.
[238] DUNLAVEY, D. C., and SEABORG, G. T. *Phys. Rev.,* **92:** 206, 1953.
[239] HULET, E. K., THOMPSON, S. G., and GHIORSO, A. *Phys. Rev.,* **89:** 878, 1953.
STUDIER, M. H., and HUIZENGA, J. R. *Phys. Rev.,* **96:** 545, 1954.
FIELDS, P. R., STUDIER, M. H., MAGNUSON, L. B., and HUIZENGA, J. R. *Nature* (London), **174:** 266, 1954.
MAGNUSON, L. B., STUDIER, M. H., FIELDS, P. R., STEVENS, C. M., MECH, J. F., FRIEDMAN, A. M., DIAMOND, H., and HUIZENGA, J. R. *Phys. Rev.,* **96:** 1576, 1954.
CHOPPIN, G. R., HARVEY, B. G., THOMPSON, S. G., and GHIORSO, A. *Phys. Rev.,* **98:** 1519, 1955.

[240] Hill, D. L., and Wheeler, J. A. *Phys. Rev.*, **89**: 1102, 1953; *UFN* ("Advances of Physical Sciences"), **52**: 83, 239, 1954.
[241] Hill, R. D. *Phys. Rev.*, **98**: 1272, 1955.
[242] Zel'dovich, Ya., and Zysin, Yu. *ZhETF* ("Jour. Exper. Theoret. Phys."), **10**: 831, 1940.
[243] Segrè, E., and Wiegand, C. E. *Phys. Rev.*, **75**: 39, 1949; **81**: 284, 1951; Leininger, R. F., Segrè, E., and Wiegand, C. E. *Phys. Rev.*, **76**: 897, 1949.
[244] Bainbridge, K. T., Goldhaber, M., and Wilson, E. *Phys. Rev.*, **84**: 1260, 1951.
[245] Scolman, T. T., Quisenberry, K. S., and Nier, A. O. *Phys. Rev.*, **102**: 1076, 1956.
[246] Giese, C. F., and Benson, J. L. *Phys. Rev.*, **110**: 712, 1958.
[247] Johnson, W. H., and Nier, A. O. *Phys. Rev.*, **105**: 1014, 1957.
[248] Collins, T. L., Rourke, F. M., and White, F. A. *Phys. Rev.*, **105**: 196, 1957.
[249] Awshalom, M. *Bull. Amer. Phys. Soc.*, **1**: 31, 1956.
[250] Swiatecki, W. J. *Phys. Rev.*, **100**: 937, 1955.
[251] Goldschmidt, V. M. *Sbornik: "Osnovnyye idei geokhimii,"* vyp. 1 (Collected Volume: *Fundamental Ideas of Geochemistry*), issue 1, p. 270, 1933; *Naturwiss.*, **18**: 999, 1930.
[252] Cherdyntsev, V. V. *Vestnik kazfiliala AN SSSR* ("News Herald, Kazakh Branch Acad. Sci. U.S.S.R."), **1**: 15, 1945; *Vestnik AN Kaz SSR* ("News Herald Acad. Sci. Kazakh SSR"), **9**: 30, 1946.
[253] Oddo, G. *Zeitschr. f. anorg. Chem.*, **87**: 253, 1914.
[254] Harkins, W. D. *Phys. Rev.*, **38**: 1270, 1931.
[255] Cherdyntsev, V. V. *DAN SSSR* ("Repts. Acad. Sci. U.S.S.R."), **25**: 19, 1941.
[256] Alpher, R. A. *Phys. Rev.*, **74**: 1577, 1948.
[257] Frank, F. C. *Proc. Phys. Soc., London,* **60**: 211, 1948.
[258] Chackett, K. F., and Martin, G. R. *Proc. Phys. Soc., London,* **61**: 197, 1948.
[259] Weizsäcker, C. F. von. *Phys. Zeitschr.*, **38**: 176, 1937.
[260] Macnamara, J., Collins, C. B., and Thode, H. G. *Phys. Rev.*, **78**: 129, 1950.
[261] Frenkel', Ya. I. *Printsipy teorii atomnykh yader,* izd. AN SSSR ("Principles of the Theory of Atomic Nuclei"). Acad. Sci. U.S.S.R., 1950.
[262] Selinov, I. P. *Sistema atomnykh yader i nekotoryye zakonomernosti v svoistvakh izotopov,* prilozheniye II v knige ("System of Atomic Nuclei and Some Regularities in the Properties of Isotopes), Appendix II, p 261.
[263] Suess, H. E., and Brown, H. *Phys. Rev.*, **83**: 1254, 1951.
[264] Ambartsumian, V. A. *Uchenyye zapiski LGU, ser. mat. astr.,* ("Scientific Notes, Leningrad State University, math. astr. ser.), issue 4, 1938; *Evolutsiya zvezd i astrofizika,* izd. AN Arm. SSR ("The Evolution of Stars and Astrophysics"). Acad. Sci. Armenian SSR, Erevan, 1947.
[265] Russell, H. N. *Proc. Roy. Soc. London, A,* **99**: 84, 1921.

[266] RUTHERFORD, E. *Nature* (London), **123**: 313, 1929.

[267] PICCARD, A. *Arch. d. Genève,* **44**: 161, 1917.

[268] ATKINSON, R. D' E., and HOUTERMANS, F. G. *Zeitschr. f. Phys.,* **54**: 656, 1930.

[269] BETHE, H. *Astrofizicheskii sbornik,* IL (in "Astrophysical Collected Volume"), p. 116, 1949.

[270] LANDAU, L. D. *DAN SSSR* ("Repts. Acad. Sci. U.S.S.R."), **17**: 301, 1937.

[271] CHERDYNTSEV, V. V. *Astr. zhur.* ("Astr. Jour."), **17**: No. 5, 1, 1940.

[272] CHANDRASEKHAR, S. *Vvedeniye v ucheniye o stroyenii zvezd,* IL, 1950. Orig. *An Introduction to the Study of Stellar Structure.* Chicago: University of Chicago Press, 1939.

[273] BAADE, W., and ZWICKY, F. *Proc. Nat. Acad. Sci.,* **20**: 254, 259, 1934.

[274] OPPENHEIMER, J. R., and VOLKOFF, G. M. *Phys. Rev.,* **55**: 374, 1939.

[275] KUKARKIN, B., and PARENAGO, P. *Peremennyye zvezdy,* Vol. **1**, ONTI (*Variable Stars,* Vol. **1**). 1937.

[276] AHRENS, L. H. *Geochim. et Cosmochin. Acta,* **7**: 294, 1955.

[277] ALPHER, R. A., and HERMAN, R. C. *Rev. Mod. Phys.,* **22**: 153, 1950.

[278] PERRIN, J. *Rev. du mois,* **21**: 113, 1920.

[279] ATKINSON, R. D' E. *Astrophys. Jour.,* **73**: 250, 308, 1931; **84**: 73, 1936.

[280] WEIZSÄCKER, C. F. VON. *Phys. Zeitschr.* **38**: 623, 1937; **39**: 633, 1938.

[281] ALPHER, R. A., BETHE, H., and GAMOW, G. *Phys. Rev.,* **73**: 803, 1948.

[282] SMART, J. S. *Phys. Rev.,* **74**: 1882, 1948; **75**: 1379, 1949.

[283] GUREVICH, L. E. *Voprosy kosmogonii,* Vol. **2**, izd. AN SSSR ("Problems of Cosmogony," Vol. **2**), p. 151, 1954; *Trudy I sessii komissii po opredeleniyu absolutnogo vozrasta geologicheskikh formatsii,* izd. AN SSSR ("Proc. of the I Session of the Commission on Determination of the Absolute Age of Geologic Formations"), p. 79. Acad. Sci. U.S.S.R., 1954.

[284] TOLMAN, R. C. *Jour. Amer. Chem. Soc.,* **44**: 1902, 1922.
UREY, H. C., and BRADLEY, C. A. *Phys. Rev.,* **38**: 718, 1931.

[285] POKROVSKII, G. I. *Phys. Zeitschr.,* **32**: 374, 1931.

[286] FARKAS, L., and HARTECK, P. *Naturwiss.,* **19**: 705, 1931.

[287] STERNE, T. *Monthly Not. Roy. Astr. Soc.,* **93**: 736, 767, 1933.

[288] CHANDRASEKHAR, S., and HEINRICH, L. R. *Astrophys. Jour.,* **95**: 288, 1942.

[289] ALBADA, G. B. VON. *Astrophys. Jour.,* **105**: 393, 1947.

[290] KLEIN, O., BESKOW, G., and TREFFENBERG, L. *Ark. f. mat., astr. fys.,* **33**: 1, 1946.
BESKOW, G., and TREFFENBERG, L. *Ark. f. mat., astr., fys.,* **34**: 13, 1947.

[291] GEHENIAU, G., PRIGOGINE, P., and DEMEUR, M. *Physics,* **13**: 429, 1947.
SALA, O., and WARAGHIN, G. *Phys. Rev.,* **70**: 430, 1946.

[292] CHERDYNTSEV, V. V. *Astr. zhur.* ("Astr. Jour."), **18**: 1, 1941; *Trudy I sessii komissii po opredeleniyu absolutnogo vozrasta geologicheskikh formatsii,* izd. AN SSSR ("Proc. of the I Session of the Commission on Determination of the Absolute Age of Geologic Formations"), p. 92. Acad. Sci. U.S.S.R., 1954.

[293] WALKE, H. *Phil. Mag.,* **18**: 795, 1934; **19**: 33, 341, 1935.

[294] Mayer, M. G., and Teller, E. *Phys. Rev.,* **76:** 1226, 1949.
[295] Humason, M. L., Mayall, N. U., and Sandage, A. R. *Astr. Jour.,* **61:** 97, 1956.
[296] Salpeter, E. E. *Astrophys. Jour.,* **115:** 326, 1952.
[297] Fowler, W. A., Burbidge, G. R., and Burbidge, E. M. *Astrophys. Jour.,* **122:** 271, 1955.
[298] Cameron, A. G. W. *Phys. Rev.,* **93:** 932, 1954.
[299] Salpeter, E. E. *Phys. Rev.,* **107:** 516, 1957.
[300] Burbidge, G. R., Hoyle, F., Burbidge, E. M., Christy, R. F., and Fowler, W. A. *Phys. Rev.,* **103:** 1145, 1956.
[301] Minkowski, R. *Pub. Astr. Soc. Pacific,* **53:** 224, 1941.
[302] Baade, W. *Astrophys. Jour.,* **102:** 309, 1945.
[303] Borst, L. *Phys. Rev.,* **78:** 807, 1950.

Appendix

Fundamental Tables

TABLE I

ABUNDANCE OF CHEMICAL ELEMENTS IN EARTH'S CRUST AND METEORITES

Z	Element	Abundance (Weight Per Cent)						
		Earth's Crust	Lithosphere		Meteorites			
					Brown (1949)		Urey (1952, 1956)	
		Fersman (1939)	Vinogradov (1949)	Goldschmidt (1937) with Suppl. by Rankama (1952)	Silicate Phase	Metal Phase	Chondrites (1952)	Chondrites, revised (1956) * Si = 1 × 10^6 atoms
1	H	1.00	0.15	...	0.063	...	...	...
2	He	1×10^{-6}	...	3×10^{-7}	...	...	...	...
3	Li	5×10^{-3}	6.5×10^{-3}	6.5×10^{-3}	3×10^{-4}	...	5×10^{-4}	100
4	Be	4×10^{-4}	6×10^{-4}	6×10^{-4}	1×10^{-4}	...	1×10^{-4}	16
5	B	5×10^{-3}	3×10^{-4}	3×10^{-4}	3×10^{-4}	...	1.5×10^{-4}	20
6	C	0.35	0.1	0.03	0.04	0.11	...	...
7	N	0.04	0.01	0.0046	9×10^{-5}	...	...	...
8	O	49.13	47.2	46.6	41.02	...	...	...
9	F	0.08	0.027	0.06–0.09	4×10^{-3}	...	4×10^{-3}	300
10	Ne	5×10^{-7}	...	7×10^{-9}	...	...	...	...
11	Na	2.40	2.64	2.83	0.78	...	0.75	4.38×10^4
12	Mg	2.35	2.10	2.09	15.8	0.032	13.55	9.12×10^5
13	Al	7.45	8.80	8.13	1.7	0.004	1.43	9.48×10^4
14	Si	26.00	27.6	27.72	20.6	0.004	18.0	1.0×10^6
15	P	0.12	0.08	0.118	0.16	0.22	0.15	5.0×10^3
16	S	0.10	0.05	0.052	1.79	0.036	2.01	9.8×10^4

TABLE I—*Continued*

Z	Element	Abundance (Weight Per Cent)						
		Earth's Crust	Lithosphere		Meteorites			
					Brown (1949)		Urey (1952, 1956)	
		Fersman (1939)	Vinogradov (1949)	Goldschmidt (1937) with Suppl. by Rankama (1952)	Silicate Phase	Metal Phase	Chondrites (1952)	Chrondrites, revised (1956) * Si = 1×10^6 atoms
17	Cl	0.20	0.045	0.031	0.09	...	0.047	2100
18	Ar	4×10^{-4}	...	4×10^{-6}	...	...	...	...
19	K	2.35	2.60	2.59	0.20	...	0.09	3160
20	Ca	3.25	3.6	3.63	2.0	0.05	1.43	4.90×10^4
21	Sc	6×10^{-4}	6×10^{-4}	5×10^{-4}	5.8×10^{-4}	...	5×10^{-4}	28
22	Ti	0.61	0.6	0.44	0.093	0.01	0.058	2440
23	V	0.02	0.015	0.015	9×10^{-3}	6×10^{-4}	5×10^{-3}	220
24	Cr	0.03	0.02	0.02	0.345	0.024	0.27	7800
25	Mn	0.10	0.09	0.10	0.30	0.03	0.24	6850
26	Fe	4.20	5.10	5.0	15.6	90.8	24.1	6.00×10^5
27	Co	2×10^{-3}	3×10^{-3}	2.3×10^{-3}	0.02	0.63	0.11	1800
28	Ni	0.02	8×10^{-3}	8×10^{-3}	0.14	8.6	1.45	2.74×10^4
29	Cu	0.01	0.01	0.007	1.6×10^{-4}	0.031	0.017	212
30	Zn	0.02	0.005	0.013	3.4×10^{-4}	0.012	7.6×10^{-3}	180
31	Ga	1×10^{-4}	1.5×10^{-3}	1.5×10^{-3}	5×10^{-5}	5×10^{-3}	4.6×10^{-4}	11.4
32	Ge	4×10^{-4}	7×10^{-4}	7×10^{-4}	1×10^{-3}	1.9×10^{-2}	5.3×10^{-3}	65
33	As	5×10^{-4}	5×10^{-4}	5×10^{-4}	2.0×10^{-3}	3.6×10^{-2}	1.8×10^{-3}	4.0
34	Se	8×10^{-5}	6×10^{-5}	9×10^{-6}	1.3×10^{-3}	3×10^{-4}	6.7×10^{-4}	24
35	Br	1×10^{-3}	1.6×10^{-4}	1.6×10^{-4}	2.5×10^{-3}	1×10^{-4}	2.5×10^{-3}	49(?)
36	Kr	2×10^{-8}	...	...	...	...	...	...
37	Rb	8×10^{-3}	0.03	0.031	4.5×10^{-4}	...	8.4×10^{-4}	6.5
38	Sr	0.035	0.04	0.03	2.6×10^{-3}	...	2.3×10^{-3}	18.9
39	Y	5×10^{-3}	2.8×10^{-3}	2.8×10^{-3}	6.6×10^{-4}	...	5.5×10^{-4}	8.9
40	Zr	0.025	0.02	0.022	1×10^{-2}	8×10^{-4}	8×10^{-3}	54.5
41	Nb	3.2×10^{-5}	1×10^{-3}	2.4×10^{-3}	5×10^{-5}	2×10^{-5}	4.1×10^{-5}	0.8
42	Mo	1×10^{-3}	3×10^{-4}	2.5×10^{-4}–1.5×10^{-3}	2.5×10^{-4}	1.7×10^{-3}	3.6×10^{-4}	2.42
44	Ru	5×10^{-6}	5×10^{-7}	...	0	1.06×10^{-3}	1.4×10^{-4}	2.1

TABLE I—*Continued*

Z	Element	Abundance (Weight Per Cent)						
		Earth's Crust	Lithosphere		Meteorites			
					Brown (1949)		Urey (1952, 1956)	
		Fersman (1939)	Vinogradov (1949)	Goldschmidt (1937) with Suppl. by Rankama (1952)	Silicate Phase	Metal Phase	Chondrites (1952)	Chondrites, revised (1956)* $Si = 1 \times 10^6$ atoms
45	Rh	1×10^{-6}	1×10^{-7}	1×10^{-7}	0	4.1×10^{-4}	4.7×10^{-5}	0.71
46	Pd	5×10^{-6}	1×10^{-6}	1×10^{-6}	0	3.7×10^{-4}	9.2×10^{-5}	1.3
47	Ag	1×10^{-5}	1×10^{-5}	1×10^{-5}	0	3.3×10^{-4}	1.35×10^{-4}	0.35
48	Cd	5×10^{-4}	5×10^{-5}	1.5×10^{-5}	1.6×10^{-4}	8×10^{-4}	1.6×10^{-4}	1.9
49	In	1×10^{-5}	1×10^{-5}	1×10^{-5}	2.4×10^{-5}	1×10^{-4}	2×10^{-5}	0.26
50	Sn	8×10^{-3}	4×10^{-3}	4×10^{-3}	3×10^{-4}	7.7×10^{-3}	1.4×10^{-3}	1.33
51	Sb	5×10^{-5}	4×10^{-4}	1×10^{-4}	1×10^{-5}	2×10^{-4}	6.4×10^{-5}	0.12
52	Te	1×10^{-6}	1×10^{-6}	1.8×10^{-7}	...	...	1.3×10^{-5}	0.16
53	I	1×10^{-4}	3×10^{-5}	3×10^{-5}	1.26×10^{-4}	6×10^{-5}	1.3×10^{-4}	1.5
54	Xe	3×10^{-9}	...	...	...	...	...	...
55	Cs	1×10^{-3}	7×10^{-4}	7×10^{-4}	1×10^{-5}	...	1.1×10^{-4}	1.3
56	Ba	0.05	0.05	0.025	9×10^{-4}	...	2.9×10^{-4}	8.8
57	La	6.5×10^{-4}	1.8×10^{-3}	1.8×10^{-3}	2.2×10^{-4}	...	1.9×10^{-4}	2.1
58	Ce	2.9×10^{-3}	4.5×10^{-3}	4.6×10^{-3}	2.5×10^{-4}	...	2.1×10^{-4}	2.3
59	Pr	4.5×10^{-4}	7×10^{-4}	5.5×10^{-4}	1.0×10^{-4}	...	8.8×10^{-5}	0.96
60	Nd	1.7×10^{-3}	2.5×10^{-3}	2.4×10^{-3}	3.7×10^{-4}	...	3.0×10^{-4}	3.3
62	Sm	7×10^{-4}	7×10^{-4}	6.5×10^{-4}	1.3×10^{-4}	...	1.1×10^{-4}	1.1
63	Eu	2×10^{-5}	1.2×10^{-4}	1.1×10^{-4}	3.3×10^{-5}	...	2.7×10^{-5}	0.28
64	Gd	7.5×10^{-4}	1×10^{-3}	6.4×10^{-4}	2.0×10^{-4}	...	1.7×10^{-4}	1.6
65	Tb	1×10^{-4}	1.5×10^{-4}	9×10^{-5}	6.4×10^{-4}	...	5.2×10^{-5}	0.52
66	Dy	7.5×10^{-4}	4.5×10^{-4}	4.5×10^{-4}	2.5×10^{-4}	...	2.1×10^{-4}	2.0
67	Ho	1×10^{-4}	1.3×10^{-4}	1.2×10^{-4}	7.2×10^{-5}	...	6.0×10^{-5}	0.57
68	Er	6.5×10^{-4}	4×10^{-4}	2.5×10^{-4}	2.1×10^{-4}	...	1.7×10^{-4}	1.6
69	Tm	1×10^{-4}	8×10^{-5}	2×10^{-5}	3.8×10^{-5}	...	3.1×10^{-5}	0.29
70	Yb	8×10^{-4}	3×10^{-4}	2.7×10^{-4}	2.0×10^{-4}	...	1.7×10^{-4}	1.5
71	Lu	1.7×10^{-4}	1×10^{-4}	7.5×10^{-5}	6.5×10^{-5}	...	5.4×10^{-5}	0.48
72	Hf	4×10^{-4}	3.2×10^{-4}	4.5×10^{-4}	1×10^{-4}	...	1.6×10^{-4}	0.55

TABLE I—*Continued*

Z	Element	Abundance (Weight Per Cent)							
		Earth's Crust	Lithosphere		Meteorites				
					Brown (1949)		Urey (1952, 1956)		
		Fersman (1939)	Vinogradov (1949)	Goldschmidt (1937) with Suppl. by Rankama (1952)	Silicate Phase	Metal Phase	Chondrites (1952)	Chrondrites, revised (1956)* Si = 1×10^6 atoms	
73.......	Ta	2.4×10^{-5}	2×10^{-4}	2.1×10^{-4}	3.8×10^{-5}	6×10^{-6}	2.8×10^{-5}	0.32	
74.......	W	7×10^{-3}	1×10^{-4}	1.5×10^{-4}–7×10^{-3}	1.8×10^{-3}	8.1×10^{-4}	1.6×10^{-3}	13.0	
75.......	Re	1×10^{-7}	1×10^{-7}	1×10^{-7}	...	8.5×10^{-5}	8×10^{-6}	0.05	
76.......	Os	5×10^{-6}	5×10^{-6}	...	...	7.6×10^{-4}	1.2×10^{-4}	0.97	
77.......	Ir	1×10^{-6}	1×10^{-7}	1×10^{-7}	0	3×10^{-4}	3.8×10^{-5}	0.31	
78.......	Pt	2×10^{-5}	5×10^{-7}	5×10^{-7}	8.3×10^{-6}	1.9×10^{-3}	1.9×10^{-4}	1.5	
79.......	Au	5×10^{-7}	5×10^{-7}	5×10^{-7}	0	1.8×10^{-4}	2.5×10^{-5}	0.140	
80.......	Hg	5×10^{-6}	7×10^{-6}	8×10^{-6}–5×10^{-4}	1×10^{-6}	...	...	0.006	
81.......	Tl	1×10^{-5}	3×10^{-4}	3×10^{-5}–3×10^{-4}	1.5×10^{-5}	...	1.5×10^{-5}	0.11	
82.......	Pb	1.6×10^{-3}	1.6×10^{-3}	1.6×10^{-3}	2×10^{-4}	6×10^{-3}	...	0.47	
83.......	Bi	1×10^{-5}	2×10^{-5}	2×10^{-5}	...	5×10^{-5}	2×10^{-6}	0.144	
90.......	Th	1×10^{-3}	8×10^{-4}	1.2×10^{-3}	2×10^{-4}	4×10^{-6}	...	...	
92.......	U	4×10^{-4}	3×10^{-4}	4×10^{-4}	4×10^{-5}	7×10^{-7}	...	...	

* The data are published in the paper by H. E. Suess and H. C. Urey (*Rev. Mod. Phys.*, **28**: 53–74, 1956). The values are the empirical abundances for chondritic stones modified in accordance with new analytical data. The elements which have been redetermined since 1956 include the following:

1. *Germanium*, by S. A. Wardani (*Geochim. et Cosmochim. Acta*, **10**: 321–22, 1956).
2. *Cesium*, by B. M. Gordon, L. Friedman, and G. Edwards (*Geochim. et Cosmochim. Acta*, **12**: 170–71, 1957).
3. *Tin*, by H. Onishi and E. B. Sandell (*Geochim. et Cosmochim. Acta*, **12**: 262–70, 1957).
4. *Uranium and barium*, by H. Hamaguchi, G. W. Reed, and A. Turkevich (*Geochim. et Cosmochim. Acta*, **12**: 337–47, 1957).
5. *Cesium*, by R. K. Webster, J. W. Morgan, and A. A. Smales (*Geochim. et Cosmochim. Acta*, **15**: 150–52, 1958).
6. *Bismuth, thallium, and mercury*, by W. D. Ehmann and J. R. Huizenga (*Geochim. et Cosmochim. Acta*, **17**: 125–35, 1959).
7. *Rhodium, silver, and indium*, by U. Schindewolf and M. Wahlgren (*Geochim. et Cosmochim. Acta*, **18**: 36–41, 1960).
8. *Scandium, chromium, and europium*, by G. L. Bate, H. A. Potratz, and J. R. Huizenga (*Geochim. et Cosmochim. Acta*, **18**: 101–7, 1960).
9. *Gold*, by E. A. Vincent and J. H. Crocket (*Geochim. et Cosmochim. Acta*, **18**: 143–48, 1960).
10. *Barium, mercury, thallium, lead, bismuth, and uranium*, by G. W. Reed, K. Kigoshi, and A. Turkevich (*Geochim. et Cosmochim. Acta*, **20**: 122–40, 1960).
11. *Ruthenium*, by T. Hara and E. B. Sandell (*Geochim. et Cosmochim. Acta*, **21**: 145–50, 1960).
12. *Potassium, rubidium, and cesium*, by P. Gast (*Geochim. et Cosmochim. Acta*, **19**: 1–4, 1960).
13. *Selenium and tellurium*, by Ann du Fresne (*Geochim. et Cosmochim. Acta*, **20**: 141–48, 1960), and by U. Schindewolf (*Geochim. et Cosmochim. Acta*, **19**: 134–38, 1960).
14. *Iodine and tellurium*, by G. G. Goles and E. Anders (*Jour. Geophys. Res.*, **65**: 4181–84, 1960)

TABLE II

ABUNDANCE OF CHEMICAL ELEMENTS (IN LOGARITHMS OF RELATIVE NUMBER OF ATOMS Q) IN ATMOSPHERE OF SUN ($Q_\odot$), PLANETARY NEBULA NGC 7027 (Q_N), EARTH'S CRUST (Q_E), IRON METEORITES (Q_I), STONY METEORITES (Q_S), PARTICULARLY CHONDRITES (Q_{Ch})

Z (1)	Element (2)	$Q_\odot$ (3)	Q_N (4)	Q_E (5)	Q_I (6)	Q_S (7)	Q_{Ch} (8)	$Q_E - Q_\odot$ (9)	$Q_S - Q_\odot$ (10)	$Q_I - Q_\odot$ (11)
1	H	12.35	11.7	8.5	...	7.4	...	−4.1	−5.0	...
2	He	11.65	11.0	1.9	...	...	...	−10.2	...	...
3	Li	2.0	<8	5.4	...	4.2	4.2	3.4	2.2	...
4	Be	1.8	<8	4.1	...	3.6	3.4	2.3	1.8	...
5	B	5	<9	5.2	...	4.0	3.5	0.2	−1.0	...
6	C	9.24	7.8	7.0	6.8	7.1	...	−2.2	−2.1	−2.4
7	N	9.43	8.8	6.0	...	3.4	...	−3.5	−6.0	...
8	O	9.0	9.0	9.0	...	9.0	...	...	...	...
9	F	6.6(K)	⩽6	6.1	...	4.9	4.7	−0.5	−2.7	...
10	Ne	9.0(A)	8	1.9	...	...	...	...	...	...
11	Na	6.68	<7	7.5	...	7.1	6.9	0.8	0.4	...
12	Mg	7.92	7^+	7.5	4.9	8.1	8.1	−0.4	0.2	−3.0
13	Al	6.52	...	8.0	4.0	7.4	7.1	1.4	0.9	−2.5
14	Si	7.47	...	8.5	3.9	8.5	8.2	1.0	1.0	−3.5
15	P	5.8(K)	...	6.1	5.6	6.3	6.1	0.3	0.5	−0.2
16	S	7.1(K)	8	6.0	4.8	7.3	7.2	−1.1	0.2	−2.3
17	Cl	7.0(K)	7^+	6.3	...	6.0	5.0	−0.7	−1.0	...
18	Ar	8.0(K)	7	3.5	...	...	...	...	...	...
19	K	5.36	6^+	7.3	...	6.3	5.7	1.9	0.9	...
20	Ca	6.81	7^-	7.4	4.9	7.3	6.9	0.6	0.5	−1.9
21	Sc	3.6	...	3.6	...	3.7	3.4	0.0	0.1	−1.1
22	Ti	5.2	...	6.6	4.1	5.9	5.5	1.4	0.7	−1.1
23	V	5.0 4.3(A) }	...	5.1	2.9	4.8	4.4	0.1	−0.2	−2.1
24	Cr	5.7	...	5.3	5.5	6.3	6.1	−0.4	0.6	−0.2
25	Mn	5.9	...	5.8	4.5	6.3	6.0	−0.1	0.4	−1.4
26	Fe	8.0	7^+	7.4	8.0	8.0	8.0	−0.6	0.0	...
27	Co	5.6	...	4.0	5.8	5.1	5.7	−1.6	−0.5	0.2

TABLE II—*Continued*

Z (1)	Element (2)	$Q_\odot$ (3)	Q_N (4)	Q_E (5)	Q_I (6)	Q_S (7)	Q_{Ch} (8)	$Q_E - Q_\odot$ (9)	$Q_S - Q_\odot$ (10)	$Q_I - Q_\odot$ (11)
28	Ni	6.0	...	5.0	7.0	6.0	6.8	−1.0	0.0	1.0
29	Cu	5.15	...	4.7	4.5	3.0	4.8	−0.4	−2.2	−0.7
30	Zn	4.87	...	5.0	4.0	3.3	4.4	0.1	−1.6	−0.8
31	Ga	2.0	...	2.7	3.7	2.5	3.2	0.7	0.5	1.7
32	Ge	3.0	...	3.3	4.2	3.7	4.2	0.3	0.7	1.2
33	As	...	...	3.3	4.5	4.0	4.8	...	...	...
34	Se	...	...	2.5	2.4	3.8	3.3	...	...	...
35	Br	...	...	3.6	1.9	4.1	3.9	...	...	...
36	Kr	...	...	−1.1	...	...	...	...	...	...
37	Rb	1.7	...	4.5	...	3.3	3.4	2.8	1.6	...
38	Sr	3.23	...	5.1	...	4.1	3.8	1.9	0.8	...
39	Y	2.6 / 3.6(A)	...	4.3	...	3.5	3.2	1.7	0.9	...
40	Zr	2.5	...	5.0	2.7	4.6	4.3	2.5	2.1	0.2
41	Nb	1.0 / 2.6(A)	...	2.0	2.1	2.3	2.0	1.0	1.3	1.1
42	Mo	1.4	...	3.5	3.0	3.0	3.9	2.1	1.6	1.6
44	Ru	1.7	...	1.2	3.8	...	2.5	−0.5	...	2.1
45	Rh	0.5	...	0.5	2.4	...	2.0	0.0	...	1.9
46	Pd	1.1	...	1.2	2.3	...	2.3	0.1	1.2	1.2
47	Ag	1.0	...	1.5	2.3	...	2.5	0.5	1.3	1.5
48	Cd	2.2	...	3.2	2.6	2.7	2.5	1.0	0.5	0.4
49	In	0.0	...	1.5	1.7	1.9	1.6	1.5	1.9	1.7
50	Sn	1.2	...	4.3	3.6	3.0	3.5	3.1	1.8	2.4
51	Sb	0.8	...	2.1	2.0	1.5	2.1	1.4	0.7	1.2
52	Te	...	...	0.4	...	...	2.4	...	...	...
53	I	...	...	2.4	2.5	2.6	2.4	...	...	...
54	Xe	...	...	−2.1	...	...	...	...	...	...
55	Cs	...	...	3.4	...	2.5	2.3	...	...	...
56	Ba	2.73	...	5.1	...	3.4	2.7	2.4	0.7	...
57	La	1.8	...	3.2	...	2.8	2.5	1.4	1.0	...

TABLE II—*Continued*

Z (1)	Element (2)	$Q_{\odot}$ (3)	Q_N (4)	Q_E (5)	Q_I (6)	Q_S (7)	Q_{Ch} (8)	$Q_E - Q_{\odot}$ (9)	$Q_S - Q_{\odot}$ (10)	$Q_I - Q_{\odot}$ (11
58	Ce	2.4	...	3.8	2.6	2.9	...	1.4	0.5	...
59	Pr	0.6	...	3.0	...	2.4	2.2	2.4	1.8	...
60	Nd	2.0	...	3.6	...	3.0	2.7	1.6	1.0	...
62	Sm	1.5	...	3.2	...	2.5	2.2	1.7	1.0	...
63	Eu	1.4	...	1.6	...	1.9	1.6	0.2	0.5	...
64	Gd	1.1	...	3.2	...	2.7	2.4	2.1	1.6	...
65	Tb	...	...	2.3	...	2.2	1.9	...	...	...
66	Dy	1.6	...	3.2	...	2.8	2.5	1.6	1.2	...
67	Ho	...	...	2.3	...	2.2	2.0	...	...	...
68	Er	0.1	...	3.1	...	2.7	2.4	3.0	2.6	...
69	Tm	0.5	...	2.3	...	1.9	1.6	1.8	1.4	...
70	Yb	1.0	...	3.2	...	2.7	2.4	2.2	1.7	...
71	Lu	1.0	...	2.5	...	2.2	1.9	1.5	1.2	...
72	Hf	0.4	...	2.9	...	2.3	2.3	2.5	1.9	...
73	Ta	0.0	...	2.6	0.3	1.9	1.6	2.6	1.9	0.3
74	W	0.2	...	4.1	2.4	3.6	3.3	3.9	3.4	2.2
75	Re	...	...	−0.8	1.5	...	1.0	...	...	...
76	Os	0.5	...	0.9	2.4	...	2.2	0.4	...	1.9
77	Ir	−0.2	...	0.2	2.0	...	1.7	0.4	...	2.2
78	Pt	1.6	...	1.5	2.8	1.2	2.4	−0.1	−0.4	1.2
79	Au	...	...	−0.1	2.7	...	1.5	...	...	...
80	Hg	3.33	...	0.9	...	0.3	...	−2.4	−3.0	...
81	Tl	...	...	1.2	...	1.5	1.2	...	...	...
82	Pb	1.2 } 2.8(A) }	...	3.4	3.3	2.6	...	2.2	1.4	2.1
83	Bi	...	...	1.2	1.2	...	0.3	...	...	...
90	Th	...	...	3.2	0.0	2.5	...	...	...	...
92	U	...	...	2.7	−0.7	1.8	...	...	...	...

TABLE III

Table of Isotopes

Z	Element	A	Content (Per Cent)	Abundance in Earth's Crust (Atom Per Cent) [4]	A − Z	Isotope Mass	Binding Energy (Mev)
(1)	(2)	(3)	(4)	(5)	(6)	(7)	(8)
1.	H	1	99.9851	17.25	0	1.008142	0.00
		2	0.0149	2.5×10^{-3}	1	2.0147425	1.11
2.	He	3	10^{-4}–10^{-5}	10^{-12}	1	3.0169807	2.57
		4	100	4×10^{-6}	2	4.0038761	7.07
3.	Li	6	7.52	9×10^{-4}	3	6.0170404	5.33
		7	92.48	0.011	4	7.0182389	5.61
4.	Be	9	100	1×10^{-3}	5	9.0150566	6.46
5.	B	10	18.45–18.98	1.3×10^{-3}	5	10.0161236	6.47
		11	81.02–81.55	5.7×10^{-3}	6	11.012810	6.93
6.	C	12	98.892	0.5	6	12.0038167	7.68
		13	1.108	6×10^{-3}	7	13.0074929	7.47
7.	N	14	99.635	0.05	7	14.0075263	7.48
		15	0.365	1.8×10^{-4}	8	15.0048793	7.70
8.	O	16	99.759	53.2	8	16.00 (standard)	7.98
		17	0.037	0.02	9	17.0045364	7.75
		18	0.204	0.11	10	18.0048843	7.77
9.	F	19	100	0.07	10	19.0044429	7.78
10.	Ne	20	90.92	3.6×10^{-7}	10	19.9987953	8.03
		21	0.257	1×10^{-9}	11	21.0005209	7.97
		22	8.82	3.5×10^{-8}	12	21.9983777	8.08
11.	Na	23	100	1.82	12	22.9970913	8.11
12.	Mg	24	78.60	1.35	12	23.9926713	8.26
		25	10.11	0.174	13	24.9937832	8.22
		26	11.29	0.194	14	25.9908541	8.33
13.	Al	27	100	4.80	14	26.9901111	8.33
14.	Si	28	92.27	14.87	14	27.985821	8.44
		29	4.68	0.75	15	28.985701	8.45
		30	3.05	0.49	16	29.983288	8.52
15.	P	31	100	0.07	16	30.9836126	8.47
16.	S	32	95.018	0.048	16	31.9822388	8.49
		33	0.750	3.8×10^{-4}	17	32.9819473	8.50
		34	4.215	2.1×10^{-3}	18	33.9786635	8.58
		36	0.017	8.5×10^{-6}	20	35.9785253	8.57

TABLE III—*Continued*

Z (1)	Element (2)	A (3)	Content (Per Cent) (4)	Abundance in Earth's Crust (Atom Per Cent) [4] (5)	$A - Z$ (6)	Isotope Mass (7)	Binding Energy (Mev) (8)
17.	Cl	35	75.4	0.075	18	34.9799720	8.55
		37	24.6	0.025	20	36.9776573	8.57
18.	A	36	0.337	5.7×10^{-7}	18	35.9789823	8.52
		38	0.063	1.1×10^{-7}	20	37.9748023	8.61
		40	99.600	1.7×10^{-4}	22	39.9750926	8.59
19.	K	39	93.08	0.98	20	38.9761002	8.56
		40	0.0119	1.25×10^{-4}	21	39.9767094	8.54
		41	6.91	7.3×10^{-2}	22	40.9748556	8.58
20.	Ca	40	96.97	1.37	20	39.9752931	8.55
		42	0.64	9.0×10^{-3}	22	41.9719674	8.61
		43	0.145	2.0×10^{-3}	23	42.9724439	8.60
		44	2.06	0.03	24	43.9694714	8.66
		46	0.0033	4.7×10^{-5}	26	45.9682984	8.67
		48	0.185	2.4×10^{-3}	28	47.9677766	8.67
21.	Sc	45	100	2.5×10^{-3}	24	44.9702122	8.62
22.	Ti	46	7.95	0.017	24	45.9672420	8.65
		47	7.75	0.017	25	46.9666862	8.67
		48	73.45	0.162	26	47.9631912	8.72
		49	5.51	0.012	27	48.9634294	8.73
		50	5.34	0.012	28	49.9606687	8.76
23.	V	50	0.24	1.7×10^{-5}	27	49.963045	8.77
		51	99.76	7×10^{-3}	28	50.9601754	8.74
24.	Cr	50	4.31	3.9×10^{-4}	26	49.9619308	8.70
		52	83.76	7.5×10^{-3}	28	51.9570263	8.77
		53	9.55	8.6×10^{-4}	29	52.9574817	8.76
		54	2.38	2.1×10^{-4}	30	53.9560231	8.77
25.	Mn	55	100	0.03	30	54.9555234	8.76
26.	Fe	54	5.84	7.6×10^{-2}	28	53.9567590	8.74
		56	91.68	1.20	30	55.9527252	8.79
		57	2.17	2.8×10^{-2}	31	56.953513	8.79
		58	0.31	4.1×10^{-3}	32	57.951736	8.77
27.	Co	59	100	9×10^{-4}	32	58.951919	8.77
28.	Ni	58	67.67	4.3×10^{-3}	30	57.953767	8.73
		60	26.16	1.57×10^{-3}	32	59.949823	8.78
		61	1.25	7.5×10^{-5}	33	60.950460	8.76
		62	3.66	2.2×10^{-4}	34	61.948033	8.79
		64	1.16	7.0×10^{-5}	36	63.948339	8.78
29.	Cu	63	69.1	2.1×10^{-3}	34	62.949607	8.75
		65	30.9	9×10^{-4}	36	64.948427	8.76

TABLE III—*Continued*

Z (1)	Element (2)	*A* (3)	Content (Per Cent) (4)	Abundance in Earth's Crust (Atom Per Cent) [4] (5)	*A* − *Z* (6)	Isotope Mass (7)	Binding Energy (Mev) (8)
30.......	Zn	64	48.89	3.5×10^{-3}	34	63.949472	8.73
		66	27.81	1.4×10^{-3}	36	65.947013	8.76
		67	4.11	2.1×10^{-4}	37	66.948418	8.73
		68	18.56	9.3×10^{-4}	38	67.946456	8.75
		70	0.62	3.1×10^{-5}	40	69.947572	8.73
31.......	Ga	69	60.2	1.5×10^{-5}	38	68.9478	8.71
		71	39.8	1.0×10^{-5}	40	70.9475	8.74
32.......	Ge	70	20.55	5.0×10^{-6}	38	69.9464	8.74
		72	27.37	6.8×10^{-6}	40	71.9445	8.73
		73	7.67	1.9×10^{-6}	41	72.9467	8.71
		74	36.74	1.0×10^{-5}	42	73.9447	8.72
		76	7.67	1.9×10^{-6}	44	75.9456	8.71
33.......	As	75	100	1×10^{-4}	42	74.9457	8.70
34.......	Se	74	0.87	1.3×10^{-7}	40	73.9462	8.68
		76	9.02	1.4×10^{-6}	42	75.9436	8.70
		77	7.58	1.1×10^{-6}	43	76.9446	8.69
		78	23.52	3.5×10^{-6}	44	77.9423	8.70
		80	49.82	7.5×10^{-6}	46	79.9421	8.71
		82	9.19	1.5×10^{-6}	48	81.9429	8.68
35.......	Br	79	50.52	1×10^{-4}	44	78.9437	8.68
		81	49.48	1×10^{-4}	46	80.9423	8.69
36.......	Kr	78	0.354	1.4×10^{-11}	42	77.9451	8.66
		80	2.27	9×10^{-11}	44	79.9419	8.68
		82	11.56	4.6×10^{-10}	46	81.9397	8.71
		83	11.55	4.6×10^{-10}	47	82.9406	8.69
		84	56.90	2.3×10^{-9}	48	83.9384	8.71
		86	17.37	7.0×10^{-10}	50	85.9383	8.71
37.......	Rb	85	72.15	1.5×10^{-3}	48	84.9392	8.69
		87	27.85	5.5×10^{-4}	50	86.9371	8.71
38.......	Sr	84	0.56	3.9×10^{-5}	46	83.9401	8.66
		86	9.86	6.9×10^{-4}	48	85.9368	8.72
		87	7.02	4.9×10^{-4}	49	86.9367	8.72
		88	82.56	5.8×10^{-3}	50	87.9341	8.74
39.......	Y	89	100	1×10^{-3}	50	88.93421	8.71
40.......	Zr	90	51.46	2.6×10^{-3}	50	89.9331	8.71
		91	11.23	5.6×10^{-4}	51		
		92	17.11	8.6×10^{-4}	52	91.9328	8.70
		94	17.40	8.7×10^{-4}	54	93.9361	8.67
		96	2.80	1.4×10^{-4}	56	95.940	8.60
41.......	Nb	93	100	6×10^{-6}	52	92.9354	8.68

TABLE III—*Continued*

Z (1)	Element (2)	A (3)	Content (Per Cent) (4)	Abundance in Earth's Crust (Atom Per Cent) [4] (5)	A − Z (6)	Isotope Mass (7)	Binding Energy (Mev) (8)
42	Mo	92	15.86	3.2×10^{-5}	50	91.9341	8.68
		94	9.12	1.8×10^{-5}	52	93.9349	8.66
		95	15.70	3.1×10^{-5}	53		
		96	16.50	3.3×10^{-5}	54	95.936	8.64
		97	9.45	1.9×10^{-5}	55		
		98	23.75	4.8×10^{-5}	56	97.93610	8.64
		100	9.62	1.9×10^{-5}	58	99.9386	8.61
44	Ru	96	5.7	5.7×10^{-8}	52	95.939	8.48
		98	2.2	2.2×10^{-8}	54		
		99	12.8	1.3×10^{-7}	55		
		100	12.7	1.3×10^{-7}	56	98.944	8.48
		101	17.0	1.7×10^{-7}	57		
		102	31.3	3.1×10^{-7}	58		
		104	18.3	1.8×10^{-7}	60		
45	Rh	103	100	1.5×10^{-7}	58		
46	Pd	102	0.8	1.2×10^{-8}	56	101.9375	8.58
		104	9.3	1.4×10^{-7}	58	103.9364	8.59
		105	22.6	3.4×10^{-7}	59	104.9390	8.57
		106	27.2	4.1×10^{-7}	60	105.9368	8.57
		108	26.8	4.1×10^{-7}	62	107.9380	8.66
		110	13.5	2.0×10^{-7}	64	109.9406	8.54
47	Ag	107	51.35	7.7×10^{-7}	60	106.948	8.47
		109	48.65	7.3×10^{-7}	62	108.947	8.47
48	Cd	106	1.215	9.7×10^{-7}	58	105.9398	8.54
		108	0.875	7.0×10^{-7}	60	107.9386	8.55
		110	12.39	1.0×10^{-5}	62	109.93873	8.54
		111	12.75	1.0×10^{-5}	63	110.9398	8.53
		112	24.07	1.9×10^{-5}	64	111.9388	8.54
		113	12.26	1.0×10^{-5}	65	112.9406	8.52
		114	28.86	2.3×10^{-5}	66	113.9400	8.53
		116	7.58	6.0×10^{-6}	68	115.9420	8.50
49	In	113	4.23	5.5×10^{-8}	64	112.9404	8.52
		115	95.77	1.25×10^{-6}	66	114.9404	8.51
50	Sn	112	0.95	9.5×10^{-6}	62	111.9407	8.51
		114	0.65	6.5×10^{-6}	64	113.9394	8.52
		115	0.34	3.4×10^{-6}	65	114.9401	8.51
		116	14.24	1.4×10^{-4}	66	115.9385	8.52
		117	7.57	7.6×10^{-5}	67	116.9412	8.50
		118	24.01	2.4×10^{-4}	68	117.9398	8.51
		119	8.58	8.6×10^{-5}	69	118.9412	8.50
		120	32.97	3.3×10^{-4}	70	119.9404	8.50
		122	4.71	4.7×10^{-5}	72	121.9425	8.48
		124	5.98	6.0×10^{-5}	74	123.9448	8.46

TABLE III—*Continued*

Z (1)	Element (2)	*A* (3)	Content (Per Cent) (4)	Abundance in Earth's Crust (Atom Per Cent) [4] (5)	*A* − *Z* (6)	Isotope Mass (7)	Binding Energy (Mev) (8)
51.......	Sb	121	57.25	4×10^{-6}	70	120.9426	8.48
		123	42.75	3×10^{-6}	72	122.9430	8.47
52.......	Te	120	0.089	1.3×10^{-10}	68	119.9429	8.47
		122	2.46	3.7×10^{-9}	70	121.9419	8.47
		123	0.87	1.3×10^{-9}	71	122.9437	8.46
		124	4.61	6.9×10^{-9}	72	123.9428	8.46
		125	6.99	1.05×10^{-8}	73	124.9446	8.45
		126	18.91	2.8×10^{-8}	74	125.9427	8.46
		128	31.79	4.8×10^{-8}	76	127.9471	8.43
		130	34.49	5.2×10^{-8}	78	129.9467	8.43
53.......	I	127	100	1.5×10^{-5}	74	126.9434	8.45
54.......	Xe	124	0.096	4×10^{-13}	70	123.9459	8.43
		126	0.090	4×10^{-13}	72	125.9448	8.43
		128	1.919	7.7×10^{-12}	74	127.9445	8.44
		129	26.44	1.0×10^{-10}	75	128.9456	8.43
		130	4.08	1.6×10^{-11}	76	129.9481	8.44
		131	21.18	8.5×10^{-11}	77	130.94670	8.42
		132	26.89	1.1×10^{-10}	78	131.94611	8.41
		134	10.44	4.2×10^{-11}	80	133.94799	8.41
		136	8.87	3.5×10^{-11}	82	135.950419	8.39
55.......	Cs	133	100	1.5×10^{-4}	78	132.94738	8.41
56.......	Ba	130	0.101	6×10^{-6}	74	129.94481	8.40
		132	0.097	6×10^{-6}	76	131.94716	8.41
		134	2.42	1.45×10^{-4}	78	133.94683	8.41
		135	6.59	4.0×10^{-4}	79	134.94845	8.40
		136	7.81	4.7×10^{-4}	80	135.94758	8.40
		137	11.32	6.8×10^{-4}	81	136.94906	8.39
		138	71.66	4.3×10^{-3}	82	137.94873	8.39
57.......	La	138	0.089	7×10^{-8}	81	137.95059	8.38
		139	99.911	8×10^{-5}	82	138.95020	8.38
58.......	Ce	136	0.193	7.7×10^{-7}	78	135.95028	8.37
		138	0.250	1×10^{-6}	80	137.94987	8.38
		140	88.48	3.5×10^{-4}	82	139.94976	8.38
		142	11.07	4.4×10^{-5}	84	141.95441	8.35
59.......	Pr	141	100	6×10^{-5}	82	140.95128	8.35
60.......	Nd	142	27.13	5.4×10^{-5}	82	141.95260	8.34
		143	12.20	2.4×10^{-5}	83	142.95502	8.33
		144	23.87	4.7×10^{-5}	84	143.95556	8.33
		145	8.30	1.7×10^{-5}	85	144.95814	8.31
		146	17.18	3.4×10^{-5}	86	145.95908	8.31
		148	5.72	1.1×10^{-5}	88	147.96349	8.28
		150	5.60	1.1×10^{-5}	90	149.96849	8.25

TABLE III—*Continued*

Z (1)	Element (2)	A (3)	Content (Per Cent) (4)	Abundance in Earth's Crust (Atom Per Cent) [4] (5)	A − Z (6)	Isotope Mass (7)	Binding Energy (Mev) (8)
62.......	Sm	144	3.16	2.5×10^{-7}	82	143.95741	8.30
		146	<0.00008	$<8 \times 10^{-11}$	84	145.95929	8.29
		147	15.07	1.2×10^{-5}	85	146.96120	8.29
		148	11.27	9.0×10^{-6}	86	147.96145	8.28
		149	13.84	1.1×10^{-5}	87	148.96415	8.26
		150	7.47	6.0×10^{-6}	88	149.96457	8.26
		152	26.63	2.1×10^{-5}	90	151.96767	8.24
		154	22.53	1.8×10^{-5}	92	153.97087	8.22
63.......	Eu	151	47.77	1.5×10^{-6}	88	150.96753	8.24
		153	52.23	1.5×10^{-6}	90	152.9692	8.23
64.......	Gd	152	0.20	1.6×10^{-7}	88		
		154	2.15	1.7×10^{-6}	90		
		155	14.73	1.2×10^{-5}	91	154.977	8.18
		156	20.47	1.6×10^{-5}	92	155.976	8.19
		157	15.68	1.2×10^{-5}	93	156.976	8.19
		158	24.87	2.0×10^{-5}	94		
		160	21.90	1.8×10^{-5}	96		
65.......	Tb	159	100	1×10^{-5}	94		
66.......	Dy	156	0.0524	4×10^{-8}	90		
		158	0.0902	7×10^{-8}	92		
		160	2.294	1.8×10^{-6}	94		
		161	18.88	1.5×10^{-5}	95		
		162	25.53	2.0×10^{-5}	96		
		163	24.97	2.0×10^{-5}	97		
		164	28.18	2.3×10^{-5}	98		
67.......	Ho	165	100	1×10^{-5}	98		
68.......	Er	162	0.136	1×10^{-7}	94		
		164	1.56	1.1×10^{-6}	96		
		166	33.41	2.3×10^{-5}	98		
		167	22.94	1.6×10^{-5}	99		
		168	27.07	1.9×10^{-5}	100		
		170	14.88	1.0×10^{-5}	102		
69.......	Tm	169	100	1×10^{-5}	100		
70.......	Yb	168	0.140	1×10^{-7}	98		
		170	3.03	2.4×10^{-6}	100		
		171	14.31	1.1×10^{-5}	101		
		172	21.82	1.7×10^{-5}	102		
		173	16.13	1.3×10^{-5}	103		
		174	31.84	2.5×10^{-5}	104		
		176	12.73	1.0×10^{-5}	106		
71.......	Lu	175	97.40	1×10^{-5}	104		
		176	2.60	2.6×10^{-7}	105		

TABLE III—*Continued*

Z (1)	Element (2)	A (3)	Content (Per Cent) (4)	Abundance in Earth's Crust (Atom Per Cent) [4] (5)	$A-Z$ (6)	Isotope Mass (7)	Binding Energy (Mev) (8)
72.......	Hf	174	0.18	7.2×10^{-8}	102		
		176	5.15	2.1×10^{-6}	104	175.992	8.09
		177	18.39	7.4×10^{-6}	105	177.994	8.08
		178	27.08	1.1×10^{-5}	106		
		179	13.78	5.5×10^{-6}	107		
		180	35.44	1.4×10^{-5}	108	180.003	8.03
73.......	Ta	180	0.0123	3×10^{-10}	107		
		181	99.99	2.3×10^{-6}	108	181.003	8.03
74.......	W	180	0.135	1×10^{-6}	106		
		182	26.4	1.85×10^{-4}	108	182.003	8.03
		183	14.4	1.0×10^{-4}	109	183.006	8.03
		184	30.6	2.15×10^{-4}	110	184.005	8.00
		186	28.4	2.0×10^{-4}	112		
75.......	Re	185	37.07	3.7×10^{-9}	110		
		187	62.93	6.3×10^{-9}	112		
76.......	Os	184	0.018	9×10^{-11}	108		
		186	1.59	8.0×10^{-9}	110		
		187	1.64	8.2×10^{-9}	111		
		188	13.3	6.7×10^{-8}	112		
		189	16.1	8.1×10^{-8}	113		
		190	26.4	1.32×10^{-7}	114		
		192	41.0	2.05×10^{-7}	116		
77.......	Ir	191	38.5	3.9×10^{-8}	114		
		193	61.5	6.2×10^{-8}	116		
78.......	Pt	190	0.012	5×10^{-11}	112		
		192	0.78	3.1×10^{-9}	114		
		194	32.8	1.3×10^{-7}	116	194.026	7.92
		195	33.7	1.3×10^{-7}	117	195.026	7.93
		196	25.4	1.0×10^{-7}	118	196.027	7.93
		198	7.23	3.0×10^{-8}	120		
79.......	Au	197	100	4.0×10^{-7}	118		
80.......	Hg	196	0.146	1×10^{-8}	116		
		198	10.02	7×10^{-7}	118	198.03264	7.89
		199	16.84	1.2×10^{-6}	119	199.03446	7.89
		200	23.13	1.6×10^{-6}	120	200.03477	7.89
		201	13.22	9.2×10^{-7}	121	201.03703	7.88
		202	29.80	2.1×10^{-6}	122	202.03767	7.88
		204	6.85	4.8×10^{-7}	124		
81.......	Tl	203	29.50	2.4×10^{-7}	122	203.04041	7.87
		205	70.50	5.6×10^{-7}	124	205.0442	7.89

TABLE III—*Continued*

Z (1)	Element (2)	A (3)	Content (Per Cent) (4)	Abundance in Earth's Crust (Atom Per Cent) [4] (5)	$A - Z$ (6)	Isotope Mass (7)	Binding Energy (Mev) (8)
82.......	Pb	204	1.48	1.5×10^{-6}	122	204.04081	7.86
		206	23.6	2.4×10^{-5}	124	206.04519	7.85
		207	22.6	2.3×10^{-5}	125	207.04725	7.85
		208	52.3	5.2×10^{-5}	126	208.04754	7.91
83.......	Bi	209	100	8×10^{-7}	126	209.05325	7.82
90.......	Th	232	100	1×10^{-4}	142	232.1165	7.60
92.......	U	235	0.715	3×10^{-7}	143	235.12517	7.56
		238	99.285	4×10^{-5}	146	238.13232	7.55

TABLE IV

Natural Radioactive Elements

Element	Z	A	Radiation	Half-Life	Decay Products	Decay Energy (Mev)	Content of Isotope (Per Cent)	Abundance of the Isotope in Earth's Crust (Weight Per Cent)	Av. Energy per Gm of Earth's Crust (Mev/Min)
K........	19	40	β, K $\beta/K = 8$	1.5×10^9	Ca^{40} Ar^{40}	1.33 (β) 1.63 (K)	0.0119	3.1×10^{-4}	39
Ca........	20	48	2β	$\geqslant 1.6 \times 10^1$	Ti^{48}	4.1	0.185	6.6×10^{-3}	$\leqslant 1 \times 10^{-6}$
V........	23	50	β, K (?)	?	Cr^{50} Ti^{50}	1.18 (β) 2.39 (K)	0.24	3.6×10^{-5}	?
Rb.......	37	87	β	6.0×10^{10}	Sr^{87}	0.27	27.85	8.4×10^{-3}	3.4
Zr........	40	96	2β	$\geqslant 6 \times 10^{16}$	Mo^{96}	3.8	2.8	5.6×10^{-4}	$\leqslant 3 \times 10^{-8}$
In........	49	115	β	6×10^{14}	Sn^{115}	0.63	95.77	1×10^{-5}	7×10^{-7}
Te........	52	130	2β	$\sim 10^{21}$	Xe^{130}	...	34.49	3.5×10^{-7}	$\sim 10^{-14}$
La........	57	138	β, K $K/\beta = 16$	2×10^{11}	Ba^{138} Ce^{138}	? (K) 1.0 (β)	0.089	6×10^{-6}	10^{-4}
Nd.......	60	144	α	$\sim 5 \times 10^{15}$	Ce^{140}	1.9	23.87	6.0×10^{-4}	6×10^{-7}
Sm.......	62	147	α	1.25×10^{11}	Nd^{143}	2.18	15.07	1.1×10^{-4}	0.040
Lu........	71	176	β	7.5×10^{10}*	Hf^{176}	0.40	2.6	8.3×10^{-6}	5.0×10^{-3}

TABLE IV—*Continued*

Element	Z	A	Radiation	Half-Life	Decay Products	Decay Energy (Mev)	Content of Isotope (Per Cent)	Abundance of the Isotope in Earth's Crust (Weight Per Cent)	Av. Energy per Gm of Earth's Crust (Mev/Min)
Ta........	73	180	β, K(?)	?	W^{180}, Hf^{180}	...	0.0123	3×10^{-10}	...
Re........	75	187	β	8×10^{10}†	Os^{187}	0.008 (0.001(?))	62.9	1×10^{-7}	$\leqslant 10^{-3}$
Bi........	83	209	α	$\geqslant 2 \times 10^{17}$	Tl^{205}	3.1	100	2×10^{-5}	$\leqslant 2 \times 10^{-7}$
Th........	90	232	α, f $\alpha/f = 1.5 \times 10^8$	1.39×10^{10}	Pb^{208}, fragments decay series	4.01 51.55	100 ...	8×10^{-4} ...	7.7 98
U........	92	235	α, f $\alpha/f = 2.7 \times 10^8$	7.13×10^8	Pb^{207}, fragments decay series	4.66 46.39	0.715 ...	2.2×10^{-6} ...	0.46 4.6
U........	92	238	α, f $\alpha/f = 1.7 \times 10^6$	4.49×10^9	Pb^{206}, fragments decay series	4.18 50.01	99.28 ...	3×10^{-4} ...	9.2 110

* See footnote on p. 75.
† See n. 70, p. 76.

TABLE V

Even-Mass Isobars

A (1)	Element (2)	*Z* (3)	Content in Isotopic Composition of Element (Per Cent) (4)	Abundance in Earth's Crust According to Fersman (Per Cent) (5)	χ_1* (6)	χ_2* (7)	δ (8)
36........	S Ar	16 18	0.017 0.337	0.048 5.7×10^{-7}	0.050	...	0
40........	Ar Ca	18 20	99.60 96.97	1.7×10^{-4} 1.37	1.03	...	0
46........	Ca Ti	20 22	0.0033 7.95	4.7×10^{-5} 0.017	4.2×10^{-4}	2.8×10^{-3}	$-\frac{1}{2}$
48........	Ca Ti	20 22	0.185 73.45	2.4×10^{-3} 0.162	2.5×10^{-3}	0.015	−1
50........	Ti Cr	22 24	5.34 4.31	0.012 3.9×10^{-4}	1.24	31	$+\frac{1}{2}$
54........	Cr Fe	24 26	2.38 5.84	2.1×10^{-4} 7.6×10^{-2}	0.41	2.7×10^{-3}	$+\frac{1}{2}$
58........	Fe Ni	26 28	0.31 67.76	4.1×10^{-3} 4.3×10^{-3}	4.6×10^{-3}	0.95	$+\frac{1}{2}$
64........	Ni Zn	28 30	1.16 48.89	7.0×10^{-5} 3.5×10^{-3}	0.024	0.02	0
70........	Zn Ge	30 32	0.62 20.55	3.1×10^{-5} 5.0×10^{-6}	0.03	6.2	0
74........	Ge Se	32 34	36.74 0.87	1.0×10^{-5} 1.3×10^{-7}	42.2	77	$+\frac{1}{2}$
76........	Ge Se	32 34	7.67 9.02	1.9×10^{-6} 1.4×10^{-6}	0.85	1.36	$-\frac{1}{2}$
78........	Se Kr	34 36	23.52 0.354	3.5×10^{-6} 1.4×10^{-11}	66.4	...	$+\frac{1}{2}$
80........	Se Kr	34 36	49.82 2.27	7.5×10^{-6} 9×10^{-11}	22.0	...	0
82........	Se Kr	34 36	9.19 11.56	1.5×10^{-6} 4.6×10^{-10}	0.80	...	$+\frac{1}{2}$
84........	Kr Sr	36 38	56.90 0.56	2.3×10^{-9} 3.9×10^{-5}	102	...	$+\frac{1}{2}$
86........	Kr Sr	36 38	17.37 9.86	7.0×10^{-10} 6.9×10^{-4}	1.78	...	$-\frac{1}{2}$

TABLE V—*Continued*

A (1)	Element (2)	*Z* (3)	Content in Isotopic Composition of Element (Per Cent) (4)	Abundance in Earth's Crust According to Fersman (Per Cent) (5)	χ_1* (6)	χ_2* (7)	δ (8)
92	Zr	40	17.11	8.7×10^{-4}	1.08	27	$+\frac{1}{2}$
	Mo	42	15.86	3.2×10^{-5}			
94	Zr	40	17.40	8.7×10^{-4}	1.91	48	$-\frac{1}{2}$
	Mo	42	9.12	1.8×10^{-5}			
96	Zr	40	2.80	1.4×10^{-4}			−1
	Mo	42	16.50	3.3×10^{-5}	0.17	4.2	+1
	Ru	44	5.7	5.7×10^{-8}	2.9	...	
98	Mo	42	23.75	4.8×10^{-5}	1.86	...	0
	Ru	44	12.8	1.3×10^{-7}			
100	Mo	42	9.62	1.9×10^{-5}	0.76	...	−1
	Ru	44	12.7	1.3×10^{-7}			
102	Ru	44	31.3	3.1×10^{-7}	39	26	$+\frac{1}{2}$
	Pd	46	0.8	1.2×10^{-8}			
104	Ru	44	18.3	1.8×10^{-7}	2.0	1.3	$-\frac{1}{2}$
	Pd	46	9.3	1.4×10^{-7}			
106	Pd	46	27.2	4.1×10^{-7}	2.24	...	$+\frac{1}{2}$
	Cd	48	1.215	9.7×10^{-7}			
108	Pd	46	26.8	4.1×10^{-7}	30.6	...	0
	Cd	48	0.875	7.0×10^{-7}			
110	Pd	46	13.5	2.0×10^{-7}	1.09	...	$-\frac{1}{2}$
	Cd	48	12.39	1.0×10^{-5}			
112	Cd	48	24.07	1.9×10^{-5}	25.3	...	$+\frac{1}{2}$
	Sn	50	0.95	9.5×10^{-6}			
114	Cd	48	28.86	2.3×10^{-5}	44.4	...	$+\frac{1}{2}$
	Sn	50	0.65	6.5×10^{-6}			
116	Cd	48	7.58	6.0×10^{-6}	0.53	...	−1
	Sn	50	14.24	1.4×10^{-4}			
120	Sn	50	4.71	3.3×10^{-4}	53	...	$+\frac{1}{2}$
	Te	52	0.089	1.3×10^{-10}			
122	Sn	50	4.71	4.7×10^{-5}	1.91	...	0
	Te	52	2.46	3.7×10^{-9}			
124	Sn	50	5.98	6.0×10^{-5}	1.30		−1
	Te	52	4.61	6.9×10^{-9}		...	
	Xe	54	0.096	4×10^{-13}	48.0		+1

TABLE V—*Continued*

A (1)	Element (2)	*Z* (3)	Content in Isotopic Composition of Element (Per Cent) (4)	Abundance in Earth's Crust According to Fersman (Per Cent) (5)	χ_1* (6)	χ_2* (7)	δ (8)
126........	Te Xe	52 54	18.71 0.090	2.8×10^{-8} 4×10^{-13}	208	...	$+\frac{1}{2}$
128........	Te Xe	52 54	31.79 1.919	4.8×10^{-8} 7.7×10^{-12}	16.6	...	$-\frac{1}{2}$
130........	Te Xe Ba	52 54 56	34.49 4.08 0.101	5.2×10^{-8} 1.6×10^{-11} 6×10^{-6}	8.45 40.4	...	-1 $+1$
132........	Xe Ba	54 56	26.89 0.097	1.1×10^{-10} 6×10^{-6}	277	...	$+\frac{1}{2}$
134........	Xe Ba	54 56	10.44 2.42	4.2×10^{-11} 1.45×10^{-4}	4.3	...	$-\frac{1}{2}$
136........	Xe Ba Ce	54 56 58	8.87 7.81 0.193	3.5×10^{-11} 4.7×10^{-4} 7.7×10^{-7}	1.11 40.5	... 610	-1 $+1$
138........	Ba Ce	56 58	71.66 0.250	4.3×10^{-3} 1×10^{-6}	287	4300	$+\frac{1}{2}$
142........	Ce Nd	58 60	11.07 27.13	4.4×10^{-5} 5.4×10^{-6}	0.41	8.3	$-\frac{1}{2}$
144........	Nd Sm	60 62	23.87 3.16	4.7×10^{-6} 2.5×10^{-6}	7.56	1.9	$+1$
148........	Nd Sm	60 62	5.72 11.27	1.1×10^{-6} 6.0×10^{-6}	0.494	0.12	-1
150........	Nd Sm	60 62	5.60 7.47	1.1×10^{-6} 6.0×10^{-6}	0.75	0.18	$-\frac{3}{2}$
152........	Sm Gd	62 64	26.63 0.20	2.1×10^{-5} 1.6×10^{-7}	133	133	0
154........	Sm Gd	62 64	22.53 2.15	1.8×10^{-5} 1.7×10^{-6}	10.5	10.5	$-\frac{1}{2}$
156........	Gd Dy	64 66	20.47 0.0524	1.6×10^{-5} 4×10^{-8}	391	391	$+1$
158........	Gd Dy	64 66	24.87 0.0902	2.0×10^{-5} 7×10^{-8}	276	276	$+\frac{1}{2}$
160........	Gd Dy	64 66	21.90 2.294	1.8×10^{-5} 1.8×10^{-6}	9.55	9.55	$-\frac{1}{2}$

TABLE V—*Continued*

A (1)	Element (2)	Z (3)	Content in Isotopic Composition of Element (Per Cent) (4)	Abundance in Earth's Crust According to Fersman (Per Cent) (5)	χ_1* (6)	χ_2* (7)	δ (8)
162........	Dy Er	66 68	25.53 0.136	2.0×10^{-5} 1×10^{-7}	188	200	+1
164........	Dy Er	66 68	28.18 1.56	2.3×10^{-5} 1.1×10^{-6}	18.1	21	$+\frac{1}{2}$
168........	Er Yb	68 70	27.07 0.140	1.9×10^{-5} 1×10^{-7}	193	190	$+\frac{1}{2}$
170........	Er Yb	68 70	14.88 3.03	1.0×10^{-5} 2.4×10^{-6}	4.91	4.9	$-\frac{1}{2}$
174........	Yb Hf	70 72	31.84 0.18	2.5×10^{-5} 7.2×10^{-8}	177	350	$+\frac{1}{2}$
176........	Yb Hf	70 72	12.73 5.15	1.0×10^{-5} 2.1×10^{-6}	2.47	4.8	$-\frac{1}{2}$
180........	Hf W	72 74	35.44 0.135	1.4×10^{-5} 1×10^{-6}	262	14	$+\frac{1}{2}$
184........	W Os	74 76	30.6 0.018	2.15×10^{-4} 9×10^{-11}	1700	...	$+\frac{1}{2}$
186........	W Os	74 76	28.4 1.59	2.0×10^{-4} 8×10^{-9}	17.8	...	0
190........	Os Pt	76 78	26.4 0.012	1.32×10^{-7} 5×10^{-11}	2200	...	$+\frac{1}{2}$
192........	Os Pt	76 78	41.0 0.78	2.05×10^{-7} 3.1×10^{-9}	53	66	0
196........	Pt Hg	78 80	25.4 0.146	1.0×10^{-7} 1.0×10^{-8}	174	...	$+\frac{1}{2}$
198........	Pt Hg	78 80	7.23 10.02	3.0×10^{-8} 7×10^{-7}	0.722	...	$-\frac{1}{2}$
204........	Hg Pb	80 82	6.85 1.48	4.8×10^{-7} 1.5×10^{-6}	4.63	...	0

* χ_1 and χ_2 denote the ratio of the abundances of isobars with $Z - 1$ and $Z + 1$ in the isotopic composition of the elements and in the earth's crust. For the isobars which belong to the elements lost by the earth, the value of χ_2 is not given.

TABLE VI

TABLE OF α-EMITTERS

Z (1)	A (2)	Element; Symbol of Isotope (3)	Possibility and Probability of K-Capture or β-Decay (4)	T_α (5)	Energy of α-Particles (Mev) (6)
83...........	<198	Bismuth, Bi	...	1.7 minutes	6.2
	198	Bismuth, Bi	$K/\alpha = 2000$	10 days	5.83
	199	Bismuth, Bi	$K/\alpha = 10^4$	180 days	5.47
	201	Bismuth, Bi	$K/\alpha \approx 3 \times 10^5$	400 years	5.15
	203	Bismuth, Bi	$K/\alpha \approx 10^7$	10^4 years	4.85
	209	Bismuth, Bi	None	$>2 \times 10^{18}$ years	2.9
	210	Bismuth, RaE	$\beta/\alpha = 2 \times 10^6$	3×10^4 years	...
	211	Bismuth, AcC	$\beta/\alpha = 3.2 \times 10^{-3}$	2.16 years	6.618
	212	Bismuth, ThC	$\beta/\alpha = 1.97$	2.0 hours	6.086
	213	Bismuth, Bi	$\beta/\alpha = 50$	1.6 days	5.86
	214	Bismuth, RaC	$\beta/\alpha = 2.5 \times 10^3$	34 days	5.505
84...........	196	Polonium, Po	...	1.9 minutes	6.14
	197	Polonium, Po	...	4 minutes	6.04
	198	Polonium, Po	...	6 minutes	5.846
	200	Polonium, Po	K	>11 minutes	5.770
	201	Polonium, Po	K	>18 minutes	5.671
	202	Polonium, Po	$K/\alpha = 50$	42 hours	5.575
	204	Polonium, Po	$K/\alpha = 100$	160 days	5.37
	205	Polonium, Po	$K/\alpha = 1350$	84 days	5.2
	206	Polonium, Po	$K/\alpha = 10–20$	73–870 days	5.218
	207	Polonium, Po	$K/\alpha = 10^4$	6 years	5.10
	208	Polonium, Po	$K/\alpha \ll 1$	2.93 years	5.108
	209	Polonium, Po	$K/\alpha \approx 0.005$	103 years	4.877
	210	Polonium, Po	None	138.3 days	5.298
	211	Polonium, AcC′	None	0.52 second	7.434

TABLE VI—*Continued*

Z (1)	A (2)	Element; Symbol of Isotope (3)	Possibility and Probability of K-Capture or β-Decay (4)	T_α (5)	Energy of α-Particles (Mev) (6)
	212	Polonium, ThC′	None	3.04×10^{-7} second	8.776
	213	Polonium, Po	None	4.2×10^{-6} second	8.336
	214	Polonium, RaC′	None	1.637×10^{-4} second	7.680
	215	Polonium, AcA	β(?)	1.83×10^{-3} second	7.365
	216	Polonium, ThA	None	0.158 second	6.774
	217	Polonium, Po	. . .	<10 second	6.54
	218	Polonium, RaA	β(?)	3.05 minutes	5.998
85.	<202	Astatine, At	K	>43 seconds	6.50
	<203	Astatine, At	K	>1.7 minutes	6.35
	203	Astatine, At	K	>7 minutes	6.10
	205	Astatine, At	K	>25 minutes	5.90
	207	Astatine, At	$K/\alpha \approx 9$	20 hours	5.75
	208	Astatine, At	$K/\alpha \approx 200$	14 days	5.65
	209	Astatine, At	$K/\alpha \approx 19$	110 hours	5.65
	210	Astatine, At	$K/\alpha \approx 600$	210 hours	5.519
	211	Astatine, At	$K/\alpha = 1.44$	18 hours	5.862
	212	Astatine, At	. . .	0.22 second	(7.7)
	213	Astatine, At	K(?)	. . .	9.2
	214	Astatine, At	K(?)	2×10^{-6} second	8.78
	215	Astatine, At	None	10^{-4} second	8.00
	216	Astatine, At	(K, β)(?)	3×10^{-4} second	7.79
	217	Astatine, At	β(?)	0.018 second	7.02
	218	Astatine, At	$\beta/\alpha \approx 10^{-3}$	1.5–2.0 seconds	6.63
	219	Astatine, At	$\beta/\alpha \approx 3 \times 10^{-2}$	0.9 minute	6.27
86.	204	Emanation, Em	. . .	3 minutes	6.28
	206	Emanation, Em	$K/\alpha \approx 0.5$	~10 minutes	6.25
	207	Emanation, Em	$K/\alpha = 24$	4.5 hours	6.4

TABLE VI—*Continued*

Z (1)	A (2)	Element; Symbol of Isotope (3)	Possibility and Probability of K-Capture or β-Decay (4)	$T\alpha$ (5)	Energy of α-Particles (Mev) (6)
86 *Continued*	208	Emanation, Em	$K/\alpha \cong 4$	2 hours	6.34
	209	Emanation, Em	$K/\alpha = 5$	3 hours	6.037
	210	Emanation, Em	$K/\alpha = 0.04$	2.7 hours	6.037
	211	Emanation, Em	$K/\alpha = 3$	2.7 days	5.847
	212	Emanation, Em	None	23 minutes	6.262
	215	Emanation, Em	None	$\sim 10^{-6}$ second	8.6
	216	Emanation, Em	None	$\sim 10^{-4}$ second	8.01
	217	Emanation, Em	None	$\sim 10^{-3}$ second	7.74
	218	Emanation, Em	None	0.019 second	7.12
	219	Emanation, An	β(?)	3.92 seconds	6.824
	220	Emanation, Tn	None	54.5 seconds	6.282
	221	Emanation, Em	$\beta/\alpha = 4$	2 hours	...
	222	Emanation, Rn	None	3.825 days	5.486
87............	212	Francium, Fr	$K/\alpha = 1.3$	44 minutes	6.409
	217	Francium, Fr	K(?)	...	8.3
	218	Francium, Fr	K(?)	5×10^{-3} second	7.85
	219	Francium, Fr	None	0.02 second	7.30
	220	Francium, Fr	β, K(?)	27.5 seconds	6.69
	221	Francium, Fr	β(?)	4.8 minutes	6.30
	222	Francium, Fr	$\beta/\alpha \approx 10^3$–$10^4$	10–100 days	...
	223	Francium, AcK	$\beta/\alpha = 2.5 \times 10^4$	1 year	5.6
88............	213	Radium, Ra	K(?)	2.7 months	6.90
	219	Radium, Ra	K(?)	10^{-3} second	8.0
	220	Radium, Ra	None	3×10^{-2} second	7.43
	221	Radium, Ra	None	30 seconds	6.71

TABLE VI—*Continued*

Z (1)	A (2)	Element; Symbol of Isotope (3)	Possibility and Probability of K-Capture or β-Decay (4)	T_α (5)	Energy of α-Particles (Mev) (6)
88 *Continued*	222	Radium, Ra	None	38 seconds	6.51
	223	Radium, AcX	None	11.2 days	5.86
	224	Radium, ThX	None	3.64 days	5.681
	226	Radium, Ra	None	1622 years	4.777
89.	221	Actinium, Ac	$K(?)$	Small	7.6
	222	Actinium, Ac	$K(?)$	5.5 seconds	6.96
	223	Actinium, Ac	$K/\alpha \approx 0.01$	2.2 minutes	6.64
	224	Actinium, Ac	$K/\alpha = 9$; $\beta(?)$	1.2 days	6.17
	225	Actinium, Ac	None	10.0 days	5.80
	227	Actinium, Ac	$\beta/\alpha = 82$	1800 years	4.942
90.	223	Thorium, Th	$K(?)$	0.1 second	7.55
	224	Thorium, Th	$K(?)$	1 second	7.13
	225	Thorium, Th	$K/\alpha \approx 1/9$	9 minutes	6.57
	226	Thorium, Th	None	30.9 minutes	6.30
	227	Thorium, RdAc	None	18.6 days	6.030
	228	Thorium, RdTh	None	1.90 years	5.423
	229	Thorium, Th	None	7340 years	5.02
	230	Thorium, Io	None	8×10^4 years	4.682
	232	Thorium, Th	None	1.39×10^{10} years	3.98
91.	225	Protactinium, Pa	$K(?)$	2.0 seconds	. . .
	226	Protactinium, Pa	$K(?)$	1.8 seconds	6.81
	227	Protactinium, Pa	$K/\alpha = 0.2$	46 minutes	6.46
	228	Protactinium, Pa	$K/\alpha = 50$	46 days	6.09
	229	Protactinium, Pa	$K/\alpha = 400$	600 days	5.69
	230	Protactinium, Pa	$K + \beta/\alpha = 3 \times 10^4$	1600 years	. . .
	231	Protactinium, Pa	None	3.43×10^4 years	5.042

TABLE VI—*Continued*

Z (1)	A (2)	Element; Symbol of Isotope (3)	Possibility and Probability of K-Capture or β-Decay (4)	Tα (5)	Energy of α-Particles (Mev) (6)
92.	227	Uranium, U	None	1.3 minutes	6.8
	228	Uranium, U	$K/\alpha \approx 0.25$	12 minutes	6.67
	229	Uranium, U	$K/\alpha = 4$	5 hours	6.42
	230	Uranium, U	None	20.8 days	5.85
	231	Uranium, U	$K/\alpha = 1.8 \times 10^3$	20 years	5.45
	232	Uranium, U	None	73.6 years	5.31
	233	Uranium, U	None	1.62×10^5 years	4.823
	234	Uranium, UII	None	2.48×10^5 years	4.763
	235	Uranium, AcU	None	7.13×10^8 years	4.58
	236	Uranium, U	None	2.39×10^7 years	4.499
	238	Uranium, UI	None	4.49×10^9 years	4.18
93.	231	Neptunium, Np	None	50 minutes	6.28
	233	Neptunium, Np	$K/\alpha \approx 10^5$	6.6 years	5.53
	235	Neptunium, Np	$K + L + M/\alpha = 6 \times 10^4$	5×10^4 years	5.06
	237	Neptunium, Np	None	2.20×10^6 years	4.77
94.	232	Plutonium, Pu	$K/\alpha \geqslant 50$	$\geqslant$1.25 days	6.58
	233	Plutonium, Pu	$K/\alpha = 800$	11 days	6.30
	234	Plutonium, Pu	$K + L/\alpha = 16$	6 days	6.19
	235	Plutonium, Pu	$K/\alpha = 3.3 \times 10^4$	1.7 years	5.85
	236	Plutonium, Pu	None	2.7 years	5.75
	237	Plutonium, Pu	$K/\alpha = 3 \times 10^4$	1.7×10^4 years	5.65
	238	Plutonium, Pu	None	89.6 years	5.492
	239	Plutonium, Pu	None	2.436×10^4 years	5.150
	240	Plutonium, Pu	None	6.58×10^3 years	5.162
	241	Plutonium, Pu	$\beta/\alpha = 2.5 \times 10^4$	3.3×10^5 years	4.893
	242	Plutonium, Pu	None	1×10^6 years	4.88
	244	Plutonium, Pu	. . .	7.6×10^7 years	(4.53)

TABLE VI—*Continued*

Z (1)	A (2)	Element; Symbol of Isotope (3)	Possibility and Probability of K-Capture or β-Decay (4)	T_α (5)	Energy of α-Particles (Mev) (6)
95	237	Americium, Am	$K/\alpha = 2 \times 10^4$	3 years	6.01
	239	Americium, Am	$K/\alpha = 3.3 \times 10^4$	45 years	5.75
	241	Americium, Am	None	470 years	5.546
	242	Americium, Am	$\beta/\alpha \approx 100$	10^4 years	5.44
	243	Americium, Am	...	7950 years	5.339
96	238	Curium, Cm	$K/\alpha > 9$	>1 day	6.50
	240	Curium, Cm	None	26.8 days	6.25
	241	Curium, Cm	$K/\alpha = 100$	10 years	5.95
	242	Curium, Cm	None	162.5 days	6.11
	243	Curium, Cm	$K/\alpha = 0.0026$	35 years	6.061
	244	Curium, Cm	None	17.9 years	5.801
	245	Curium, Cm	None	8×10^3 years	5.36
	246	Curium, Cm	None	6600 years	5.37
	247	Curium, Cm	None	$\geqslant 4 \times 10^7$ years	(5.29)
	248	Curium, Cm	$\alpha/f = 8$	4.7×10^5 years	5.05
	250	Curium, Cm	$\alpha/f \cong 0$	2×10^4 years	...
97	243	Berkelium, Bk	$K/\alpha \approx 700$	120 days	6.72
	244	Berkelium, Bk	$K/\alpha = 1.6 \times 10^4$	8 years	6.67
	245	Berkelium, Bk	$K/\alpha \approx 900$	12 years	6.33
	247	Berkelium, Bk	None	10^4 years	5.67
	249	Berkelium, Bk	$\beta/\alpha \approx 4 \times 10^4$	4×10^4 years	5.4
98	244	Californium, Cf	...	25 minutes	7.17
	245	Californium, Cf	$K/\alpha = 7/3$	2.3 hours	7.11
	246	Californium, Cf	None	35.7 hours	6.75
	248	Californium, Cf	None	350 days	6.26

TABLE VI—*Continued*

Z (1)	A (2)	Element; Symbol of Isotope (3)	Possibility and Probability of K-Capture or β-Decay (4)	Tα (5)	Energy of α-Particles (Mev) (6)
98 *Continued*	249	Californium, Cf	None	360 years	6.19
	250	Californium, Cf	None	10.9 years	6.02
	251	Californium, Cf	None	~800 years	(6.17)
	252	Californium, Cf	$f/\alpha = 0.03$	2.2 years	6.11
	253	Californium, Cf	(α, β)	18 years	6.01
	254	Californium, Cf	$\alpha/f \cong 0$	55 days	...
99	246	Einsteinium, E	K	>7.3 minutes	7.35
	247	Einsteinium, E	...	7.3 minutes	7.3
	248	Einsteinium, E	$K/\alpha \approx 300$	6 days	6.87
	249	Einsteinium, E	$K/\alpha = 770$	65 days	6.76
	251	Einsteinium, E	$K/\alpha \approx 190$	285 days	6.48
	252	Einsteinium, E	None	140 days	6.64
	253	Einsteinium, E	None	20.0 days	6.636
	254	Einsteinium, E	None	480 days	6.42
100	250	Fermium, Fm	K	⩾30 minutes	7.43
	251	Fermium, Fm	$K/\alpha \approx 100$	30 days	6.89
	252	Fermium, Fm	None	22.7 hours	7.04
	253	Fermium, Fm	$K/\alpha = 8.5$	43 days	6.05
	254	Fermium, Fm	None	3.24 hours	7.20
	255	Fermium, Fm	None	21.5 hours	7.03
	256	Fermium, Fm	$\alpha/f = 0$	Several days(?)	...
102	254	...	...	3 seconds	8.7

TABLE VII

CONTENT OF ISOTOPES OF SAME TYPE FOR DIFFERENT ELEMENTS*

Z (1)	Element (2)	A (3)	Content of Isotope (Per Cent; $n_{A \pm 1}$) (4)	$\frac{n_{A-1}}{n_{A+1}}$ (5)
8.	Oxygen	16 18	99.759 0.204	488
10.	Neon	20 22	90.92 8.82	10.3
12.	Magnesium	24 26	78.60 11.29	6.96
14.	Silicon	28 30	92.27 3.05	30.3
16.	Sulfur	32 34	95.018 4.215	22.5
17.	Chlorine	35 37	75.4 24.6	3.07
19.	Potassium	39 41	93.08 6.91	13.5
20.	Calcium	42 44	0.64 2.06	0.31
22.	Titanium	47 49	7.75 5.51	1.41
28.	Nickel	60 62	26.16 3.66	7.15
29.	Copper	63 65	69.1 30.9	2.24
30.	Zinc	66 68	27.81 18.56	1.50
31.	Gallium	69 71	60.2 39.8	1.51
35.	Bromine	79 81	50.52 49.48	1.02
42.	Molybdenum	95 97	15.70 9.45	1.66
44.	Ruthenium	99 101	12.8 17.0	0.75
47.	Silver	107 109	51.35 48.65	1.06

* Isotopes which form isobars are excluded.

TABLE VII—*Continued*

Z	Element	A	Content of Isotope (Per Cent; $n_{A\pm 1}$)	$\frac{n_{A-1}}{n_{A+1}}$
(1)	(2)	(3)	(4)	(5)
50.	Tin	117 119	7.57 8.58	0.88
54.	Xenon	129 131	26.44 21.18	1.25
56.	Barium	135 137	6.59 11.32	0.58
60.	Neodymium	143 145	12.20 8.30	1.47
62.	Samarium	147 149	15.07 13.84	1.09
63.	Europium	151 153	47.77 52.23	0.91
64.	Gadolinium	155 157	14.73 15.68	0.94
66.	Dysprosium	161 163	18.88 24.97	0.76
70.	Ytterbium	171 173	14.31 16.13	0.89
72.	Hafnium	177 179	18.39 13.78	1.33
77.	Iridium	191 193	38.5 61.5	0.63
80.	Mercury	199 201 200 202	16.84 13.22 23.13 29.80	1.27 0.78
81.	Thalium	203 205	29.50 70.50	0.42

Author Index

Subject Index

Printed in U.S.A.